THE GREAT NATURALISTS EXPLORE SOUTH AMERICA

CHARLES DARWIN
As a Young Man

The Great Naturalists Explore South America

BY PAUL RUSSELL CUTRIGHT

Essay Index Reprint Series

BOOKS FOR LIBRARIES PRESS
FREEPORT, NEW YORK

This edition is reprinted 1968 by arrangement with
The Macmillan Company

LIBRARY OF CONGRESS CATALOG CARD NUMBER:
68-8454

PRINTED IN THE UNITED STATES OF AMERICA

TO
MIMI AND PAUL

FOREWORD

THE present volume is divided into two parts. The first is a résumé of the travels and experiences of the great naturalists, such as Alexander von Humboldt, Charles Darwin, Alfred Russel Wallace, and W. H. Hudson, who explored and wrote of South America during the nineteenth and twentieth centuries. The second part is a series of chapters on several of the mammals, birds, reptiles, fish, and insects indigenous to South America. Each chapter gives attention to the more important observations made on these animals by the naturalists as well as to the classification, geographical distribution, general description, and habits, so that each may be considered an epitome of a century and a half of observation on the animal in its own environment.

I have not attempted to describe all the animals mentioned in the works of the naturalists (an obviously impossible task) but have considered rather those which they found most important or most interesting.

I take pleasure in making acknowledgments to: L. Wehekind, Port-of-Spain, Trinidad, who supplied information relative to the life of Eugène André; to Julius M. Johnson for the pictures of the night monkey and two-toed sloth; to Mark Mooney, Jr., of the Philadelphia Zoological Society for his cooperation in furnishing photographs; to Robert K. Enders of Swarthmore College, who gave assistance with the illustrations; to Leo E. Miller, Raymond L. Ditmars, George K. Cherrie, Frank M. Chapman, and William Beebe for permission to use material from their works on South America; to E. P. Dutton & Co. for permission to quote from *Six Years in Bolivia* by A. V. L. Guise and from *The Naturalist in La Plata* by W. H. Hudson; and to Dodd, Mead & Co. for permission to quote from *Head Hunters of the Amazon* by F. W. Up de Graff.

I am especially indebted to Dr. L. M. Peairs, Professor of Entomology, West Virginia University, who read the manuscript and offered valuable criticisms, and to Dr. John Marshall Saunders, Nashville, Tennessee, who has followed with interest the preparation of the book and given constant encouragement. I wish also to thank Miss Blanche Schwartz who typed the manuscript. To many others who were of assistance I am deeply grateful.

PAUL RUSSELL CUTRIGHT

CONTENTS

PART ONE

PART TWO

Contents

ILLUSTRATIONS

Illustrations

PART ONE

SOUTH AMERICA AND THE NATURALISTS

THE most extensive tract of virgin forest in the world lies equatorially located in South America. It extends from the Atlantic to the Andes and from the Brazilian state of Matto Grasso to the Caribbean Sea. More than a third of Brazil, practically all of the Guianas, much of Venezuela and Colombia, liberal portions of eastern Ecuador and Peru, and a generous section of northern Bolivia are covered by it. The immensity of this region is not fully comprehended unless a journey is made by land and by water, or by water alone—for that is possible—from one side of it to the other; a journey such as that from Puerto Maldonado on the Madre de Dios of Peru to Ciudad Bolívar on the Orinoco. This forest is not a solid mass of vegetation from end to end; here and there are interspersed treeless oases, some of them like our northern plains and meadows and of considerable scope. Neither is the densely wooded part all jungle —a word too often applied to any or all parts of the equatorial forest. Much of the tropical forest in South America clearly deserves that term but its universal application must be objected to on the ground that there are great areas resembling neither the thicket nor the tangle characteristic of the true jungle. Immense regions are open woods through which a traveler may wander with as much freedom and ease as in a beech forest of New England. Other sections bordering the large streams are covered with water during several months of the year, and these no more deserve the appellation "jungle" than do the open woods. On the other hand a South American jungle to many people is not jungle unless it fairly reeks with boa constrictors, slithering crocodiles, and naked savages.

The statement is made from time to time that there is no land left on our planet to explore. Perhaps the most striking feature of this boundless forest is the fact that vast expanses of it are entirely unexplored. Exploration of it in the past has been, for the most part, a matter of travel up and down the various rivers draining this huge area. Excursions into the regions between the streams have been in many instances hazardous, and usually unsuccessful. As a result such great inland mesopotamias as that between the Xingú and Tapajóz, or the Tapajóz and Madeira, or the Purús and Solimões are virtually unknown to civilized man. Take a look at the map of that vast expanse of jungle in southeastern Colombia drained by affluents of the Rio Negro and the Japurá; much of this is a *terra incognita* where, so far as is known, no white foot has ever trod. Much the same may be said for parts of southern and eastern Venezuela, large areas of northern Brazil, and smaller portions of Ecuador, Peru, and Bolivia. No surer proof of how little is known about this great northern wilderness is needed than the recent discovery of Mt. Auyan-tepui, in the eastern part of Venezuela. This mountain is another vestige, like Mt. Roraima and Mt. Duida, of a great tableland that once covered this part of the world. Mt. Auyan-tepui was discovered from the air and is estimated to be some twenty miles long and at least eight thousand feet high. Mt. Roraima and Mt. Duida are about four hundred miles apart, and both have been climbed and explored—Roraima on several occasions—yet the existence of another mountain in the same general region was not known until recently. Under the leadership of G. H. H. Tate of the American Museum of Natural History, an expedition has just returned from exploring this, another, "Lost World."

There are sound reasons, of course, why the great forest covering Brazil and adjoining countries has not been more fully explored. In the first place much of it is impenetrable; there is such a rank undergrowth that, even with a machete, progress can be made through it only after great exertion. In the second place literally millions of acres are flooded during the wet season. In the third place certain regions are inhabited by irrepressible, warlike tribes of Indians. These resent the attempts of any people —white, red, or black—to encroach upon their territory. As they are well armed with blowguns and poisoned arrows they have so far been successful in repelling intruders.

The great majority of animals and plants indigenous to South America are to be found in this forest. There is not the wealth of large game animals so inviting to the big-game hunter, but there is a profusion of smaller forms—mammals, birds, reptiles, insects—that make this tropical wilderness a perennial source of delight to the naturalist. It is here that butterflies and beetles, parrots and toucans, snakes, lizards, and monkeys abound, and it is into this area that most of the naturalists venture when collecting in South America. As an example of how numerous animals are, Bates, in the eleven years he spent in South America, collected the enormous total of over 14,000 species. The representation was as follows:

Mammals	52 species
Birds	360
Reptiles	140
Fishes	120
Insects	14,000
Mollusks	35

These figures show that he collected four species of animals, on an average, every day of those eleven years. Bates declared that 8,000 of the 14,000 were species new to science. Even though Bates was on virtually new ground, could any fact more clearly demonstrate the profusion of animal life existing in South America? Many naturalists have come and gone since Bates was in this forest, and each one has brought out many additional forms for the taxonomists to add to an already cumbersome list; yet there is little doubt that thousands of species remain undiscovered in South America. Most of the forms unknown to science are insects. Entomologists have described already something like 700,000 species, but estimate that this number will probably increase to the staggering total of 2,000,000 when, and if, all existing forms are finally described. Surely a goodly proportion of those still unknown in the world inhabit the great equatorial forest of South America where they await discovery by some future naturalist.

However, other regions than this spacious tract of forest primeval challenge the scientist in South America: there are the widespreading plains of southern Brazil, Paraguay, and Uruguay, the grass-covered pampas of the Argentine, the wind-swept terrains of Patagonia, and the declivities and plateaus incident to the Andean cordillera. Each of these extensive regions has its own particular biota to attract the zoologist and the botanist.

South America and the Naturalists

That South America still remains less well known than any other continent is true from more than a biological standpoint. It is said that not much more than a quarter of the continent has been surveyed. Great areas exist in the Andes that have yet to be seen by either a geographer or a biologist. In every republic through which the cordillera extends, from Panama to Punta Arenas, there are localities about which little or nothing is known. For example, there are great upland areas in Peru, such as the Gran Prajonal between the Alto Ucayali and Perené rivers and the Pampa de Sacramento east of the Huallago. These are said to be inhabited by fierce tribes of Indians who have been successful in driving away all interlopers.

For three centuries following the discovery of South America the prospect of gold—a shining, irresistible magnet—drew, first, the Iberian conquistadores and, later, adventurers from all parts of the northern world, to the Spanish Main and lands to the south. In this mad scramble for wealth little thought was expended on the natural history of the continent. Such names as Francisco Pizarro, Sebastian de Belalcazar, Gonzalo Ximenes de Quesada, and Sir Walter Raleigh will forever be associated with the early history of South America. They, and many others who might be mentioned, were giants among men in their day, but they had only one motive as they conducted their expeditions into the interior of the continent: they sought gold. In the accounts of these and other expeditions made by the conquerors there is little mention of the fauna and flora of the regions they explored, and such descriptions as were written are, for the most part, fantastical. As an example, Raleigh wrote: "The armadillo is a beast which seemeth to be all barred over with small plates somewhat like to a *Renocero,* with a white horne growing in his hinder parts, as big as a great hunting horne, which they vse to winde in steed of a trumpet. *Monardus* writeth that a little of the powder of the horne put into the eare, cureth deafnes."

It was not until the close of the eighteenth century that a naturalist, in the true sense of the word, visited South America intent on studying its plant and animal life. Since then many others have ascended turbulent Brazilian streams, climbed treacherous Bolivian trails, and suffered from tropical fevers and jungle parasites in the interior of Ecuador, Guiana, and Venezuela, in their search for new and interesting animals or plants. Others have collected in Uruguay, Paraguay, and Argentina where conditions of climate and travel were not so harassing. Several of these naturalists have written of their experiences and discoveries in South America, and much is to be learned from their accounts about the natural riches of the country. In years to come these volumes will become of increasing value to South Americans. As the forests are leveled and species after species becomes extinct, these early accounts of the jungle and of the profusion of strange and fascinating creatures which once peopled it will fascinate readers of them much as Parkman's *Oregon Trail* and Cooper's Leatherstocking Tales entrance young and old of the United States today. The authors of these volumes were skilled naturalists, and some of them were equally skillful with the pen. Several of them resided in South America as long as five to fifteen years. They came to know the wild life of that vast country as no others have known it. In their protracted period of residence they became, it might be said, a part of the land itself.

The first naturalist of distinction to travel in South America was ALEXANDER VON HUMBOLDT. His *Personal Narrative of Travels to the Equinoctial Regions of America* was the first written account describing in detail, and with a considerable degree of accuracy, the animals and plants of that continent. On earlier occasions some few individuals—Felix de Azara for one—made contributions to the knowledge of natural history in South America, and the value of their work is not to be overlooked; but the true or modern investigative spirit made its entrance into that continent with Humboldt and his companion Aimé Bonpland, a botanist.

Humboldt (1769–1859) was born in Berlin on September 14, 1769. At the age of twenty he made a scientific expedition up the Rhine and was so enthusiastic over the results that he determined to become a scientific explorer instead of devoting his life to the political career toward which his parents had directed him. To that end he studied foreign languages, biology, astronomy, and geology for the next few years in the best schools of Germany. His next venture into the field of scientific exploration was a field trip to Switzerland and Italy in the year 1795. The successful issue of this journey, together with the publication of several scientific papers, gave him prestige, and he was invited to join an expedition preparing to circumnavigate the globe. Bonpland was invited to go on this trip as botanist. When this venture was postponed Humboldt and Bonpland, after an ineffective attempt to reach Egypt, went to Madrid. This was a most fortunate move, for there they received the unexpected assistance of the minister d'Urquijo, who paved the way for their visit to Spanish America. After considerable preparation they sailed on the *Pizarro* from Corunna on June 5, 1799.

Humboldt and Bonpland landed in the little town of Cumana, in the northeastern part of what is now Venezuela, on July 16, 1799, some ten years before Simon Bolívar led his countrymen in open revolt against the Spanish yoke. After a residence of some months in that place during which they diligently explored the surrounding country, they went to Caracas, the present capital. It was here that plans materialized for an expedition up the Orinoco to the Rio Negro and Casiquiare.

The first stage of this trip took Humboldt and Bonpland due south across Venezuela to San Fernando on the Apure River, a western tributary of the Orinoco. They arrived here March 27, 1800, and soon found conveyance down the river to the Orinoco. In the weeks that followed they ascended the Orinoco past the great cataracts of Atures and Maipures and reached the small mission station of San Fernando de Atabapo, situated near the confluence of the Orinoco, Atabapo, and Guaviare. Instead of continuing the ascent of the Orinoco from this point they ascended the Atabapo as far as practicable, crossed the watershed between the Orinoco and Amazon, and then descended the Pimichín onto the Rio Negro. This journey was concluded on May 6, 1800, and a few days later Humboldt and Bonpland found themselves on the Casiquiare, the remarkable stream which connects the Amazon with the Orinoco. One of the major purposes of Humboldt's journey was to verify, or to disprove, the persistent report that such an aquatic conjunction did exist. It is probable that no other experience in South America gave Humboldt more satisfaction than the discovery that the Casiquiare was a reality. He determined not only that it existed, but that it was a relatively large stream navigable throughout the year, and that it flows from the Orinoco into the Rio Negro. He was the first naturalist to travel the entire length of it although, according to Whitney, a Spaniard, Lope de Aguirre, the "Wanderer," made the traverse in the year 1561 looking for El Dorado, and was probably the first white man to do so. However, the existence of it was not made known to the world at large until much later, after the Jesuit Father Manoel Roman passed through the Casiquiare in 1744 on a visit to the missions of the Guaviare. The men who have traveled on the Casiquiare did not tarry long; Humboldt, Spruce, Whitney all agree in saying that this region is a rendezvous for all the mosquitoes in northern South America.

After reaching the Orinoco, Humboldt and Bonpland lost little time in returning to civilization. They descended the Orinoco to Angostura (now Ciudad Bolívar), where they arrived in the middle of June. The exploration of this region in the year 1800 was difficult and not without danger, but it could be accomplished then with less peril than at the present date. At that time the Spaniards were still in control of the country, and missionaries were stationed at every native village bearing a name along the Orinoco, Atabapo, Rio Negro, and Casiquiare. As a result Humboldt was able to secure food and assistance at each of these places; at no time was he far distant from a village in charge of a missionary from whom he might expect help if necessary. During the century and a half since Humboldt's journey of exploration many of the remote places he visited, inhabited then, have been deserted.[1]

The account of this journey, the first of its kind into South America, takes rank with the great explorers' records. It gave the world its first realistic picture of the great South American forest and of the abundance and exuberance of life therein. The observations made by Humboldt and Bonpland on electric eels, manatees, piranhas, howler monkeys, turtles, capybaras, and many other forms were the first of consequence to reach the civilized world. Considering the time at which Humboldt wrote and the fact that

[1] The difficulties of travel in this region at the present time are interestingly related in a recent book by Earl P. Hanson, entitled *Journey to Manaos.*

he was writing of animals practically unknown to him, his descriptions are remarkably free from error. His chief and abiding fault —in common with that of many another traveler—was that of accepting the words of the Indians too freely. That Humboldt did make mistakes in observation is, after all, somewhat beside the point. The fact that matters above everything else is that he was the first scientist to go into this region; consequently his narrative describing the natural history had a profound effect on the civilized world.

All natural agencies and events, from the grandest to the most common, interested Humboldt. He was equally interested in determining the elevation of a mountain, the food habits of a tribe of Indians, the nature of the galvanic action in an electric eel, and the structure of the larynx in a howling monkey. He sought to arrive at the mutual relations of all natural phenomena. His activities of mind in this respect have seldom been equaled.

Humboldt's second, and last, journey in South America started from Cartagena near the mouth of the Magdalena River. A journey by boat of several days up the Magdalena brought him to a small place called Honda where he debarked to travel by muleback to Bogotá. After a stay of several weeks in this city during which he and Bonpland were engrossed in the botany, zoology, and geology of the region, they crossed the Andes to Popayán and then proceeded to Quito, now the capital of Ecuador, where they arrived January 6, 1802. The manner in which Humboldt occupied himself on the west coast of South America for the next few months is, for the most part, of less interest to the biologist than to the geologist or physicist.

He utilized most of his time in climbing and studying the great mountain peaks—Pichincha and Chimborazo—of that region. He did make a journey across the Andes to the headwaters of the Amazon, but his efforts there were chiefly in revising the chart of that region made by the French astronomer Condamine.

In his studies of the mountain peaks he became acquainted with the condor, and his observations on this great vulture are of considerable interest to the naturalist. Of great importance were his researches on the cold current of water flowing north along the coasts of Peru and Ecuador. In recognition of these studies the current now bears his name. Humboldt also made a study of the guano found on the desert islands off the Peruvian coast and was responsible for the first shipments of this valuable fertilizer to Europe.

The *Personal Narrative* was first published in French and appeared in several volumes over the course of several years. Later (1852) a three-volume edition in English divested of considerable material of limited interest was published. The influence of these volumes on the civilized world was pronounced. Charles Darwin read them while still a student at Cambridge and declared, "This work stirred up in me a burning zeal to add even the most humble contribution to the noble structure of Natural Science." After he had himself looked upon South America and walked in some of its magnificent forests he wrote, "From what I have seen Humboldt's glorious descriptions are & will forever be unparalleled."

Following his return from America, Humboldt's popularity was second only to that enjoyed by Napoleon. Scientific societies everywhere sought his membership, and Frederick William III of Prussia made him a royal chamberlain and gave him a pension of 2,500 thalers, later doubled. He made Paris his home and was lionized as the master spirit of the age. In 1827, upon the insistence of his sovereign, he returned regretfully to Berlin. Although he had prepared himself for a lifetime of travel he made only one more expedition. This was a rapid trip across Russia and Siberia to the Yenesei River, too rapid to be of any great value, although he discovered diamonds in the Ural Mountains. The journey was made from May to November 1829. The later years of his life were spent in research, in the completion of the *Kosmos*—an encyclopedic account and explanation of the physical universe—and in the fulfillment of various diplomatic missions. He died in Berlin, May 6, 1859, and was buried with royal honors.

Humboldt did not at any time return to South America but his companion, Bonpland, did. Bonpland (1773–1858) was born at La Rochelle, France, August 22, 1773. Before joining Humboldt he served for a time as surgeon in the French army but found time to acquire considerable botanical knowledge that later was to be of value to him. Some years after he and Humboldt returned to Europe from America he was invited to become a professor in the

University of Buenos Aires. He accepted and made the journey to Argentina. Later, while on a botanical expedition, he fell into the hands of Dr. Francia, the mad dictator of Paraguay. For ten years, from 1821 to 1831, he was held prisoner while Humboldt, Bolívar, the emperor of Brazil, and several European monarchs tried in vain to effect his release. However, we are led to believe that Bonpland did not lead such an unhappy existence during his period of captivity, for he continued his botanical studies in the vicinity of Cerrito, where he was detained and treated somewhat as an honored guest, although under surveillance. After gaining his freedom he continued to reside in South America and died at Santa Anna, May 4, 1858. Father Zahm, when with Roosevelt in South America, discovered to his delight a small town in northern Argentina by the name of Bonpland. The French botanist deserved the honor, for while he was with Humboldt he discovered six thousand species of plants, all new to science.

Some twenty-five years after Humboldt first set foot in South America (1825) there appeared in England a book entitled *Wanderings in South America.* CHARLES WATERTON (1782–1865), the author of this work, was born at Walton Hall, Yorkshire, July 3, 1782. He was educated at a Roman Catholic college, traveled somewhat in Spain, and, in 1804, went to British Guiana to look after some estates owned by his family. His father died in 1806, and he returned to England. Later he made four more journeys to British Guiana and spent altogether more than ten years in the forests of northern South America. Although he traveled rather extensively in French, Dutch, and British Guiana and in parts of Brazil and Venezuela, he gave his readers a very vague notion of just where he went. This is understandable, for the geography of the Guianas at the beginning of the nineteenth century was not any too well known, and it is clear that Waterton traveled along many streams and visited many places in the interior unheard of by the cartographers of that day.

However, it is certain that on his first journey (1812) he ascended the Demerara and the Essequibo, and probably the large western tributary of the latter, the Rupununi, and then crossed over the divide to the waters of the Rio Branco down which he traveled to São Joaquim. This ambitious trip was made some nine or ten years before the Brazilians declared their independence, and the fort at São Joaquim consequently was garrisoned by Portuguese soldiers. Waterton spent several days there recovering from a severe attack of malaria. Following his recovery, he made the return journey without apparent incident. The chief objective of the excursion to the waters of the Amazon was to obtain a quantity of the famous curare poison ("Wourali," he called it). Waterton was successful in this, and he took a quantity of the poison to England, where its potency was the subject of numerous experiments by himself and other interested scientists. The account of this first journey to America includes a lengthy description, the earliest of consequence to be written, on the preparation, effects, and virulence of curare poison.

On the second journey to South America (1816) Waterton sailed to Pernambuco (Recife), Brazil. He explored for some weeks in the vicinity of this city and thence took ship for Cayenne, French Guiana. It was his plan to go from there to Pará and then travel up the Amazon and Rio Negro to the region of the Casiquiare, whence he would return to the Guianas overland keeping a weather eye out along the way for Lake Parima and El Dorado. This plan failed to materialize and, from Cayenne, Waterton wandered instead into the Guiana forests again. Just where he went is not clear except for the fact he "left Cayenne for Paramaribo, went through the interior to the Coryntin, stopped a few days in New Amsterdam, and proceeded to Demerara," as British Guiana was called in those days. The account of this second journey to the Guianas is taken up chiefly with descriptions of many of the birds of northern South America, such as the cock-of-the-rock, hummingbird, bellbird, toucan, macaw, tinamou, and cotinga. In these pictures of bird life are incorporated the observations he made, not only on this visit to South America but on the other three as well.

On the third visit (1820) Waterton went direct to Demerara, where he apparently spent most of his time along the lower reaches of the Essequibo, although that is not certain. The narration of this stay includes descriptions of several of the mammals

—sloth, giant anteater, armadillo, and vampire bat among others—as well as descriptions of snakes, caimans, certain insect pests, and native Indian tribes.

On Waterton's fourth and final journey (1824) he visited the United States before proceeding to Demerara via the West Indies. Once again we have no precise notion of where his wanderings took him, although he probably did not journey far in any direction from Georgetown. The description of the Guiana experiences on this trip is taken up chiefly with his method of preserving birds for cabinets of natural history. This is of little general interest and might well have been omitted. However, he does give us some afterthoughts on the sloth, hummingbird, tinamou, and vampire that are worth while, and concludes with a very satisfactory account of the monkeys of the region.

Instead of attempting a day-by-day narration of his wanderings Waterton confined himself largely to descriptions of the Guiana animals—the caiman, toucan, bushmaster, jaguar, sting ray, and many others he encountered on one or another of his sojourns here. Of these creatures he writes in a simple but archaic manner that is not only informative but often delightful. Even though his rather frequent passages from Ovid or Livy are not always fully comprehensible, they do not detract from the color and the charm of the subject at hand. Waterton's observations were particularly valuable at that date, since they were the first ones upon which any degree of reliance could be placed. It must be remembered that in 1825 the ideas in Europe and the United States concerning the animals of South America were based largely upon a knowledge of museum specimens; little or nothing was known of the habits of any of these creatures. During the several years Waterton spent in the forests of the Guianas he had many opportunities to observe the general behavior of the animals of that region. This privilege had been afforded previous travelers, but none had taken advantage of it. Many of the forms of which Waterton wrote had found their way, in preservatives, into the hands of the closet naturalists of Europe and elsewhere. With these specimens before them they essayed lengthy descriptions relative to color, size, and other anatomical points. Some of these naturalists went further and tried to portray certain habits of the animals. As an example, the giant anteater was pictured by the laboratory scientists as walking on the soles of its forefeet in the same way in which other mammals generally travel. Waterton, having the advantage of residing in the anteater's natural habitat, was in a position to note the actual manner in which this peculiar beast progresses, a manner entirely different from that ascribed to it by the European biologists. The chief value of Waterton's *Wanderings*, then, lies in the graphic descriptions he gave the world of the behavior of living animals in their native environment. We must bear in mind that Waterton was not a scientist trained in twentieth century standards, and so did not have the background of scientific reserve which is now considered proper; in fact, his academic training was chiefly in the classics.

He has been criticized on the ground that he was a sensationalist who, knowing the weakness of the public for simmering adventures, did not hesitate to draw upon his imagination whenever the occasion presented itself. Some individuals believe with great difficulty—or not at all—his very colorful account of how he managed to capture and ride a large caiman; and his equally vivid story of how he captured a *coulacanara* (apparently a boa constrictor) with his bare hands.

In Waterton's defense it may be said, in the first place, that the bulk of his observations are accurate and unimagined. In the second place he was not an ordinary man: he was an eccentric. He wandered through Guiana forests always in his bare feet. At home in England, according to Koebel, he invariably slept on the hard floor with not even a rug under his body and used a block of wood for a pillow. An *ordinary* man would hardly think of attempting the capture of a large snake with his bare hands, or of sleeping on the bare floor. Perhaps, being of such a capricious nature, Waterton actually experienced the adventures which he so energetically recounted.

After his return from his last journey to the Guianas he passed the remainder of his life at Walton Hall, where he busied himself writing on natural history. Three series of these essays were published (1833, 1844, 1857). He died at Walton Hall, May 27, 1865.

The greatest of all naturalists to visit South America was

Charles Darwin. Between 1831 and 1836 Darwin, as naturalist on H.M.S. *Beagle* under Captain FitzRoy, circumnavigated the globe. Of the five years which he spent away from England, three and a half were passed either in South America or along the coast aboard ship. The *Journal of Researches into the Natural History and Geology of the Countries Visited During the Voyage Round the World of H.M.S. "Beagle,"* first published in 1839, is then a volume devoted for the most part to the South American continent.

Darwin first landed in Bahia, Brazil, February 29, 1832, and his first impressions of the tropical landscape were full of youthful enthusiasm. "The day has past delightfully," he exclaimed. "Delight itself, however, is a weak term to express the feelings of a naturalist who for the first time has wandered by himself in a Brazilian forest. The elegance of the grasses, the novelty of the parasitical plants, the beauty of the flowers, the glossy green of the foliage, but above all the general luxuriance of the vegetation filled me with admiration. To a person fond of natural history, such a day as this brings with it a deeper pleasure than he can ever hope to experience again." A day or so later he wrote in his diary: "I can only add raptures to the former raptures. I collected a great number of brilliantly colored flowers, enough to make a florist go wild. Brazilian scenery is nothing more nor less than a view in the Arabian nights, with the advantage of reality."

The *Beagle* was along the eastern coast of South America for over two years. Darwin spent a good deal of this time on board ship as it sailed to Rio de Janeiro, to Montevideo, Bahía Blanca, Tierra del Fuego, the Falkland Islands, and other specific points; but he had the opportunity of going ashore rather often and made at least five inland journeys of consequence. These were as follows: (1) Patagones to Bahía Blanca, August 11–17, 1833; (2) Bahía Blanca to Buenos Aires, September 8–20, 1833; (3) Buenos Aires to Santa Fe, September 27 to October 2, 1833; (4) Montevideo to Mercedes and return, November 14–28, 1833; (5) expedition up Santa Cruz River, April 18 to May 8, 1834.

It was on these trips that Darwin became acquainted with the animal life of Uruguay, the Argentine pampas, and Patagonia. His descriptions of the rhea, guanaco, puma, armadillo, viscacha, capybara, condor, and many other less familiar forms not only are of great interest to the reader, but were the first to be written by a scientist of note. Many of the observations on these animals found recorded in our natural histories of today are taken directly from Darwin's original words.

It was at Port Desire in Patagonia that Darwin found a new species of rhea, or South American ostrich. He sent a specimen to London and was later honored by having it named after him—*Rhea Darwini.*

In a way the most significant discovery made by Darwin was at Bahía Blanca, where he uncovered the fossilized head of a large animal. It was, so far as he was able to tell at the time, the head of some species allied to a rhinoceros. This was the first of many of those huge prehistoric animals whose remains Darwin was to encounter on more than one occasion and under more than one condition. The effect of this original discovery on Darwin's mind was, perhaps, intangible; but as subsequent discoveries were made there gradually developed the impelling conviction that the animals he saw alive in the Argentine—they were undoubtedly similar in structure to the fossilized species he unearthed—had evolved from the ones he discovered buried in the earth.

Darwin made two visits to Tierra del Fuego. He seems to have been more impressed by the wild Indians (Fuegians) of that region than by any other feature or circumstance. According to him they "exist in a lower state of improvement than in any other part of the world. I could not have believed how wide was the difference between savage and civilized man; it is greater than that between a wild and a domestic animal."

In June, 1834, the *Beagle* rounded the Horn, and after a voyage of about a month it cast anchor in Valparaiso, the chief seaport of Chile. From here Darwin made two expeditions into the interior: (1) Valparaiso to Santiago and Mendoza, March 18 to April 10, 1835; and (2) Valparaiso to Copiapó, April 27 to June 22, 1835.

The trip to Santiago and Mendoza was for the purpose of continuing his studies in geology and zoology but in an entirely new environment, that of the Andes. Most of this journey along and over the cordillera was accomplished by mule, and Darwin evidently had plenty of opportunity to study the beast, for he made this rather unusual statement about it: "The mule always appears to me a most surprising animal. That a hybrid should possess more reason, memory, obstinacy, social affection, powers of muscular endurance, and length of life, than either of its parents, seems to indicate that art has here outdone nature."

It was on the journey to Copiapó, at night, that he discovered a fact which had been doubted in England; viz., that there are such things as blood-eating bats. He not only saw the vampire bat in the act of taking a meal of blood from a horse but, after capturing it, was able to identify the species as *Desmodus d'orbignyi.*

The month spent in this journey was valuable to him chiefly for geological reasons. His references to animals are few and sketchy. He was impressed very much by his discovery of "red snow," a phenomenon caused by the presence of a red alga *(Protococcus nivalis)* growing on the snowbanks.

In July, 1835, Darwin sailed from Chile for Peru. Following a stay of several weeks there he sailed (September 7, 1835) for the Galápagos Islands.

After a careful reading of the *Journal of Researches* one finds it hard to believe that the observations and deductions revealed therein were the work of a youth who was only twenty-two years old when the expedition left England. Darwin wrote with a clarity and vigor that few men have possessed at a much more mature age, and each page bears witness to his breadth of interest, the keenness of his observations, his natural gift of description, his unbounded enthusiasm, and his passion for truth. Some scientists have one or two of these qualities; a few, three or four; mighty few have all.

In the light of what we consider an education in the twentieth century Darwin's preparation in the sciences was meager. Indeed, with the slight training he had it is a miracle that he was chosen to make the journey. There were a score or more of men in England better qualified than he, among whom might be included Charles Waterton. However, the position as naturalist was a nonremunerative one, and older men, with more responsibilities, were not so eager to work five years without emolument.

South America and the Naturalists

Darwin was educated as befitted a Victorian gentleman: he became well steeped in Latin and Greek and had little opportunity, if he wished, to learn geology and biology. He did have some scientific training under such men as Henslow the Cambridge botanist, the geologist Sedgwick, and Dr. Grant of Edinburgh, but we know that this was just a smattering. It is likely that Darwin's most valuable training came through his own efforts. From a very early age he was a collector of minerals, insects, and flowers, and gradually developed the enthusiasm characteristic of an ardent amateur.

In spite of the lack of formal training in geology and zoology, during the five years he was naturalist he made profound contributions to both of those sciences. Darwin has been termed "the perfect traveler" because of his eager interest in everything. The fields of zoology and geology attracted him more than any others; but his writings show he was never so absorbed in either of these that he could not lend an eye or an ear to other subjects, such as history, physiography, botany, and geography.

Although Darwin may be called "the perfect traveler" for the reasons just mentioned, he was far from being a good sailor. He suffered horribly from seasickness and never on the voyage was able to get his "sea legs." Five years of more or less continuous nausea may have contributed to Darwin's later invalidism.

The voyage of the *Beagle* will go down in history as one of the greatest of all sea journeys. Without it Darwin would not have written the *Origin of Species*. Confirmation of that fact may be found in the opening paragraph of that immortal work where Darwin wrote: "When on board H.M.S. *Beagle* as naturalist, I was much struck with certain facts in the distribution of the organic beings inhabiting South America, and in the geological relations of the present to the past inhabitants of that continent. These facts . . . seemed to throw some light on the origin of species—that mystery of mysteries, as it has been called by one of our greatest philosophers."

And yet Darwin narrowly missed being turned down as naturalist on the trip because of the shape of his nose! Captain Fitz-Roy thought he could judge character by a close study of the facial contour. When he saw Darwin for the first time he had serious doubts as to whether anyone with such a nose "could possess sufficient energy and determination for the voyage."

If we exclude the part the *Voyage* played in the *Origin of Species,* it still remains one of the real classics of biological exploration and deserves the careful study of every biologist. According to Theodore Roosevelt it is "the best book of its kind ever written."

In the years 1847–1848 there was published in Germany a book, *Reisen in Britisch-Guiana* (3 vols.), by RICHARD SCHOMBURGK (1811–1891), a German botanist born at Freiburg, October 5, 1811. Although deserving of wide attention, this work was not translated into English until 1922. In the preface to this recent edition the translator Walter Edmund Roth, curator of the British Guiana Museum until his death in 1933, wrote that he "was at a loss to understand how such a monumental, so interesting, and valuable work had become forgotten as it were, and had never been 'done into English,' since it deserves to rank with the highest works on South American travel and adventure."

Richard Schomburgk was the brother of the celebrated Prussian, Sir Robert Schomburgk, who traveled extensively in the Guianas and Venezuela and, commissioned by the Royal Geographical Society of London, established the Schomburgk Line between British Guiana and Venezuela. Perhaps he will longest be remembered as the discoverer of the magnificent *Victoria Regia* lily.

Richard Schomburgk landed in Georgetown, British Guiana, early in 1841—a year which came near being his last, for he had not been long in Georgetown when he fell violently ill with yellow fever. He recovered, however, and in the years 1841 to 1844 ascended or descended practically every river of importance in British Guiana and several in Brazil and Venezuela that have their headwaters close to the western border of the British possession. He made an expedition to the mouth of the Orinoco and explored the Barima and Amakura rivers. He explored the Demerara and Corentyne. He ascended the Essequibo and Rupununi and Tacatú rivers. He made an expedition to São Joaquim, the small establishment on the Rio Branco previously visited by Waterton. He traveled from there to the headwaters of the

Cotinga, and crossed the Pacaraima Mountains to the headwaters of the Caroni, a tributary of the Orinoco. While here he attempted an ascent of the then unclimbed Mt. Roraima, but failed to reach the summit. (This was not to be conquered until 1884, when Sir Everard F. im Thurn and H. I. Perkins discovered a trail leading to the top.) From this expedition Schomburgk returned to Georgetown by way of the Cuyuni. Some interest may be attached to the fact that these trips were all made possible in the beginning through the solicitation of Humboldt to the German ruler Frederick William IV in his behalf.

One of the very few rivers in British Guiana that Schomburgk did not travel was the Potaro, a small western tributary that empties into the Essequibo not a great many miles away from the coast. The emotions of Schomburgk may be surmised when he learned in 1873 of the discovery of one of the most magnificent waterfalls in the world, the Kaieteur Falls, 822 feet high, on the Potaro River. A side journey from the Essequibo of a very few miles and his name, instead of that of C. Barrington Brown, would have forever been linked with these falls.

Schomburgk's *Travels* contains a great deal of extraneous material; considerable portions are not of any great general interest, and, furthermore, there are literally hundreds of plants and animals mentioned in the text only by their scientific names. For instance, even taxonomists might be perturbed by the following typical paragraph: "More towards the neighbourhood of the stream there grew a many-coloured mixture of different species of *Dracontium, Bacopa aquatica* Aubl., which were interspersed with delicate groups of *Spennera aquatica* Mart., *Lisyanthus Coerulescens* Aubl., and the *Tocoyena longiflora* Aubl., with long red blossoms."

However, in spite of Schomburgk's tendency to wordiness, both in German and in Latin, the real merit of the *Travels* cannot be overlooked. It would be incomprehensible that a man should travel as extensively as he did, on the march more or less continuously for three years, visiting mountain regions, savannas, jungle of all types, and Indian villages, without having many varied and valuable experiences with which to interest the reader. Schomburgk had a keen pair of eyes and remarkable enthusiasm and energy, and there is an enormous amount of material in the 800-odd pages of his translation that will interest anthropologist, botanist, and zoologist alike. He was continuously with one Indian tribe or another, and his descriptions of them, their modes of life, manufacture of curare poison, methods of hunting, etc., are of signal importance. The ornithologist is well acquainted with his experiences with the cock-of-the-rock; Schomburgk was the first naturalist to witness the remarkable dance performed by this bird. He witnessed the effect of the venom from a fer-de-lance on an Indian girl who died from the bite a few hours later in spite of all he could do. He saw a piranha, the cannibal fish of South America, bite off two fingers from the hand of one of his native helpers. There is hardly a mammal, or bird, or reptile, or fish in that whole country that Schomburgk did not see and of which he did not write in greater or less detail. Schomburgk went to Australia in 1849, and in 1865 was made director of the Botanical Gardens at Adelaide. He died in Adelaide, March 24, 1891.

The first naturalist from the United States to travel and write of his experiences in South America was WILLIAM H. EDWARDS (1822–1909), a descendant of Jonathan Edwards. He was born at Hunter, New York, March 5, 1822. His early life was passed in the Catskill Mountains, where he acquired a love of nature. He graduated from Williams College in 1842 and then studied law in New York City. From February to October, 1846, Edwards was engaged in traveling and in making a collection of animals along the Amazon. His only journey of any distance into the interior was a trip from Pará to Manáos (Barra), although he made several short excursions into the forests in the immediate vicinity of Pará and somewhat longer ones to the islands of Marajó and Mexiana. The account of his experiences in tropical America was published in 1847 under the title of *A Voyage up the River Amazon.* This volume contains only about two hundred pages, but Edwards is so enthusiastic in his descriptions of the people, the vegetation, the climate, and the many kinds of animals he encountered that the reader at the end closes the book with regret.

This small volume, however, soon attracted the attention of two men who were to become famous in the history of South

American exploration. These were Alfred Russel Wallace and Henry Walter Bates. It is doubtful if they would have turned their attention to the Amazon had they not read Edwards' narrative. In Wallace's autobiography is this significant statement: "What decided our going to Pará and the Amazon rather than to any other part of the tropics was the publication in 1847, in Murray's Home and Colonial Library, of *A Voyage up the Amazon* by Mr. W. H. Edwards. This little book was so clearly and brightly written, described so well the beauty and the grandeur of tropical vegetation, and gave such a pleasing account of the people, their kindness and hospitality to strangers, and especially of the English and American merchants in Pará, while expenses of living and of traveling were moderate, that Bates and myself at once agreed that this was the very place for us to go if there was any chance of paying our expenses by the sale of our duplicate collection."

Very soon after Wallace and Bates read this volume they learned that Edwards was in London. They called upon him, secured valuable information, which increased their ardor for going to South America, and received letters of introduction from him to some of Edwards' American friends in Pará.

Edwards was a man of many interests. Soon after his return from the Amazon he was admitted to the New York Bar, and some years later, becoming interested in the coal business, he moved to Coalburg, West Virginia, a small mining town on the Great Kanawha River. Here he built railroads, opened coal mines, and led an extremely busy life. Always, though, he found time for the study of butterflies, and it is for his monumental work, *The Butterflies of North America,* a superbly illustrated set of volumes issued between 1868 and 1897, that he is best known. In 1887 Wallace visited Edwards at his West Virginia home when on a lecture tour in the United States. Edwards died at Coalburg, April 4, 1909.

Alfred Russel Wallace (1823–1913) was born at Usk, Monmouthshire, England, January 8, 1823. He early became interested in botany and somewhat later (1844–45), while an English master in a school at Leicester, met Bates, who introduced him to the study of insects. Their common interest in natural history soon led to plans for foreign travel. On May 28, 1848, Wallace and Bates arrived in South America. Their ship docked at Pará (Belém), and the two young naturalists—Wallace was twenty-five and Bates twenty-three—made this town their headquarters for almost a year and a half before leaving on expeditions up the Amazon. Wallace always insisted that the environs of Pará was the most fertile field for collecting he encountered anywhere in the Amazon Basin. More than four years all told were spent by Wallace in tropical America. Following his return to England, he published in 1853 *A Narrative of Travels on the Amazon and the Rio Negro*. This was the best general account of that part of South America, and of its animals and plants written up to that time.

Although Wallace and Bates were together much of the time after reaching Pará until they separated (March, 1850) for individual excursions up-river, they make, peculiarly enough, practically no references to each other in their written accounts of that period. Perhaps they considered that their separate accounts would be more effective if done with as little mention of each other as possible. At any rate they were together on excursions to the Tocantins River, to the islands of Marajó and Mexiana, and to other points near Pará. In these months they became accustomed to the climate, to modes of living and travel, and learned enough Portuguese to understand the language and to be understood.

On December 31, 1849, Wallace reached Manáos (then called Barra de Rio Negro), a town of five to six thousand people. Two small trips were made from here: one a short distance up the Rio Negro in search of the umbrella bird and the other to the Solimões, as the Amazon is called above its junction with the Rio Negro.

On the last day of August, 1850, Wallace left Manáos on the first of two long journeys to the upper Rio Negro. His ascent of this stream was a leisurely one, for he made many stops along the way and collected extensively. It was not until February 4, 1851, that he reached San Carlos, which was then the major Venezuelan town on the Rio Negro. Just beyond San Carlos is the mouth of the Casiquiare, but Wallace passed this famous connection and went on to the mouth of the Pimichín River. This was the stream Humboldt had descended just fifty years before when he crossed over the watershed from San Fernando de Atabapo to the Rio Negro. Wallace made his way up this same river and crossed the same watershed—probably at the same place. A walk of about ten miles from the Pimichín brought him to the village of Javita on the Temí River, a tributary of the Atabapo. He was now in country drained by the Orinoco and in a town at which Humboldt had stopped in the year 1800. There were no monks in the town to be of assistance to Wallace as there had been on Humboldt's visit; and he needed aid, for his entire crew of natives deserted him after he had been there a few days. It rained continuously during Wallace's residence, as it did during Humboldt's, but he made a large collection of many animals quite new to him—forty species of butterflies among others. He said the great blue Morphos were more plentiful here than anywhere he had been. Wallace thought that in the dry season Javita would prove to be one of the finest collecting grounds in that part of South America, especially for insects.

Following a stay of over a month, Wallace retraced his steps to the Rio Negro and returned to Manáos in September, having been absent a little more than a year.

His stay in Manáos this time was just long enough to store his miscellaneous collections and assemble supplies for his next expedition. His plan was to go up the Rio Negro again to the mouth of the Uaupés, a large western tributary, and then to ascend that stream to a point no white man had reached before. Following out his plan, Wallace, some weeks after leaving Manáos, found himself back at the small town of São Joaquim located near the mouth of the Uaupés. Here he was severely ill with malaria; but, improving, he left February 16, 1852, although still so weak he had difficulty in getting in and out of the boat. A month of extremely laborious travel through and around innumerable rapids and waterfalls brought him to the native village of Mucúra. A notable feature of this trip was that Wallace traveled almost directly on the equator for many miles; perhaps the only place in the world where a boat trip of such a nature could be made. He was now well across the Brazilian border and in Colombian territory many hundreds of miles from the mouth of the Amazon. He would have liked to push on farther; but travel was difficult, and his health was precarious. After a stay of two weeks at this remote Indian village he began his return to Manáos and Pará. He reached Manáos in May, and on July 12, 1852, sailed for England.

In his autobiography Wallace wrote that there were three great features that impressed him particularly while on the Amazon: "The first was the virgin forest, everywhere grand, often beautiful and sublime; the second, the wonderful variety and exquisite beauty of the butterflies and birds; and the third, the meeting and living with man in a state of nature—with absolutely uncontaminated savages."

Unfortunately Wallace's South American exploration was mixed with considerable misfortune and tragedy. He would have remained longer on the Rio Negro and Uaupés if ill health had not forced him to leave. He suffered from both dysentery and malaria, and the latter disease failed to respond to treatment. His younger brother, Herbert Wallace, followed him to the Amazon, collected for a time, and on the point of returning to England took yellow fever and died. At that time Wallace was on the Rio Negro, and he did not know of his brother's death in Pará until months later. Finally, the ship in which Wallace himself was returning to England caught fire, and all aboard were forced to take to the boats. His entire collection, with the exception of those specimens shipped at an earlier date, went up in flames. At the time of this catastrophe (August 6) the ship was in latitude 30° 30′ N. and longitude 52° W., seven hundred miles from the nearest land—the Bermuda Islands. After ten days in open boats, rations and water were practically exhausted, and the crew and passengers were still over two hundred miles from the Bermudas. It is doubtful whether they would have reached their goal (for a calm had settled over the ocean) if a vessel—the *Jordeson* bound from Cuba to London—had not picked them up. While being thankful that his life was saved Wallace never quite recovered from the crushing loss of his collection, upon which he had lavished so much time and care.

Fate dealt more kindly with him in later years. He soon went to the Far East, where he traveled for several years, following which *The Malay Archipelago* (1869) was published, one of the greatest of explorers' records. Subsequent books, *Island Life* and *The Geographical Distribution of Animals,* added to his fame. He is best known though as the codiscoverer with Darwin of the principle of Natural Selection. He died at Bradstone, Dorset, November 7, 1913.

HENRY WALTER BATES (1825–1892) was born at Leicester, February 8, 1825. Although his parents intended that he should become a business man some feature of his inheritance directed otherwise. While still a young man he became avidly interested in the collection of insects. The turning point in his career came when he met Wallace in 1844.

Bates collected in South America over a period of eleven years —1848 to 1859. The forests of Brazil made a tremendous impression on him. "There is something in a tropical forest akin to the ocean in its effect on the mind," he wrote. "Man feels so completely his insignificance there and the vastness of nature." As the months turned into years this country of the Amazon with its inexhaustible store of insects, birds, mammals, and plants became an increasing source of wonder and delight. He loved it as Conrad loved the sea and Hudson the Argentine pampas. Periodically he suffered from improper diet, submitted to insect ravages, and felt starved for civilized companionship; but his early impressions of grandeur and beauty in the Brazilian wilderness remained with him throughout his entire life. Just a few months before Bates returned to England he made a short excursion to a small village on the upper Amazon called São Paulo. "Although now a forest-rambler of ten years experience," he wrote, "the beautiful forest which surrounds this settlement gave me as much enjoyment as if I had only just landed for the first time in a tropical country."

One reason for Bates' profound love for Amazonia was his enthusiasm for the study of insects. He was primarily an entomologist and could have found no place on earth where insects occurred in greater profusion. The woods and open fields along the Amazon yielded a harvest of ants, wasps, beetles, moths, and butterflies that far surpassed his fondest dreams. Before he reached America he could have had little or no conception of how abundant the insect life there really was. Imagine a country like the vicinity of Pará where within an hour's walk a total of seven hundred species of butterflies could be collected!

But Bates did not confine his interest to insects. He by no means neglected the plants, reptiles, birds, and mammals. His expositions on toucans, marmosets, turtles, spider monkeys, and many other animals reveal just as much enthusiasm as those he wrote on termites, sauba ants, and heliconid butterflies. He gives us remarkably vivid pictures of the towns he visited, the people inhabiting them, and their customs. He visited some of the native tribes, and his descriptions of them would do credit to a trained anthropologist. Under no circumstances did Bates' powers of observation fail him, and he was far more than a mere collector. His eyes were clear, his brain was active, and his pen was graphic.

Bates, unlike Wallace and Humboldt, did not choose to make long, strenuous journeys far into unexplored regions of the continent. He did travel for some fourteen hundred miles along the Amazon—from Pará to Ega—but he never went far from the parent stream. Bates liked rather to settle down in a region where collecting was good and to remain there until the possibilities were exhausted or he felt he could profit more by going elsewhere. In one place we find him saying, "I wished to explore districts at my ease." As a result of this procedure he passed the greater part of his eleven years in just three regions. In each case he made some town on the Amazon his headquarters and from that point explored the region in all directions. These three towns were: Pará, near the mouth of the Amazon; Santarem, a few hundred miles upstream; and Ega, fourteen hundred miles from Pará.

The better part of three years was spent in or near Pará, although not all at one time. He made several side trips, the most ambitious of which were expeditions up the Tocantins and to the islands of Marajó and Mexiana. In these months he formed the acquaintance of men in Pará who were to be of great service to him later; he learned to speak Portuguese (the language of Brazil), became acclimated to the equatorial sun, and learned the customs of the country. It was here he made his intensive studies of the subterranean activities of the sauba, or leaf-cutting, ants and amassed large collections of butterflies and other insects. His journeys on foot into the forests made him acquainted with the commoner plants and animals to be found there. He encountered at Pará his first monkeys, anteaters, sloths, boa constrictors, iguanas, macaws, and innumerable other forms associated with a tropical American forest.

After this period of jungle apprenticeship Bates left on a journey of reconnaissance up the Amazon; he wished to discover for himself likely collecting sites to be explored by him in the future at his leisure. Following a year of travel he chose Santarem, at the mouth of the Tapajós, as a location of unusual promise. He made this his headquarters for three and a half years. From here he made trips up the Tapajós and to places of interest in the surrounding country. At Aveyros above Santarem on the Tapajós (Aveyros is not far from Fordlandia, the rubber town built by Henry Ford), Bates found another locality rich in butterflies. He spent forty days here and in that time captured or identified three hundred species within one-half hour's walk of the village. Among the interesting experiences of Bates along the Tapajós were his observations on the Indian manner of catching fish with the juices of poisonous plants; also the reactions of a native woman who had been stung by a sting ray.

Bates' most protracted stay at one place, however, was at Ega, a small village fourteen hundred miles from Pará near the mouth of the river Teffé. A study of any modern map will not reveal the location of Ega, for its name has been changed to that of the river —Teffé. Bates was here in 1850 and stayed a year. After he had concluded his long residence at Santarem he returned to Ega for three and a half years more. The South American collection of animals by Bates included approximately fourteen thousand distinct species of insects. Of this number at least half were discovered at Ega. Next to Pará this locality was the richest in its supply of butterflies; he collected five hundred and fifty species here. In our time it seems impossible that less than a hundred years ago a naturalist could find a territory where over half of the animals and plants were new to science. Ega was such a place for Bates, and almost every day spent there he added a new species of butterfly or wasp or beetle to a rapidly growing list of insects. But, as elsewhere, he found many animals to interest him other than insects. His studies of the aquatic turtles of the region were made at Ega, as were observations on the manatee, dolphin, electric eel, caiman, and other water-inhabiting animals. He enriched his knowledge on the subject of monkeys, a group of mammals which seemed to intrigue him, perhaps, more than any other.

During the last year of his stay at Ega, Bates' health became increasingly bad. Poor food reduced his resistance to infection, and malaria did the rest. He fought this disease with all the vigor at his command but, at last, was forced to admit his inability to cope with it longer. He left Ega for Pará and on June 2, 1859, embarked for England. In leaving, Bates declared that the saddest hours of his life were those spent when he realized the last links connecting him with this "land of so many pleasing recollections" were severed. Even after eleven years away from home and country, such was his love for Brazil that he saw little prospect of happiness in returning to England.

In 1863 Bates published the account of his experiences in South America under the title of *The Naturalist on the Amazons.* This book, one of the most delightfully informative volumes of scientific travel and observation in any language, would probably not have been written except for the friendly insistence of Charles Darwin. After his return to England Bates was slow in recovering his health, and as time went by gave less and less thought to the idea of transforming his voluminous notes into the form of a book. Some two years had elapsed when he made the acquaintance of Darwin. The latter was enthusiastic in his praise of Bates' scientific contributions and strongly urged him to write a book of his travels, impressing him meanwhile with the fact that such a work would be of signal value to science. Bates responded to this insistence and began the narrative at once. When the two met again Darwin once more offered encouragement.

Following the publication of *The Naturalist on the Amazons,* Darwin said Bates was second only to Humboldt in describing a tropical forest. Time, the most reliable criterion of books, has seen fit to reverse the opinion of Darwin. Scientists and laymen read Bates, even at the present time, with just as much interest and profit as they did in 1864, whereas Humboldt is used mainly for reference. It is altogether likely that future generations will find him just as interesting and stimulating. Humboldt's narrative falls down in comparison with Bates' in that it paints a very incomplete picture of any one part of South America. Bates, on the contrary, describes a single region—the Amazon valley—more accurately and completely than any one before or since has described either that region or any other. By doing this Bates has probably rendered a greater service than any other naturalist who has studied the animals of South America in their native habitats.

In 1864 Bates was appointed assistant secretary of the Royal Geographical Society, a position he held until his death, February 16, 1892.

Very few people outside of botanical circles have ever heard the name of RICHARD SPRUCE (1817–1893). Yet if Fate had not dealt unkindly with him he might have become as famous as either Wallace or Bates. Spruce was born September 10, 1817, at Ganthorpe, near York. He was educated by his father, who was a schoolmaster, and from 1839 to 1844 was a mathematics teacher in the Collegiate School at York. During these years his chief interest, though, was botany, and this avocation led him in 1845 to the Pyrenees where he collected for over a period of ten months. Upon his return he wrote a monograph on *The Musci and Hepaticae of the Pyrenees.* By this time he had made a name for himself as a botanist and was intimate with many of the most eminent plant students in England. In 1848 he went to London, where he heard of the successes Bates and Wallace were having in South America. These reports made him resolve to travel to the same region, where he thought he could easily pay expenses through the sale of sets of well-preserved plants.

Spruce landed in Pará on July 12, 1849, just a little over a year after Bates and Wallace, and lived in tropical America for a period of fifteen years—until 1864—and amassed an enormous collection of plants.

What qualities does a man possess who can break all ties with the homeland and bury himself for years in the jungle of a foreign land? The question might have been raised in connection with Bates or Wallace or Schomburgk but it more aptly applies to Spruce since he endured the hardships of jungle existence over a longer period of years than they. The major prerequisite for such a protracted period of tropical servitude is undoubtedly enthusiasm. That quality was pronounced in Bates, and in Spruce. There would be disagreement over the selection of other qualities, but surely among the most important are fearlessness, optimism, a sense of humor, and a patience that knows no end. Bates, Wallace, Waterton, and Spruce all had these qualities in good measure. It might be suggested that no one could endure the hardships of exploration long without a rugged constitution. That would appear to be true on the surface, but Spruce was in delicate health before he went to South America and periodically suffered from a chronic ailment throughout his stay. Like Bates, he would have remained longer under the equator, if ill health had not forced him to leave.

Spruce lived twenty-eight years after his return to England, but he was never free from a chronic intestinal disorder. This ailment was so severe he could walk only short distances and was unable to use a microscope for more than a few minutes at a time. Yet during the first seven years of this invalidism he published a monograph of 118 pages on *The Palms of the Amazon Valley*, and a 600-page treatise on *The Hepaticae of the Amazon and the Andes of Peru.* These works established his reputation among botanists around the world. He died December 28, 1893, without having written the narrative of his travels; but he had kept copious notes in the field, expecting to publish them. After his death these fell into the hands of Alfred Russel Wallace, who recognized their importance. However, eleven years slipped by before he got to editing them. In 1908, forty-four years after Spruce returned from South America, Wallace published *Notes of a Botanist on the Amazon and Andes.*

With good health Spruce might have written a narrative equaling that of Bates. He might have done for the vegetable world of the Amazon valley what Bates did for the animal. Spruce had one advantage over Bates and all other naturalists in South America —he lived there longer. More than that, he covered a remarkable lot of territory, considering the difficulties of travel in that day. He not only explored along the Amazon proper but traveled on the Trombetas, Rio Negro, Casiquiare, upper Orinoco as far as the great rapids of Atures and Maipures, Uaupés, Solimões, and

Huallago. In addition, he collected extensively in the Peruvian Andes and along the Pacific. While in Peru he was commissioned to secure the seeds and seedlings of the cinchona, the tree from which we get quinine. He was entirely successful in this mission and shipped the plants to India.

Wallace did remarkably well in editing Spruce's notes; but we wonder what Spruce would have told the reader if he himself could have written the complete story of his fifteen years under the tropical sun in America. We read his notes with great pleasure and profit; but the narrative is disjointed, and unquestionably much is missing which only Spruce could have told.

The fact that Spruce, Bates, and others were forced to leave South America because of illness might leave the impression that the lives of these men were cut short because of their sojourn in the tropics. The following table will speak for itself:

Humboldt	(1769–1859)	lived to the age of 89
Waterton	(1782–1865)	lived to the age of 83
Schomburgk	(1811–1891)	lived to the age of 80
Wallace	(1823–1913)	lived to the age of 90
Bates	(1825–1892)	lived to the age of 67
Spruce	(1817–1893)	lived to the age of 76

These six men who spent close to fifty years in South America lived altogether 485 years, or to an average age of 81 years.

W. H. Hudson (1841–1922) is the only native South American on our list. This remarkable ornithologist was born August 4, 1841, in the small Argentine town of Quilmes, a few miles from Buenos Aires. His parents were Americans of substantial New England stock who emigrated from Massachusetts to Argentina not many years prior to his birth.

From an early age Hudson showed a marked interest in the wild life of the pampas, and as he grew older his affection for the animals, the birds in particular, completely overshadowed all other inclinations. That this ardor was a vital part of his make-up we cannot doubt, for in all of that immense country there was no one who shared his adoration of these creatures, no one capable of assisting him at any time in his studies. As Hudson gained more freedom he began to extend his world by taking journeys farther and farther onto the plains; it was not unusual for him to ride away and be gone for days, even weeks. In this manner he learned the animals of the pampas as no one has come to know them since his day. He was not handicapped by any of the distracting elements of civilization, for the pampas then were uninhabited except for an occasional settler, and the colorful adventurous gaucho. The country was free, and the animals were untouched, unfrightened by the destructive forces associated with human populations. Hudson loved this wild, trackless country; he gloried in the vast, level prairies that stretched away interminably toward the cordillera.

Who, then, would have thought of his ever leaving it? In 1868, at the age of twenty-seven he left the Argentine for England, never to return. The reasons for his departure have not been satisfactorily explained. Both his father and mother died while he was in his twenties, and he may have felt that life on the pampas would be unendurable without them. He had a chronic heart ailment and may have thought the London physicians could put it right. Just as plausible is the notion that he went to find companionship in the field of natural history. Whatever impelling notion he had, he has revealed nothing of its character.

In England he found a new home, and we know that he eventually found a measure of happiness there. The abundant bird life afforded by the downs and the seashores was always a means of escape to him from the noisy and disagreeable surroundings of the city. As the years multiplied, the country of his childhood became somewhat of a dreamland. He could not bear the thought of witnessing the changes time and people had produced in a country so replete with beautiful memories. That is probably the reason why he never returned to Quilmes.

Following many years of poverty, ill health, and other misfortunes Hudson eventually won recognition not only as a naturalist but as a writer of fiction. He became known in literary circles as a stylist who had few, if any, living equals; and among biologists as a scientist endowed with extraordinary powers of observation and exposition. He is universally known as the author of *Green Mansions,* a masterpiece of poetic prose that will serve as an imperishable monument to his artistry.

He wrote many books in addition to *Green Mansions,* but they were for the most part about birds. Although most of his energies were devoted to the wild life of England, every so often he returned fancifully to the pampas. He wrote four books pertaining to his early life in the Argentine and his observations of its natural history between the years 1841 and 1868. In addition he collaborated with Sclater in the preparation of *The Argentine Birds.* Not one of these books was published until more than fifteen years after he had left the Argentine.

Practically our only knowledge of Hudson's youth is to be found in *Far Away and Long Ago.* This is a marvelous re-creation of his early life in which is revealed his intense, almost sacred, love for the field and forest and the creatures inhabiting them. Although a history of his youth, it was not written until 1918, fifty years after he had last looked upon the silver waters of the Río de la Plata. Fifty years—and Hudson wrote as though these events he so clearly portrayed had happened yesterday. Hudson once rebuked a friend for not keeping notes, since one's memory too often fails. Such was not his own case; a half-century of England, and the circumstances surrounding his childhood days on the pampas all came back to him with the clarity of a woodland stream. In later years he said he still remembered the characteristic notes of 154 species of South American birds. This is evidence not only of an uncommonly keen memory but of a rare affection for birds.

Far Away and Long Ago is more than an autobiography, for it gives us many delightful incidents that occurred in his youth with the animals about his home. Hudson recalled his trial of strength with an armadillo, a plover-hunting experience, the depredations of a falcon, the beautiful jaçana and its eggs, the troupial's nest, the game of hunting the ostrich, and the autumnal migration of birds.

In 1883 Hudson published *Idle Days in Patagonia.* It is thought that he was about twenty-three when he first saw the waters of the Río Negro in that "Land of the Big Feet." This volume starts out as though Hudson planned to write a book of travel, but soon it is converted into a series of essays dealing with such subjects as: The War with Nature, Bird Music in South America, Sight in

Savages, The Perfume of an Evening Primrose, and Life in Patagonia. These chapters give the reader many vivid pictures of the animals of that little known country. Although written in 1883, the observations were made about 1865, when the animal life of Patagonia was as yet undisturbed by civilization.

Of all the books on the Argentine, *The Naturalist in La Plata* is most valuable to the student of zoology. This volume was published in 1892 and consists of a score or more of essays on a variety of subjects. Birds were, as always, the principal theme, and such chapter headings as Fear in Birds, Hummingbirds, The Crested Screamer, and Dancing in Nature attest his perennial affection for these winged denizens of the plains. However, there are chapters on mammals—The Dying Huanaco, Biography of the Vizcacha, The Puma, and The Mephitic Skunk—insects, spiders, and the pampas in general. There is no book in any language that gives such an intelligible and lasting impression of the animals of the Argentine.

Birds of La Plata, published in 1920, just two years before Hudson's death, is not of so much general interest to the layman; it is more of a handbook for the ornithologist. Yet with each of the many birds Hudson described he devoted a page or more, in the delightful *Naturalist in La Plata* fashion, to some experience he had had in the fifties or the sixties. Of great interest are his notes on the migratory birds that Hudson saw occasionally, after they had made a journey of thousands of miles from Canada and the United States. The phenomenon of bird migration was perpetually a mystery to him, and a subject which never failed to fascinate him.

It has been said of Hudson that he was a man who "felt everything he said and said everything he felt." Therein is a clue to his greatness—his depth of feeling for birds and mammals, and all of nature uncontaminated by civilization. He died in London, August 18, 1922.

From 1868, the date of Hudson's departure for England, until about 1910, a period of close to half a century, the examination of the natural history of South America was practically at a standstill. In comparison with the progress made in the preceding fifty years, the results were well-nigh negligible. As a consequence, there was a proportionately meager amount of literature on the subject.

One of the authors of this period was EVERARD F. IM THURN (1852–1932). Im Thurn was born at Marlborough, England, in 1852 and graduated from Exeter College, Oxford, 1875. Before attending Oxford he had already published (1869) a book on the birds of Marlborough. In 1877 he went to British Guiana, where he became curator of the Georgetown Museum.

His most lasting monument to fame is *Among the Indians of Guiana,* which was published in 1883. Considering the date at which this was written, it is an outstanding contribution to anthropological literature. Im Thurn proved himself an authority on the indigenes of northern South America—the Arawaks, Caribs, Macusis, and several other tribes. In addition to his chapters on the natives he included one on the animals of Guiana, and here and there through the text he interpolated other significant comments on the fauna of that region. Im Thurn has been previously referred to as one of the two men who made the first ascent of the famous table-mountain of Roraima, which is surrounded on all sides by perpendicular cliffs and had baffled all previous explorers who tried to reach the summit. Im Thurn and his companion discovered a diagonal ledge in the south face of the mountain and succeeded in ascending this to the top of the plateau.

Im Thurn was appointed colonial secretary and lieutenant-governor of Ceylon in 1901, and 1904 was made governor of Fiji, high commissioner of the Western Pacific, and consul-general for the Western Pacific Islands. He retired in 1910 and returned to England. His death occurred October 8, 1932, at the age of 80.

In the latter part of the nineteenth century remnants of skins of the huge ground sloth Mylodon were discovered in certain caves of Patagonia. These finds created the thought in the mind of the British scientist E. Ray Lankester and others that the beast might still be in existence somewhere in that unexplored country. This suggestion caused quite a stir in scientific circles and an expedition was financed to undertake the task of either proving or disproving the survival of this giant Pleistocene animal.

The leadership of this expedition was entrusted to HESKETH PRICHARD (1876–1922). Prichard was born in India on November

17, 1876, six weeks after his father's death. Three months later his mother sailed with him to England. He subsequently became known as an author, sportsman, and naturalist. Before going to South America he had traveled in Panama and Haiti among other places and had published several books of fiction in collaboration with his mother under the *noms de plume* of E. and H. Heron. He had also to his credit a considerable amount of experience in the field as a hunter and naturalist before he landed in Buenos Aires in September, 1900. From that city he took passage for Patagonia, where he spent several months exploring many previously unknown parts of the land in search of the ground sloth. The account of this expedition was published in 1902 under the title *Through the Heart of Patagonia.* Prichard found no trace of a living Mylodon, although he was inclined to believe that the beast had been in existence since the Indians arrived in Patagonia and had been exterminated by them. Even though defeated in his effort to return a live ground sloth to England he was successful in bringing back many new observations on the animal life of Patagonia. He especially increased the existing knowledge of the guanaco and was instrumental in solving the riddle of a special dying place for that animal concerning which such eminent scientists as Darwin and Hudson had been mistaken.

After his return from Patagonia he traveled in Newfoundland and Labrador and continued to write. He joined the army in 1915, rose to the rank of major, and was decorated with the D.S.O. and M.C. He became an authority on the subject of sniping, and his textbook *Sniping in France* won for him much commendation. He died June 14, 1922.

One other book of this period was *A Naturalist in the Guianas* by EUGÈNE ANDRÉ, published in 1904. André was born in Trinidad January 3, 1861, and was educated at St. Mary's College, Port-of-Spain. He started collecting orchids after leaving school and went to Maturín and Cumana (Venezuela) in 1893 in search of these plants. In 1897 he made his first trip to the Caura River, an eastern tributary of the Orinoco, and in 1900–1901 he went again. On these journeys he collected for the Tring Museum and returned with not only orchids but insects and birds. *A Naturalist in the Guianas* is the account of the hardships, tragedies, and discoveries on André's second expedition, which took him to the headwaters of the Caura. The ascent of the river was made without disaster, but on the return André's boat was wrecked in the middle of the dangerous Arichi rapids. His situation was desperate —collections, food, conveyance, all lost in one split second; and he was at least two hundred miles from the nearest station where help might be expected. There were fourteen men in the party, and all they could salvage was food calculated to last them eight days and a small boat which held only four men. Between them and civilization was a river in spate and an almost impenetrable forest from which they might expect to obtain but little food. Twenty-six days later, much nearer dead than alive, André and seven of his companions reached a small settlement (La Prisión) near the mouth of the Caura; the remaining six succumbed to the jungle.

The account of this catastrophe consumes only a small portion of the book. The remainder is enlivened with many incidents of travel and valuable observations on the insects, birds, and mammals of that, heretofore, unexplored part of the continent. The Caura might well be called the "River of Tapirs," for this great beast was especially abundant along its banks. André gives some exceedingly good descriptions of its habits and the methods of hunting it. All in all, *A Naturalist in the Guianas* is a very much worth-while book. It contains information about a little known region, is interestingly written, and, without attempting to do so, reminds the reader of how quickly catastrophe and death may occur in the interior of South America.

André's ambition was to return to the Caura for further exploration, but his health was so impaired that he never realized it. Instead, he started a nursery in Port-of-Spain, and within a few years had produced several new varieties of dracaenas that were extensively imported by American firms. He continued in this business until his death, which took place December 30, 1922.

It will have been noted that, of the naturalists already described, only one, W. H. Edwards, was from the United States. Also, that the majority of these scientists were "on their own" and paid their expenses through the disposal of their collections to museums and private collectors. Not one of them went under the auspices of a museum with all expenses paid.

With the advent of 1910, a new era opened in South American exploration. In the first place practically all of the naturalists were from the United States, and in the second place they represented one or another of the large American museums, or similar institutions.

All of these men are well known in scientific circles as are their contributions to entomology, ornithology, herpetology, and mammalogy. As a consequence, the remarks about each will be brief.

This recent period was initiated by WILLIAM BEEBE, who, in collaboration with Mary Blair Beebe, published in 1910 *Our Search for a Wilderness.* This is a valuable account of the experiences of the authors in Venezuela and British Guiana.

With the experience gained on this journey Beebe was placed in charge of the Tropical Research Station at Bartica, British Guiana, established under the auspices of the New York Zoological Society. This marked the beginning of an entirely new kind of biological study, a study of the tropical wild life in its own environment. Previously the emphasis had been on collecting.

From the research of Beebe and his staff of trained scientists, four books were written: *Tropical Wild Life in British Guiana,* by Beebe, Hartley, and Howes (1917); *Jungle Peace,* by Beebe (1918); *Edge of the Jungle,* by Beebe (1921); and *Jungle Days,* by Beebe (1925).

Beebe has shown in these volumes that he possesses not only a wide horizon of interest but an extraordinary ability of expression. Minor incidents in the jungle are turned, through the magic of his pen, into extremely delightful episodes.

Originally an ornithologist—in recent years he has turned to other spheres of activity—he made significant contributions to our knowledge of the bird life of northern South America. Particularly is this true of his researches on the hoatzin, for which he has received world-wide recognition, and on such other birds as the tinamou and toucan.

LEO E. MILLER, an American naturalist who accompanied Theodore Roosevelt on a part of his journey in South America,

ALEXANDER VON HUMBOLDT
At the Age of Twenty-Six (1796)

Courtesy of Mark Mooney, Jr.

VAMPIRE BATS

published in 1918 *In the Wilds of South America.* This is a narrative of modern jungle exploration which rivals the account of Bates in content, general interest, and readability. The wanderings of Miller have taken him into practically every one of the South American republics and into many remote districts hitherto unexplored by any naturalist. Six different expeditions, including the journey made with Roosevelt, have given him the opportunity of collecting over a large area of the interior of Colombia, of traveling some fifteen hundred miles on the Orinoco, of forming an acquaintance with the life in the Guianas, and of hunting birds and mammals in the Bolivian forests and on the pampas of the Argentine. Of these expeditions he writes with a keen enthusiasm and with an ability which belongs only to the able narrator.

Until the years 1919–1920 the arid part of the west coast of Peru bathed by the Humboldt Current had not been considered as an attractive location for detailed scientific studies. From September, 1919, until February, 1920, ROBERT CUSHMAN MURPHY, under the auspices of the Brooklyn Museum, investigated the conditions responsible for the profusion of life in the waters along the coast of Peru as well as the production and disposition of guano found on the numerous coastal islands; and in 1925 he published a popular account of his researches under the title *Bird Islands of Peru.* This is at once a scientifically accurate account of the birds of that region, of which there is a greater abundance than at any other single spot on the earth's surface, and an exceedingly interesting description of the guano industry. One of the most important chapters is on the Humboldt Current, an oceanic stream of water which carries the Antarctic into the tropics. In this chapter he describes, among other things, the physical characteristics of the current, its richness of life, and the ecology of the marine organisms it contains. Every paragraph of this book proclaims Murphy to be a remarkably well-trained naturalist, a student of detail, and an able expositor.

Since the expedition of 1919 Murphy has continued his researches along the coast of South America and in 1936 brought the work to a brilliant conclusion in his *Oceanic Birds of South America,* a two-volume work that marks him as one of the outstanding ornithologists of all time.

South America and the Naturalists

Perhaps no other naturalist has seen as much of Central and South America as the stalwart explorer GEORGE K. CHERRIE. He has made, all told, some forty separate expeditions into the tropics of America, one of which was with Roosevelt down the River of Doubt. There are very few localities between Cancer and Capricorn where he has not collected natural history specimens in a long and eventful career. The high points in this life of continuous exploration have been set down in dramatic fashion in *Dark Trails,* published in 1930.

* * *

Exigencies of time and space have not allowed descriptions of other naturalists who have traveled in South America. Some of these, like Spix and von Martius, were botanists, and left little of interest to zoologists in their written travels. Others like Theodore Roosevelt were not naturalists in the same sense that Schomburgk, Bates, Wallace, and Hudson were. However, Roosevelt's *Through the Brazilian Wilderness* is one of the most important books dealing with the natural history and exploration of South America that have been published. Roosevelt's prestige and popularity caused this volume to be more widely read than any other book of its kind on South America, and consequently it has created more interest, not only in the republics through which Roosevelt journeyed, but in the natural history of that part of the world.

Other important authors and their works are: Gardner's *Travels in the Interior of Brazil* (1849); Rodway's *In the Guiana Forest* (1894); Gates' *A Botanist in the Amazon Valley* (1927); Guenther's *A Naturalist in Brazil* (1931); Hingston's *A Naturalist in the Guianas* (1932); Rusby's *Jungle Memories* (1933); Simpson's *Attending Marvels* (1934); von Hagen's *Off with Their Heads* (1937).

We would not fail to mention Belt's *A Naturalist in Nicaragua* (1874). Much of the content applies just as well to the tropical countries south of Panama. This volume should be included in any list of the four or five best books on the natural history of tropical America. In the same category may be mentioned Chapman's *My Tropical Air Castle* (1929) and *Life in an Air Castle*

(1938). Some unusually interesting material is found, also, in *Autobiography of a Bird-Lover,* by Chapman; for the dean of American ornithologists has traveled extensively in South America.

Raymond L. Ditmars has had considerable experience in Central America, the West Indies, and northern South America; and in two of his recent books, *Thrills of a Naturalist's Quest* (1932) and *Confessions of a Scientist* (1934), there are quite a few chapters on such forms as the bushmaster, fer-de-lance, and vampire bat that are valuable.

Several other naturalists, such as Ernest G. Holt, William Mann, and G. H. H. Tate, have made journeys into the American tropics in search of new discoveries but they have not yet written their experiences in book form. It is hoped that some of these may still do so.

We should like to list also a few men who, although not professed naturalists, were exceedingly capable observers and have left in their books material of much value to the biologist. Particular mention is made of C. Barrington Brown's *Canoe and Camp Life in British Guiana* (1877) and of *Fifteen Thousand Miles on the Amazon and Its Tributaries,* by the same author in collaboration with Lidstone (1878); Musters' *At Home with the Patagonians* (1879); Whitney's *The Flowing Road* (1912); and Up de Graff's *Head Hunters of the Amazon* (1923).

PART TWO

THE VAMPIRE BAT

THE word "vampire" takes one far back into the Middle Ages when superstitious Europe was parasitized by certain spectral, ghoulish creatures that, according to popular imagination, arose from the bodies of the interred dead and proceeded to kill their ill-fated human victims by a rapid, painless phlebotomy. The early references to these creatures suggest that they were werewolves, sometimes snakes, cats, or dogs, but never bats. Only later, after the discovery of America, does the "vampire" take the form of a bat such as that described in the immortal, sleep-dispelling *Dracula* of Bram Stoker.

The real vampire bats, the ones possessing an insatiable appetite for blood, are confined to tropical America. Their history has never been connected at any time with Europe or with any other part of the eastern world. Three species have been described *(Desmodus rotundus, Diphylla centralis,* and *Diaemus youngi)* and there is nothing mythological or legendary about their existence. They are abundant in many parts of Central and South America, and reports of their activities have not been unduly exaggerated.

The conquistadores, the missionaries, even the early naturalists were mistaken in their notions as to which of the bats were vampires. Among the several species in South America there is a great deal of variation in size and facial characteristic; some of them are very large with wing spreads of two to three feet and with faces suggestive of the underworld. It is probably only natural that the early explorers were of one accord in believing that these largest bats, and those of most diabolical countenance, were the vampires. That Cabeza de Vaca had this idea is evident from his writing. "These bats are a bad kind of vermin, and there are many of them on the river [Paraguay], and they are about the size of turtledoves."

The same misconception was expressed three centuries later by Captain Richard F. Burton. "It must be like a Vision of Judgment," he wrote, "to awake suddenly and to find on the tip of one's nose, in the act of drawing one's life blood, that demonical face with deformed nose, satyrlike ears, and staring fixed saucer eyes, backed by a body measuring two feet from wing-end to wing-end."

The first naturalist to capture a vampire in the act of feeding on an animal was Darwin. He discovered that it is a comparatively small creature with a body length of about four inches and a wing spread of only twelve or thirteen. Concerning this experience Darwin wrote: "The whole circumstance has lately been doubted in England; I was therefore fortunate in being present when one was actually caught on a horse's back. We were bivouacked late one evening near Coquimbo, in Chile, when my servant, noticing that one of the horses was very restive, went to see what was the matter, and fancying he could distinguish something, suddenly put his hand on the beast's withers, and secured the vampire. In the morning the spot where the bite had been inflicted was easily distinguished from being slightly swollen and bloody." Darwin determined that this bat belonged to the genus Desmodus *(D. d'orbignyi* Wat., he called it) and not to one of the genera including the large frugivorous species.

Repeated discoveries of this nature have shown the vampires parasitize many vertebrate animals. Whether they ever eat flesh or vegetable matter is not certain; the structure of the alimentary tract would indicate that they do not. The amount of blood which they take from a large beast during a single feeding is negligible, and the animal is not seriously inconvenienced. However, repeated feedings may weaken the victim and, if continued, may lead directly or indirectly to its death. The smaller the animal, the greater is the proportionate amount of blood lost; consequently it is the tiny inhabitants of the forest that suffer most.

In some parts of South America the natives who have attempted to raise domestic animals have found it almost hopeless. Chickens, cattle, sheep, goats, mules, pigs, dogs, and horses have suffered alike from periodical visits of these "winged leeches." Vampires were extremely common on the island of Mexiana, at the mouth of the Amazon, when it was visited by Wallace in 1848. He saw many horses and cattle greatly weakened by successive bleedings and was told that hundreds of cattle had been killed during previous years. At São Gabriel, Spruce learned that the sheep were regularly bled, and fowls that roosted in the open air frequently died after they had been reduced to a state of lethal anemia by repeated tappings. Murphy found vampires in large numbers on the guano island, Asia, off the coast of Peru, a barren, desolate region where the discovery of any mammalian forms, particularly vampire bats, came as a distinct surprise. In order to account for their presence on Asia and other islands along the Peruvian coast, Murphy thought that they must feed on the sea lions or some of the large birds since neither man nor domestic animals were common there.

In crossing the Bolivian highlands, Miller had more than his share of trouble with vampires. At one place he awoke to find that his mules had been so severely bled he was unable to proceed with them and was forced to get others. A little farther along his route in Bolivia, he reached a small village where the vampires literally swarmed. In order to protect his mules he tied canvas sheets over their backs and sides, but all to no avail. The bats attacked the exposed parts, and the mules attempting to free themselves from the unwelcome visitors rolled on the ground with the result that the covers were loosened. Miller discovered that the bats were not easily frightened. He was able to get quite close to them as they settled on the mules and began boring through the thick hides, making a grating noise with their teeth all the while. If he grabbed for one of them with his hand it immediately flew up into the air a short distance and then came to rest on the opposite side of the mule where it started drilling again. Each morning the mules were covered with blood and had to be bathed in the river and the wounds disinfected. After three days Miller had to drive them to another town in order to save them; they were on the point of collapse.

Vampires attack human beings just as readily as they do the wild beasts of the jungle or the domesticated animals. To them blood is life, and it apparently matters little whether it comes from a macaw, a capuchin monkey, or a human being. Practically all explorers who have been any length of time in South America have been tapped at one time or another. There is some evidence at hand, though, that bats demonstrate a preference when they have more than one individual from which to choose. Bates wrote: "The fact of their sucking the blood of persons sleeping, from wounds which they make in the toes, is now well established; but it is only a few persons who are subject to this blood-letting." Im Thurn stated that on many occasions while other members of his party were being attacked he was never, at any time, molested. "They seem to have a special liking for some people," he said, "an abhorrence of others." And Wallace was in accord when he wrote, "Many persons are particularly annoyed by bats, while others are free from their attacks." Humboldt's experience was a similar one. To use his own words, "In the course of several years, notwithstanding we slept so often in the open air, in climates where Vampire bats and other analogous species are so common, we were never wounded." Waterton's experience with bats was a disappointment to him, for he was never bitten. He related how he was literally surrounded by vampires on occasion, but never molested. He eagerly coveted the experience of being bled; he wanted to be able to say that it had actually happened to him. Night after night he carefully exposed his extremities, but all in vain. Waterton was very much perplexed, and not a little annoyed. He greatly envied a certain Scotch gentleman by the name of Tarbet who, one night, had several ounces of blood siphoned away. This man, on the contrary, was loath to part with his vascular fluid; he was thoroughly irate and did not take kindly to Waterton's condoling remark that "an European surgeon would not have been so generous as to have blooded him without making a charge." Apparently this preference for one individual among several is not confined to humans, for Enders wrote that in Panama the bats had been known to bleed only one horse although others were present.

The weapons that serve the vampires in their operations are the highly specialized front teeth, or incisors, that are sharp with the keenness of a razor blade and curved in a manner which suggests a scooplike mechanism. With the aid of these surgical tools the bats shave away the epidermis of the skin until the underlying capillaries are reached. There is no bungling in the operation; it is executed with the nicety born of long experience. Vampires have been seen to complete the incision in only a few seconds; the jaws worked rapidly back and forth a few times, after which the blood began to flow.

The wounds, as described by Up de Graff, "are perfectly cylindrical, about an eighth of an inch in diameter, and a sixteenth of an inch deep, made in the form of a cone, as if by a counter-sink for a screwhead." Spruce wrote, "The wound is a round piece of the skin taken completely out as if cut out with a knife."

The nature of the operation as we know it was not so clear in the minds of some of the earlier naturalists. Gardner was of the opinion that the puncture was made "by the sharp hook nail of its thumb, and that from the wound thus made, it abstracts the blood by the suctorial powers of its lips and tongue." Wallace asserted: "It can hardly be a bite, as that would awake the sleeper, it seems most probable that it is either a succession of gentle scratches with the sharp edge of the teeth, gradually wearing away with the skin, or a triturating with the point of the tongue, till the same effect is produced. My brother was frequently bitten by them, and his opinion was that the bat applied one of its long canine teeth to the part, and then flew round and round on that as a centre, till the tooth acting as an awl, bored a small hole; the wings of the bat serving at the same time to fan the patient into a deeper slumber."

On one point there is not the shadow of a doubt: the vampire is capable of making an opening through the skin without causing the slightest pain, and without awakening the sleeper. Spruce affirmed positively that no one of his acquaintance had ever been awakened by the surgical maneuvers of the vampire. Referring to the two times he had been bled, Wallace stated, "In neither case did I feel anything, but awoke after the operation was completed."

McGovern makes the statement that "not a single case is known in which a sleeper has awakened while the Vampires were at their work." While this statement is true in general, there are exceptions.

Up de Graff recounted that one night on the headwaters of the Amazon he happened to kick away the covering which he had laid over his feet. Some time later he was awakened by a sharp pain in one of his toes. He immediately made a light and found that his foot was covered with blood, although the culprit responsible for the pain was nowhere near his bed. As his eyes became accustomed to the shadows he looked up; and there above him, flying around under the roof of his shack, was a vampire. This bat was no ordinary vampire for, even though it had been frightened away and there was now a lamp burning, it dropped onto the bed and attacked again. As a rule, vampires do not disturb individuals while a light is burning. Im Thurn related that a boy in his service, who was nearly bled to death by vampires, found that a burning light was no protection.

Since a lighted lamp does tend to keep the vampires away, "the bedroom light is almost the last thing of which the poor man will allow himself to be denied," Rusby wrote when speaking of the numerous venesections caused by vampires in certain parts of the Amazon basin. "If it comes to a question of no bread or no light," he continued, "he is quite likely to invest his last money to maintain the light."

In certain sections where the bats are especially numerous and hungry, men are tapped night after night, sometimes in several places. Spruce found them abundant at São Gabriel on the Rio Negro in 1852. The house he occupied had stains on the floor from the blood of quondam victims. On the first night he spent there his two men were bitten, one of them having four punctures. Practically every night thereafter was similar. One of the soldiers at the fort was so covered with wounds and blood that Spruce concluded he had fallen into a bed of prickly palms. This unfortunate fellow had eight incisions in one toe. Spruce was very careful to cover his hands and feet, and usually placed a handkerchief over his face. Probably as a result of these precautions, he was not molested.

About the year 1851 at Jauarite on the Uaupés several members of Wallace's party were bitten by vampires. He himself escaped through the simple expedient of wrapping the exposed parts of his skin in blankets. However, on other occasions he was bitten, once on his toe and once on the tip of the nose.

Although Bates had a protracted stay in South America he was attacked only once by a vampire. This was not in the interior of the continent but at Caripi, a small village just a few miles from

Pará where he spent some few weeks. The house he secured at this place seemed perfectly satisfactory when he looked at it in broad daylight; but at night he discovered that it was inhabited by a large number of bats. The first night was peaceful enough, but the second he was awakened by enormous numbers of bats flying about the room in all directions. They put out his lamp and, after he had relighted it, extinguished it a second time. The following night they took more liberties; one of them got into his hammock and bit him on the hip. There were four different species all told, but he was confused as to which ones were the phlebotomists.

The most perplexing question about the vampire is: how exactly can it make a puncture through the skin of a human being without causing enough pain, or discomfort, to awaken the sleeper? These parasites have been known to light on such sensitive parts of the body as the nose and forehead, to bore a cavity therein, and, without awakening the victim, to lap up the blood which flows from the wound. This period of feeding to the point of satiety lasts ten minutes or more.

Early in the nineteenth century Waterton made this written statement: "The teeth of the Vampire are very sharp, and not unlike those of a rat. If it be that he inflicts the wounds with his teeth (and he seems to have no other instruments) one would suppose that the acuteness of the pain would cause the person who is sucked, to awake. We are in darkness in this matter; and I know of no means by which we might be enabled to throw light upon it." More than one hundred years of scientific achievement have elapsed since Waterton wrote the above, and there is still no clear-cut answer to this question. We are still "in darkness in this matter."

Ditmars had the opportunity to examine the wound made by a vampire on the back of a goat and noted that the hair had dropped from the skin immediately surrounding it. The wound itself showed up as a cicatrice not more than a quarter of an inch in diameter, but the region from which the hair had fallen was the size of a thumbnail. This very important observation suggests that possibly some irritant had been secreted by the bat. We may conjecture that this substance was employed by the vampire as a local anesthetic to deaden the pain of biting teeth as they flashed again and again into the skin. However, it is nothing more than conjecture; for this salivary agent, if it really does exist, may have another function. As Ditmars states, all we can say definitely is "that something abnormal has happened to the tissue besides the opening of a mere wound by specialized and lancing incisor teeth."

An ancient supposition is that the vampire is a bloodsucker, and that, after making its incision, it applies its lips to the wound in order to secure the blood. Apparently nothing is to be found in literature until recently which says one word to the contrary. In the *Journal of Preventive Medicine* (1932) is this statement by Dr. Dunn: "The Vampire does not suck blood, as popularly believed, but takes it up with its tongue, seldom placing its mouth on the wound except when the latter is first made or when the bleeding is very slow. If the wound bleeds freely, the bat simply laps up the blood, hardly touching the tissues, while if the bleeding is scant the bat licks the wound." Quite recently Ditmars has verified the above and made moving pictures of this method of feeding.

The wounds made by the vampire continue to bleed, often profusely, for some time after the beast has finished indulging its appetite. Long ago on the Amazon, Wallace wrote, "The wound is a small round hole, the bleeding of which it is difficult to stop"; and, nearly half a century later, Im Thurn declared, "The danger lies not so much in the quantity of blood sucked up by the animals, as in that which flows from the unnoticed wound." Practically all of the naturalists and explorers who have been subjected to the debilitating effect of the vampire's lust are agreed that much blood does flow after the bat has taken its leave, and they have much to say upon this subject. On the contrary the same authors have been very sparing in their remarks about the cause of this unnatural bleeding. The blood of humans, unless it is lacking in that particular element known as fibrinogen, ordinarily clots within a very short time. The coagulation time, even in severe cuts and lacerations, is fairly short. What then is responsible for the excessive bleeding which follows the vampire's activities?

It has been suspected that the vampire secretes a substance which temporarily prevents the clotting of the blood as it seeps from the recently made orifice. This is borne out by the findings of a recent worker[1] (Bier, of the Biological Society of São Paulo, Brazil) who, according to Ditmars, examined the salivary secretion of the vampire for the presence of any such substance. The results of this investigation indicated that there is an anticoagulant present in the vampire's saliva, but that this substance is not present in the saliva of the other species of bats. Could it be that one and the same substance acts as a local anesthetic and an anticoagulant?

With the spirit of the true scientist Beebe determined to stay awake one night and to discover for himself something concerning the operations of the vampire as it goes about securing its nocturnal potation of blood. His vigil was productive of interesting results. He made himself as comfortable as possible in order to be completely relaxed. He covered himself with the exception of one arm. Before many minutes had elapsed the bats began winging their way about the room, many of them almost touching his face. Not all of these bats were vampires; some were the larger fruit-eating forms. None of them hovered over him in autogiro fashion, or made any attempt to fan him with its wings. The notion that the vampires produced a drowsiness in their victims through a languid flapping of wings was one of long standing in South America.

Presently Beebe felt that one bat in particular was flying closer and closer. Sure enough, in a few minutes he was conscious of a slight tap as the bat made a four-point landing on his chest. The idea had prevailed in some circles that these bats did not settle on the human body at all but kept their wings continually in motion as they fed. It was known, of course, that they lighted on the bodies of domesticated animals; but, for some reason or other, it was considered that they had a special technique for dealing with man.

Beebe remained perfectly still after the bat had landed; but,

[1] Bier, O. G., "Action anticoagulante et fibrinolytique de l'extrait des glandes salivaires d'une chauvesouris hématophage (Desmodus rufus)," *C.R. Soc. Biol. Paris,* Vol. 110 (1932), pp. 129–131.

feeling no other motion, he concluded that it had taken flight again. Several tense minutes ensued, and then he became conscious of a tickling on his wrist; the vampire had dropped onto his arm in such a manner that he experienced nothing more than a tickling sensation. From the wrist it now slowly made its way up the forearm to the elbow. Beebe said that if he had been asleep none of these movements would have been sufficient to wake him.

There now followed a period of quiet and then a gentle tickling again. Presently this sensation changed to a tingling one, like an arm in the early stages of going to sleep, and Beebe's imagination began to play tricks on him. He thought he felt the teeth of the bat nipping at his flesh and, a moment later, his warm blood flowing out onto his forearm. The time had come, he felt sure, to nab this loathsome creature. Very carefully he moved his free hand close to the bat and then, as quickly as possible, grabbed at it. However, the bat eluded his fingers and escaped. The next morning he found only a scratch on his arm. He had interrupted the bat in its initial efforts at making an opening. The experiment ended abruptly and prematurely, but it was far from failure. It served to show, (1) that bats do not produce drowsiness in their victim by languid wing action, (2) that they actually light on the body of the animal they parasitize, and (3) that they will start operations on a human being who is wide awake.

Although many misdeeds have been attributed to the vampire, there is still another, entirely unsuspected until recently, that remains to be mentioned. This offense is more serious, too, than that of bloodletting. Many of the ectoparasites that suck blood—the Anopheles and Aedes mosquitoes, the tsetse fly, the flea, and the tick, to name some of the worst offenders—serve also as transmitters of deadly diseases. To this list must now be added the vampire bat. It has been proved at the Gorgas Memorial Laboratory in Panama that the cattle of the Canal Zone harbor a trypanosome in their blood. The cattle are immune to this microscopic protozoan, but horses and mules are not. Cattle and horses often feed together at night, and bats have unwittingly carried the germs from the cattle to the horses. As a result many of the latter have died.

Then there is the possibility that another disease, paralytic rabies, may be transmitted by the vampire. This disease has been known for some time to occur among cattle on the island of Trinidad. However, human beings have also died of the same malady within recent years, and it is now suspected that bats are the transmitting agents.

ARMADILLOS

IN THE year 1833 Darwin resided for a time in Montevideo and took pleasure in making daily journeys into the surrounding country. On one of these trips he stopped near an estancia to investigate a report concerning some large bones that were said to have been found there. He was rewarded by the discovery of "some large portions of a gigantic armadillo-like animal."

Paleontological knowledge has progressed at such a rate since Darwin's eventful discovery that it is now safe to say that the history of the armadillo family in South America probably goes back forty-five to fifty million years. Early in the Cenozoic period, so geologists say, the land which now forms the Isthmus of Panama sank below sea level so that South America was completely isolated from the rest of the world. This separation persisted for several million years, and then the land was elevated once more in this region and connections were reestablished between the two Americas. Previous to this, for several millions of years, the armadillos had lived entirely to themselves in what is now South America, unaffected by contact with animals of North America or any other continent. After the isthmus was re-formed, new avenues of migration were established, and the armadillos were free to make incursions into North America. That they did so is abundantly confirmed by the discovery of their bones in many of the North American rocks.

Armadillos were much more plentiful then than now, particularly so in the later epochs of the Cenozoic; and many of the species were far larger than any now existing. They were seemingly more abundant in what is now the Argentine than anywhere else. So many fossils have been found in that region—many of them armadillos—that Darwin was led to say: "I believe a straight line drawn in any direction through the pampas would cut through some skeleton or bones. We may conclude that the whole area of the pampas is one wide sepulchre of these extinct gigantic quadrupeds."

Armadillos

No more singular mammals are known to man than the armadillos, or armadillolike creatures, that inhabited the western hemisphere in glacial and interglacial times. The oddest, most inconceivable of all were the glyptodonts—huge, turtlelike animals, some of them twelve to fourteen feet long and five feet or more in height, that roamed at great leisure, in company with the mammoths, saber-tooth tigers, and giant ground sloths, over all of South and Central America, and the southern part, at least, of the United States. No knight of old could boast of a protective armor so completely enveloping and so impenetrable as that possessed by these antediluvian monsters. A great, thick, dome-shaped carapace covered the trunk and extended almost to the ground on each side; this was so heavy and massive that it furnished perfect protection against all the predacious enemies of that age, especially so when the glyptodont drew in its head and squatted low on the ground. The carapace was not of movable parts or bands, as in our present-day forms, but consisted of one solid piece made up of a perfect mosaic of thick polygonal plates of bone immovably fitted together. The tails, which in some glyptodonts were almost as long as the body itself, were also enclosed in heavy bony plates which formed a sheath. Extending from these plates were frequently long spines; for example, one glyptodont *(Daedicurus)* had a tail approximately five feet long terminating in a large knob that fairly bristled with large spines. If the beast were capable of swinging this caudal appendage from side to side with any considerable force it must have found it of great value as a protection from its enemies.

There are now not more than a dozen kinds of armadillos, a feeble remnant of bygone days, and of these none may be considered large. The largest of all, the so-called giant armadillo *(Priodon giganteus)* is not over three feet in length, exclusive of the tail, and rarely, if ever, attains a weight of more than one hundred pounds. The remaining species range down the scale to the little *pichiciago (Chlamydophorus truncatus)* that is scarcely six inches in length from the end of its snout to the tip of its tail. The nine-banded armadillo *(Dasypus novemcinctus)* found in the United States is one of the larger species, and it weighs only twelve to fifteen pounds.

There is one point in common between the forms of today and those of the past, and that is the extent of their distribution. The armadillos of the present are still found only in South America, Central America, and southern United States and are to this day more common in the Argentine than elsewhere.

There is more variation in our present-day forms than might be expected; not so much in size, but in the nature of the armature and the amount of hair on the body. In the nine-banded armadillo, the head is covered by a shield and the tail by a sheath. The back and sides are protected by the carapace which is a bony covering of three parts: an anterior and a posterior buckler and, between the two, an intermediate portion made up of nine movable, overlapping bands. The latter allow a sufficient amount of flexibility to the body. Only the ears, belly, and insides of the legs are unprotected. In some of the other species, however, the plates which constitute the armor are greatly reduced in size, and the growth of hair, which is scanty in the nine-banded armadillo, forms quite a heavy covering. The number of overlapping bands, in other forms, varies from three to thirteen.

Popular notion has it that armadillos always coil themselves into tight balls for the sake of protection when they are attacked by their enemies. Colonel Roosevelt confessed that he had that idea when he went to South America. Just how far he was wrong may be gathered from an experience which he related in *Through the Brazilian Wilderness*. While riding through a patch of open country in western Brazil he encountered two armadillos of the nine-banded variety that were feeding along a sandy stretch of ground between two clumps of rather dense vegetation. The dogs Roosevelt had with him at once charged the two beasts. To his surprise neither of the armadillos curled up into a ball; both ran from the dogs as fast as their short dumpy legs would take them and succeeded in reaching their holes and escaping. With one exception this is the customary reaction of all armadillos when in danger.

The exception is the little *apar,* or three-banded armadillo *(Tolypeutes tricinctus),* which is found in Argentina and southern Brazil. "The *apar,* commonly called *mataco,*" Darwin wrote, "is remarkable by having only three movable bands: the rest of its tessellated covering being nearly inflexible. It has the power of rolling itself into a perfect sphere, like one kind of English woodlouse. In this state it is safe from the attack of dogs; for the dog, not being able to take the whole in its mouth, tries to bite one side, and the ball slips away. The smooth hard covering of the *mataco* offers a better defence than the sharp spines of the hedgehog."

This, then, is the only one of the dozen species of armadillos that can actually convert itself into a sphere, although popular imagination has attributed this ability to all of the rest. Even if the others made the effort, they would find the protection entirely inadequate. In the first place, the shells are not so hard as is commonly believed, for they can usually be indented by strong pressure with the thumb. In the second place, the under parts are not covered at all. It would be absolutely profitless for them to curl up in the face of a jaguar, puma, or even a coyote. As a matter of fact, the remains of the nine-banded armadillo that have been killed and devoured by coyotes are commonly found in the southwestern part of the United States.

The armadillos' favorite method of escape is burrowing. They are capable of digging a hole so rapidly that an observer may be misled into the belief that they are sinking into the soil. Darwin had not been long in Argentina before he noted this trait in connection with the *pichy (Dasypus minutus),* a form common near Bahía Blanca. "The instant one was perceived," he wrote, "it was necessary, in order to catch it, almost to tumble off one's horse; for in soft soil the animal burrowed so quickly, that its hinder quarters would almost disappear before one could alight."

Schomburgk captured an armadillo in the Guiana forest and conceived the novel idea of tying a cord to one of its legs to prevent its escape. In almost less time than it takes to relate the fact, the beast had burrowed into the ground out of sight. He said that even in hard ground the armadillo can cover itself completely in three minutes; that it makes the hole with its forefeet and scrapes the loose earth back with its hind ones in such a manner that no opening is left in its wake.

A decidedly interesting story concerned with the burrowing prowess of an armadillo is told by Hudson in *Far Away and Long Ago.* As a boy he was watching some workmen pump noxious fumes into rat holes, these rodents having multiplied and become a great nuisance around their home. Evidently an armadillo had taken a liking to one of these dugouts for, suddenly, one bolted from a hole, ran to near where Hudson stood, and began to dig a retreat of its own in the soft floor of the pampa. The idea came quickly to him that here was a marvelous opportunity to capture a live armadillo which he could carry home in triumph. Putting his thought into immediate action he grasped the creature by its long, horn-covered tail and began to pull. However, much to his surprise he found he was engaged in a tug-of-war in which the victory was not easily to be won. In fact the truth slowly was borne in upon him that, instead of pulling the armadillo from the ground into his eager hands, the animal was in the process of pulling him into the hole after it. To say that this was humiliating was putting it mildly, and he put all of his juvenile strength into the task of winning the victory which he had thought would be so easy, for, after all, the armadillo was no larger than a common house cat. But Hudson found his strength inferior to that of the much smaller animal in its native environment. His hands were first drawn into the ground, then his wrists, and finally his forearms; and he had to admit defeat.

The nine-banded armadillo is unique among animals in that it almost always gives birth to four young at a time. These are of the same sex and are identical in almost every respect, even down to the number and arrangement of the scutes in the armor and to the number of hairs which protrude from between the scutes. Our information on the embryology of the other species of armadillos is incomplete, but, so far as is known, none of them produces identical quadruplets. Apparently the genus Dasypus is polyembryonic, while all other genera produce either one young at a time or twins.

How is it possible for two, three, four, or even five individuals to be born that resemble each other so much they are said to be identical twins, quadruplets, or quintuplets? The armadillos have given us the answer to this question. A detailed study of the embryological development of these animals has revealed that only one egg is fertilized; but when this divides, the two cells separate instead of adhering to each other as is normally the case. These

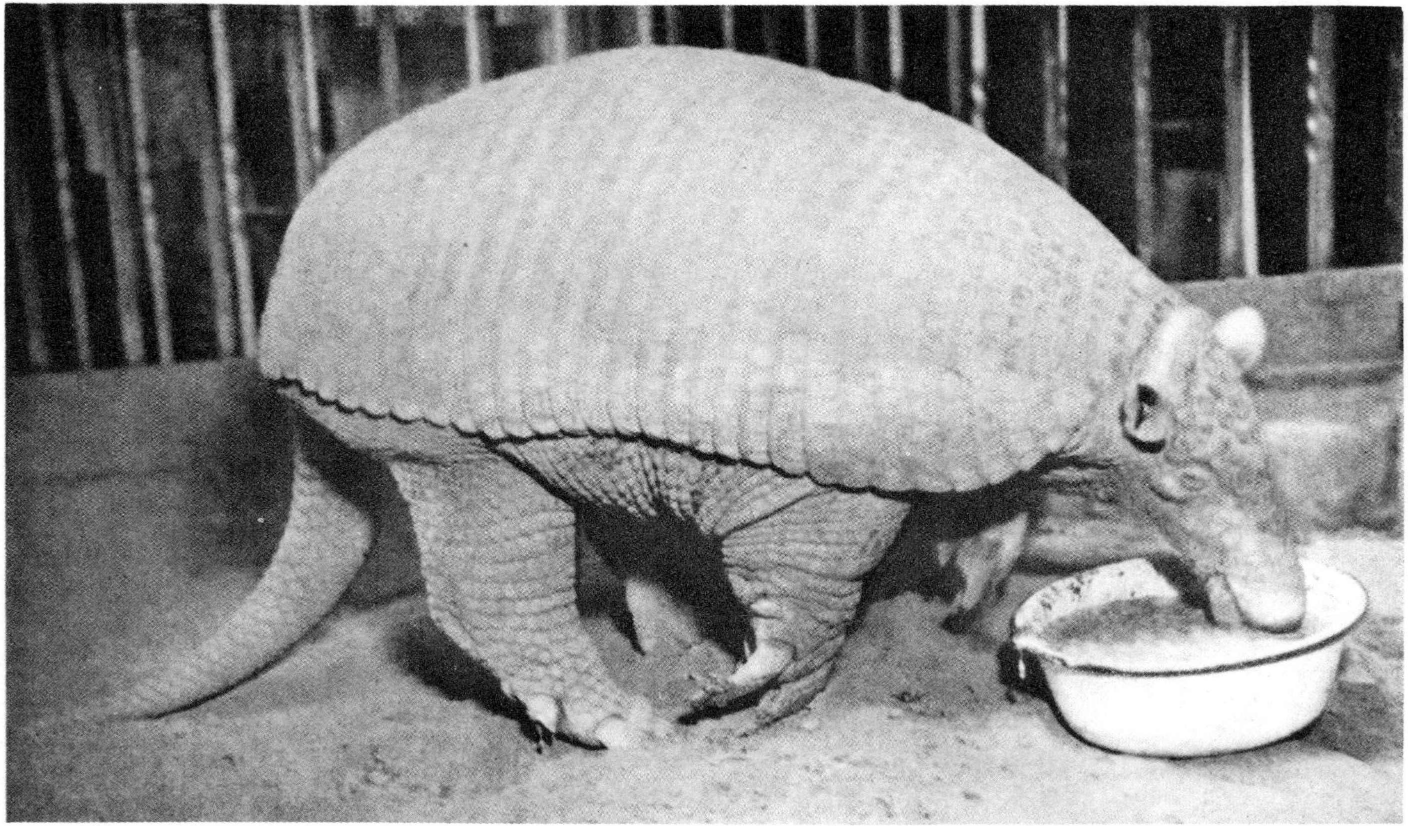

Courtesy of Zoological Society of ***Philadelphia***

GIANT ARMADILLO

Courtesy of Julius Johnson

TWO-TOED SLOTH

Courtesy of N.Y. Zoological Society

THREE-TOED SLOTH

two cells now divide and there is again a complete separation. As a result there are four cells, each of which possesses the same chromosomal make-up. From these four cells the young develop and, since the chromosome constitution is the same in all, the resultant animals are identical. Although this phenomenon has not been observed in human beings it is generally accepted as a fact that the same sequence of events takes place. This should suffice as an explanation for all the multiple births where the offspring are identical, even for the Dionne quintuplets of recent fame and fortune. Whenever multiple births occur in which the individuals are not at all alike, apparently two or more eggs—each with a different chromosome make-up—have been fertilized.

The study of armadillo quadruplets in their initial development has gone a long way toward establishing definitely the theory that sex is determined at the time of fertilization of the egg and not before or after, and in supporting the contention that closeness of resemblance among animals is in proportion to degree of kinship.

Armadillos are of considerable economic importance. All are great eaters of ants and other insects, of centipedes and scorpions. One species, at least *(Dasypus villosus),* is said to be omnivorous, feeding on everything from grass to putrefied flesh. According to Hudson this same form will even attack and kill snakes, poisonous ones as well as harmless.

The shells of these animals are frequently made into baskets. The carapace serves as the basket proper while the tail is ingeniously looped above and tied to the head as a handle. The Indians of the Southwest and of Mexico and Central America prepare many of these as attractions for tourists. However, long before there were any tourists to speak of in the Americas, the natives employed the shells as receptacles. Musters found that the Tehuelches of Patagonia put their food, paints, and other possessions into them.

The armadillo plays a surprising rôle in disease. According to scientists the armadillo *(Tatusia novemcinta)* acts as a host for the flagellate, *Trypanosoma cruzi,* which is responsible for Chagas' disease. The organism is apparently non-pathogenic so far as the armadillo is concerned, but when it is introduced into the human body (the transmitter is a species of bug—Triatoma) it causes the disease which is prevalent in the interior of Brazil.

Armadillos are in great demand for food and are eagerly sought after by the natives of South and Central America. Darwin, Prichard, Musters, and others have declared the flesh to be excellent eating, comparing it most often with young pig. Waterton related that the Indians of British Guiana considered them a delicacy and frequently dug them out of their holes.

Are the armadillos which have been a calculable part of the fauna of Hispanic America for at least fifty million years, to become extinct before the uncompromising advances of civilization? The outlook, while none too bright, has two or three hopeful aspects. Hudson said that the hairy armadillo *(Dasypus villosus)* is actually increasing in numbers since the advent of man, and will long survive the other species. It has been able to do this, however, only after some very radical changes in habit. Ordinarily armadillos feed chiefly on insects, are diurnal, and vanish from a given locality at the approach of man. The hairy armadillo has shown itself to be a distinct exception to the general rule. This particular form not only has maintained its habitat with the encroachment of man upon its estate, but has actually increased in number. More than that, Hudson declared, it has made an about-face in its habits, shuns the glare of the sun entirely, and ventures forth only late at night, after man has removed himself from the scene. Whether this has been responsible for a change in food habits cannot be said, but the hairy armadillo has digressed from a time-honored custom of eating only insects, and now feeds with equal relish upon mice, carrion, fledgling birds, grass, various grains, and almost anything that might be mentioned, even snakes.

All of this is indeed surprising, for armadillos are customarily credited with a limited intelligence at the best, and possess habits not easily changed. Hudson credited this animal with a considerable amount of craftiness and stated that the gauchos make it the "hero of many of their fables of the 'Uncle Remus' type."

There is still another species that is apparently not giving ground in the battle against man's invasion, and this is the nine-banded armadillo. This species is said to be extending its range in the United States each year; formerly its area of dispersal was Texas to Louisiana, but that has been enlarged to include some of the adjoining states. In all probability then the armadillo is in no immediate danger of extermination.

SLOTHS

The sloths of the present time are commonly distributed throughout all the forested lowlands of tropical America. In the past their range was more extensive and embraced probably all of South America and at least a fair portion of the northern continent. The Pleistocene era, which was the foremost period of mammalian abundance and dominance, fostered many more sloths than our day, and presented to the interglacial landscapes the giant ground sloths, which were among the most conspicuous animals, not only of that aspiring quadrupedal era, but of all time. Paleontologists have unearthed the bones of at least nine different genera of ground sloths and will undoubtedly discover more in the future. Tree sloths were in existence then, too, but they occupied an inconsequential niche in the Edentate household.

At least one form then living was as large as an elephant, and several of the others were not far behind in size. Three of the best-known genera were represented during the Pleistocene, in the area which is now the United States, as well as in South America. Megalonyx was apparently common in the forests between the Mississippi and the Atlantic, from Pennsylvania southward; Mylodon was found from California to the Carolinas; and Megatherium was an inhabitant of the southern states. Megalonyx was discovered in a cave in Virginia by Thomas Jefferson, and named by him.

Megatherium americanum was the largest of the ground sloths, and it was this form that reached elephantine proportions. However, one would never confuse this mammal with any of the Proboscideans. It was much longer and not so tall and, to judge from the reconstructions made of it, looked far more like an extremely large and hairy bear than an elephant.

Without a doubt these sloths lived on the ground; it would be absurd, considering their size, to imagine that they lived in trees or burrowed into the earth. The anatomists are at one in saying that they must have moved very slowly and awkwardly, and that they probably fed upon the leaves of Pleistocene trees and shrubs. They were perfectly capable of bending over trees of considerable size in order to reach the leaves. All the species had long heavy claws. For what purpose they may have been used is problematical; but self-protection, as in the case of the giant anteater, is the most likely answer.

A recent discovery in the Argentine suggests that some of these giant sloths may have inhabited South America until recently and may have lived contemporaneously with primitive man. On the floor of a small cavern at Last Hope Inlet, Patagonia, there were discovered portions of the skin of a ground sloth. The preservation was due to desiccation—the dust in the bottom of the cave being perfectly dry. This find was extremely interesting on two scores: first, perishable parts of the body such as the skin are rarely fossilized (usually only skeletal parts being preserved); and second, the nature of the material proves that it could not have been so terribly old. It has even been suggested that some of the aboriginal population of Patagonia lived in this particular cave at Last Hope Inlet and the sloth was killed by them and dragged into the cave where it was eaten. The remnants of the skin showed it to be made up of many small ossicles which were closely set together, and many long, coarse interspersing hairs. Recently, bones of the ground sloth have been found in caves in the southwestern part of the United States. The nature of these finds lends support to the contention of man's contemporaneous existence with these prehistoric Edentates. The bones not only were associated with human artifacts but were still fastened together by their ligaments; in skeletons of great age the ligaments are missing.

If the ground sloths did live contemporaneously with the American Indian, we have one clue to their extermination; but it is likely that the reason for their demise is to be sought elsewhere. If overspecialization ever brings to an end a particular species (and that has been given as one of the possible causes behind the passing of the dinosaurs, pterosaurs, and all the other Mesozoic saurians) it might very well apply here.

At the present time there are only two kinds of sloth in existence and not more than five or six species. None of these is larger than a medium-sized dog. The two kinds are the two-toed sloth, or *unau,* of which there is probably just one good species *(Choloepus didactylus)* and the three-toed sloth, or *ai,* belonging to the genus Bradypus. There are two, perhaps three, species in the genus. One of the three-toed forms has been placed in the genus Scaeopus but whether this is a good genus or merely another species remains to be determined.

The two-toed sloth is characterized by the presence of two functional toes on the forefeet and three on the hind ones, and either six or seven neck vertebrae. The three-toed sloth has three functional toes on both fore and hind feet, and nine neck vertebrae. All mammals with the exception of the sloths and two other forms have seven neck, or cervical, vertebrae. The limbs are long in all sloths as they generally are in mammals adapted to life in the trees. Although these jungle idlers have been placed in the order Edentata (derived from a Latin word meaning "without teeth") they have a very well developed set of teeth. Only the anteaters among Edentates are toothless.

If one of the hairy varieties of dog, the old English sheep dog for instance, were fastened by its legs in an upside-down position to the limb of a tree there might be a superficial resemblance to a sloth. The latter, however, has a round head with only the stub of a nose and a face devoid of all expression; its eyes hold a vacant, far-away look as though the animal were under the influence of hypnosis. The legs terminate in long, scimitarlike claws, and there is no tail at all, unless a short stump only an inch or two long is to be construed as such a caudal appendage. Of this abbreviated tail Waterton wrote: "Now had he a tail, he would be at a loss to know what to do with it in this position; were he to draw it up within his legs, it would interfere with them; and were he to let it hang down, it would become the sport of the winds."

The present-day sloths are all arboreal. Like no other animals in the world they live on the underside of the branches. "They hug the branches as if they love them," Hudson once wrote. They do not hang head downward as the bats do; their position is a horizontal one, the head and body being parallel to the limb of the tree. Their entire existence is not an upside-down one, for rather often, especially when climbing, they assume a vertical position. The three-toed sloth found on Barro Colorado Island *(Bradypus griseus)*, according to Enders, sleeps in a sitting or squatting position with the hind limbs encircling the trunk of a tree. It may feed in this position too, since the fore limbs are free for pulling food material to the mouth or for climbing. The characteristic posture of the sloth, though, is the back-downward one. For the greater part of its life the sloth sleeps suspended, moves suspended, eats suspended, gambols suspended, and makes love suspended.

A sloth is always discontent if its body is at a higher level than its feet. On the ground the legs seem incapable of supporting the body, and the belly sags to the earth. Any efforts at progression, especially if the surface of the ground is smooth, are futile. If there is any unevenness, or any object which the claws may grasp, it is able to pull itself along, however. Waterton wrote: "The sloth is as much at a loss to proceed on his journey upon a smooth and level floor, as a man would be who had to walk a mile on stilts upon a line of feather beds." And Schomburgk, in speaking of a captive sloth he had in his possession, related that when he "put it down on the smooth and hard-trodden ground under the tent cover or in the house it hardly moved a couple of feet after hours of the most violent exertion and laboured respiration which sounded very like the deep sighing of a man." The young sloth is even more helpless on the ground than the adult; it cannot progress at all, according to Beebe.

Although as helpless on the ground as a flounder, once in the trees the sloth is transformed. Its method of traveling from one part of a tree to another is unique but has been described as "sailor-like, hand over hand." Bates gives us his impression of the sloth's movements in the following words: "It is a strange sight to watch the uncouth creature, fit production of these silent shades, lazily moving from branch to branch. Every movement betrays, not indolence exactly, but extreme caution. He never looses his hold from one branch without first securing himself to the next, and when he does not immediately find a bough to grasp with the rigid hooks into which his paws are so curiously transformed, he raises his body, supported on his hind legs, and claws around in search of a fresh foothold." "Not until we invent a superlative, of which 'deliberate' is the positive, can we define a sloth with sufficient adequateness and briefness," declared Beebe.

Waterton stated that "the sloth, in a wild state, spends its whole life in the trees, and never leaves them but through force or by accident." In this contention the British naturalist was in error. Sloths not only leave the trees but they swim large rivers—streams that are in some cases a mile or more wide. They do not do this through accident or necessity. Just why they make these long aquatic journeys, no one has yet been able to ascertain. Perhaps every so often they develop the wanderlust. Granted that this is the case, why do they take to the water and not confine their peregrinations to the trees? Bates wrote of seeing a sloth swimming a river that, by his calculation, was three hundred yards wide; Hamilton Rice saw one crossing the Rio Negro just above Curituba Island; and Schomburgk and others have frequently encountered them on islands in midstream. Some of these were two-toed sloths and others three-toed. Beebe once marked a sloth and then set it free. Forty-eight days later it was recovered. In that time it had swum a mile-wide river and had then traveled "hand-over-hand" for a distance of four miles through the jungle bordering the farther side of the river. Beebe said that he had caught several sloths while they were swimming rivers a mile or more in width. He estimated they swam at the rate of a mile in three hours and twenty minutes.

Sloths subsist primarily on the leaves of the cecropia tree. The three-toed sloths apparently cannot live without this article of diet, and as a consequence are notoriously difficult to keep in captivity. If it is possible to furnish them with a supply of cecropia leaves and give them plenty of room in which to move about, they may be kept alive indefinitely. However, cecropia leaves are not procurable in temperate climes, and three-toed sloths that are brought north to our zoological gardens live only for a short while, even with the most painstaking care. On the contrary the two-toed sloths will eat many kinds of food, any and all of which appear to agree with them. Miller found that they would eat such vegetables as cabbage and lettuce and the young buds and shoots of many trees and shrubs; Enders reports that they will eat bananas, spinach, carrots, and even potatoes. According to Beebe the young baby sloths, after they are weaned from milk, are fed on cecropia leaves which are first chewed up by the mothers.

The idea once persisted that sloths completely denude cecropias of their foliage, after which they move on to other trees. No scientist has yet seen a tree completely defoliated by a sloth. Schomburgk wrote that he had seen as many as ten to twelve sloths in a tree at one time but had never seen a tree denuded by them.

Both two-toed and three-toed sloths produce just one young at a time. This is generally carried on the thorax since the breasts are pectorally located. At times, however, especially when climbing, the ventral side of the body is closely pressed against some part of the tree and the young ones, through lack of space, may have to repair to the mother's back where they hang on with their claws. If there is anything odder than an upside-down sloth it must be an upside-down baby sloth hanging to the back of its upside-down parent.

None of the species shows any particular inclination to fight when handled by humans. The sloth submits to all kinds of treatment and only rarely makes any protest. Occasionally one of them will make a desultory swing with its arm as though in mild remonstrance, but this action is not habitual. They do fight among themselves on occasion. The two-toed sloth is more active than its three-toed relative, according to Enders, and can move its legs with greater speed; its teeth, too, are better developed.

Most mammals have some active means of protection: speed of movement, well developed tusks, claws, or horns, burrowing ability, dexterity in the trees, or agility in the water. The sloth has none of these, yet it not only has survived the mishaps of innumerable centuries but will, in all likelihood, continue to weather the trials and vexations of a very uncertain future because of several interesting factors.

Perhaps the most important of these factors is its almost complete invisibility. It has been said that the sloth is so inactive that even plants grow on it. Whether its lethargy is responsible for this or not may be a matter of opinion, but plants do live on it. Certain species of unicellular, microscopic plants (algae) grow in grooves or crevices that are present on the hairs. The fur in a museum specimen of a sloth "puts you in mind of grass withered by the wintry blast," to use Waterton's simile. The hair of a live form in its native environment is, to quote Waterton again, "so much the hue of the moss which grows on the branches of the trees, that it is very difficult to make him out when he is at rest."

In the two-toed sloth as many as seven or eight grooves may be seen in a cross-section of a hair, according to Gates. Within these crevices the plants find a desirable home. The relationship between the animal and the plant is symbiotic—one of mutual benefit. The alga finds an environment to its liking and possibly a certain amount of nourishment; and the sloth benefits from the protection the green color affords it. The particular species of alga on the two-toed sloth has been named *Pleurococcus choloepi.*

The hairs on the three-toed sloth are apparently not grooved although there are transverse cracks in the cortex of the individual hairs. Herein resides another species of alga known as *Pleurococcus bradypi.* The grooves on the hairs of the two-toed sloth undoubtedly furnish a more desirable location for the plants, though it is doubtful whether they give these animals any marked advantage over the others in the matter of protective coloration.

The invisibility of the sloth is further increased by its sluggishness. It travels through the trees with such vague deliberation that even the keenest observer passes it by unnoticed. For this reason the sloth population in the tropical rain forests may be greater than is realized.

A second factor in the protection of the sloth is the almost reptilian tenacity of life which it exhibits. Like all beasts in which the brain is small in proportion to the rest of the nervous system it demonstrates an incredible ability to retain life under adverse circumstances.

Waterton removed the heart from one and found that it continued to beat for one-half hour afterward. Sloths will live after the body has been frightfully mutilated, wrote Miller, and they frequently survive after being shot several times. The natives find the flesh of the sloth very much to their liking and commonly drown the animal. However, an astonishingly long submergence is necessary before the sloth expires.

Another factor that is of aid to the sloths in their struggle for existence is their upside-down location in the trees. The inference that this inverted posture might be of any material benefit to them has not occurred to many naturalists. Yet the perennial enemies of these lethargic creatures, the jaguar and the harpy eagle, find it extremely difficult to get at their intended victims in their heels-over-head position. This is especially true if the sloths occupy a position near the end of a branch.

Certain other factors may assist the sloths in circumventing attacks by their foes. Beebe has stated that the sloth has no odor detectable by the human nostrils. If it were also true that there is no odor detectable by the olfactory senses of any of the lower animals that would indeed be a powerful asset to the sloth.

The voice of a sloth is weak, ineffectual, and perhaps ventriloquial. Only rarely does a sloth make any sound whatsoever, and then it is nothing more than a feeble, asthmatic whistle. Many jungle animals are extremely vociferous, but the sloth is among the most reticent. The roars of a howler monkey proclaim to every jaguar within a radius of two to three miles its approximate location, but the whimpers of a sloth penetrate the forest shades only a few yards. Even if some enemy is within hearing the cries are difficult to locate.

It is probable then that sloths have persisted because of their invisibility, their tenacity of life, their habitual inverted position, and other minor factors. If these have stood them in good stead in the past they may continue to do so. Certainly we do not have to agree with Buffon, who said that the sloth needed just one more defect in order to bring about its extinction. Or with Tschudi, who wrote: "This emblem of misery fixes itself on an almost leafless bough, and there remains defenseless; a ready prey to any assailant."

THE ANTEATERS

THE anteaters, sloths, and armadillos compose a trio of South American animals that for singularities of structure and behavior excel any other mammalian group. Although bearing little outward resemblance to one another, these forms are closely related and belong to the same order—Edentata. Their history has been associated with the western hemisphere since early Cenozoic days and at one time hundreds of species inhabited what is now North and South America. Only a meager remnant of this once powerful group is in existence now, and the survivors are as anachronistic as the hoatzin. Of existing anteaters there are only three: the giant anteater, the tamandua, and the two-toed anteater.

The Giant Anteater

The giant anteater *(Myrmecophaga jubata),* also called ant bear and *tamanduá bandeira,* or banded tamandua, is not such a large beast as its name implies; it is about the size of a small black bear. Measurements indicate that a full-grown specimen is about two feet tall and approximately six to seven feet long, including the tail. The dominant color is dark gray, almost black, and beginning at the throat a white band bordered with black extends obliquely on each side of the body as far back as the loin. It is this characteristic marking that has occasioned the appellation in use by the Brazilians of tamanduá bandeira.

The build of the giant anteater is unlike that of anything else on earth, except it be another anteater. It has an outlandishly elongate head with a cone-shaped muzzle sticking out into space like the handle on a gourd, a long neck, a short but slender body, and an extremely long, bushy tail. The mouth is without teeth, and the oral aperture is just large enough to permit the extrusion of a round, vermiform tongue. This particular member is unusually flexible and surprisingly long. Schomburgk measured one that had a length of sixteen inches. The eyes, nose, and ears are all tiny, and the skull encloses a very small brain. The vision is poor, according to Schomburgk, and a young one kept captive by him was constantly running against articles that were in its path.

The hind feet of the giant anteater are plantigrade, and somewhat similar to those of a bear or raccoon; but the forefeet differ markedly in being armed with three long, curved claws, the longest of which may be four inches in length. For a long time after the discovery of this ant-eating creature, at least till the time of Waterton's description of it, certain misconceptions were held regarding the position of the forefeet in locomotion. The belief was that the claws were extended forward and the anteater walked on the bottoms of its feet as any respectable animal should. Waterton was the first to point out the truth, that the claws are folded back beneath the wrist and the beast walks on the outer side of its feet. An examination of the part of the appendage that comes in contact with the ground reveals that it is hard and calloused while the soles of the feet, or what would customarily be the soles, are soft and partially covered with hair. The ant bear is comfortable in this club-footed position as it walks (indeed it would be decidedly ill at ease in any other). The only reasonable explanation for this grotesque location of the claws must be concerned with their protection. They are not retractile and if extended forward the sharp points would become dulled by being constantly thrown into contact with the earth; folded underneath, they are shielded and kept sharp.

To complete the description of this anomalous beast it is necessary only to add that the long bushy tail is two feet or more in length and may be trailed behind in circumspect manner or hoisted over the back, squirrel-fashion. It is so large and luxuriant that it has been suspected of having some very important function to perform. Schomburgk observed that the captive anteater always covered its head and shoulders with its tail when asleep, and thought it probably served the purpose of keeping the beast warm. Wallace and others have claimed that the tail serves in the capacity of an umbrella and that it is always raised above the body when rain is falling. Still others have suggested that it is of importance in driving away insects.

Some authors have not been able to reconcile themselves to

the belief that a beast as large as the giant anteater could live entirely on creatures as small as ants and termites. Any one acquainted with the profusion of these insects in practically every part of the anteater's range has no doubts as to the ability of this animal to subsist without any other additions to its larder. As a matter of fact, it does not always depend entirely on ants although Up de Graff opened the stomach of one that contained a full quart, a respectable, if not a satisfying meal even for an anteater. Cherrie found that the giant anteater is capable of climbing trees, and that it feeds on nestling birds and eggs, the soft parts of which it is capable of lapping up with its tongue.

This habit may explain how ant bears manage to subsist in certain regions of South America, such as the swampy *pantanales* of the upper Paraguay, where ants and termites are not so abundant. Then, there is no doubt but that in the act of collecting ants with their long mucus-covered tongues the anteaters must ingest a great deal of other material, vegetable and otherwise, which adheres to the tongue along with the ants. Examinations of the stomach of the giant anteater have proved this to be the case, and Schomburgk wrote that a captive specimen he fed on termites swallowed, along with the white ants, a substantial quantity of the building material of the nest.

Even though they eat nestling birds, eggs and a wide assortment of ants, anteaters apparently prefer termites (more commonly though erroneously called white ants) to any other food material. They break open termite hills with the aid of their strong claws and extract therefrom the insects with their tongues. On the savannas of British Guiana and Venezuela large ant hills, sometimes ten to twelve feet high, are frequently found that have been undermined or completely overturned by anteaters. Having once torn away the wall of a nest, exposing the termites, the ant bear employs its tongue, which shoots in and out of the mouth with lightninglike rapidity and laps up, in short order, a wholesale quantity of these insects. The sticky mucus to which the insects adhere is furnished by two enormously enlarged salivary glands.

One of the earliest accounts of their method of feeding was written by Dampier, who watched an ant bear eating army ants.

"It lays its nose down flat on the ground; close by the path that the ants travel in, (whereof here are many in this country) and then puts out its tongue athwart the path; the ants passing forwards and backwards continually, when they come to the tongue, make a stop, and in two or three minutes it will be covered all over with the ants; which she perceiving, draws in her tongue and then eats them; and after puts it out again to trapan more. They smell very strong of ants, and taste much stronger; for I have eaten of them."

They feed both at night and in the daytime although they are said to carry on most of their activities under cover of darkness. Shortage of food does not disturb the even tenor of an ant bear's life, according to Waterton, for it can go longer without feeding than almost any other mammal. Considering the abundance of ants the giant ant bear must rarely go hungry unless in captivity. The beast is so highly specialized in its food habits that the sudden, complete elimination of ants and termites from tropical America would in all likelihood bring about its early extinction. The range of the ant bear is probably coincident with the forests and llanos capable of supplying all formicine needs.

Cherrie was apparently the first naturalist to observe a giant anteater in the act of climbing a tree; but long before, Schomburgk wrote: "This species must be able to climb equally as well as the small antbear for our prisoner not only undertook excursions on level ground but also extended them to the houseposts and walls, up which he clambered with the greatest ease." It can swim, too, for Schomburgk, Beebe, and others have encountered it swimming fairly large streams. According to them, it swims unusually fast; only the tip of the snout, a small portion of the back, and the end of the tail being visible.

The anteater is decidedly inoffensive in its relations with other animals. It asks nothing better than to be left to its own pursuits. In general it gives the appearance of being absolutely defenseless. There is nothing in the way of armor, such as is possessed by its congener, the armadillo; its locomotion is so slow that even a child can overtake it; and its mouth is entirely without teeth. However, the anteater is perfectly capable of taking care of itself. Very few animals are bold enough to launch an attack against it, and the Indians are quite wary about coming into close contact with it. The reason for this caution rests in the presence of a pair of powerful, well muscled forearms provided with the long scythelike claws already mentioned.

If pursued by dogs or man the anteater does its best to escape. However, there is small chance, for its ungainly, lumbering method of progression is inadequate and it is soon overtaken. Although it can climb trees it rarely if ever attempts to escape enemies in this manner; and it never burrows into the ground. Having done its best to avoid trouble the animal will rear up on its hind limbs when closely pressed by its enemies and swing its clawed forelimbs in deadly pugilistic fashion. Unfortunate is the creature that gets in the way, for the claws are capable of tearing huge gashes in the flesh that may prove serious, if not fatal. Many a good hunting dog has come to an untimely end in this fashion. If several dogs approach from different directions the anteater may throw itself on its back and with limbs outstretched wait for one of them to leap at its throat. If one of the dogs is so venturesome it is enclosed by the forelimbs in an embrace that is certain to be mortal. If the claws do not penetrate to some vital part, as is frequently the case, the animal is so powerful in the forequarters that it will crush the dog. Its struggles to free itself or to fasten its fangs in some vulnerable part will be futile.

Whether there are any authentic instances of men being killed in this manner by the giant anteater is difficult to say. Brown wrote, "These large anteaters are very dangerous customers, and have been known to kill men." He was told of an Indian hunter who picked up a baby anteater in the forest and started home with it in his arms. He had not gone far, however, before the mother anteater came up behind him without his knowledge and threw her clawed arms about him. He managed to get to his hunting knife and plunged it deep into the body of the beast, but that did not prevent the ant bear's claws from penetrating the Indian's heart. Brown evidently did not doubt this story and, authenticity aside, there is no denying that a man once in the embrace of a giant anteater would find it difficult to escape.

Brown himself came near to experiencing the feel of an ant

bear's claws, if not the effects of its embrace. Lost, one day, he was trying to locate his path, when he almost stepped on top of a sleeping ant bear. The creature immediately sprang erect, sat up on its hindquarters, and lashed out at him with its forelimbs. Only by jumping back quickly did he manage to escape.

Gardner had a much narrower escape than he admits. Somewhere in the interior of Brazil he and his native companions encountered a giant anteater. They pursued it on foot, and Gardner caught up with it first. "Being well aware of the harmless nature of its mouth," he said, "I seized it by its long snout, by which I tried to hold it, when it immediately rose upon his hind legs, and clasping me around the middle with its powerful fore paws, completely brought me to a stand; one of the men now coming up, struck it a blow on the head with a thick stick which brought it to the ground."

The only enemies the giant anteater has to fear are the large cats—the jaguar in particular. Azara ridiculed the notion that an ant bear could ever kill a jaguar, declaring that the latter would knock the anteater dead before it could even start defensive measures. There are so many reports to the contrary, however, that they cannot all be pushed aside as fallacious. Wallace once wrote that "all travellers know that native accounts of the habits of animals, however strange they may seem, almost invariably turn out to be correct." If there is any truth in this statement, the anteater is certainly capable of killing the jaguar, for almost all of the naturalists report that the Indians believe this to be the case. They declare that while the jaguar occasionally kills the anteater, the latter is capable of defending itself vigorously and now and then manages to encircle the feline with its arms and drive its long claws to some vital part. In the meantime the jaguar has dealt a decisive blow and thus both die. The belief is that the jaguar probably never attacks the huge Edentate unless driven by hunger.

The ant bear is found over most of Central and South America but is nowhere abundant. Whether it prefers swampy, low-lying land, as Waterton contended, or the open country of the llanos, as Im Thurn declared, cannot be stated with certainty.

In some parts of South America the Indians eat the ant bear;

in other regions they will have none of it. Bates found the flesh very good and said it tasted somewhat like goose.

The Tamandua

The tamandua, or lesser anteater *(Tamandua tetradactyla)*, is about the size of a fox—not more than half the size of the giant anteater. In general shape and appearance it is like the latter, but the predominating color is yellow instead of dark gray; the bands along its sides are black without the white borders, the ears are longer, and the tail is smooth, tapering, and prehensile.

This creature is both terrestrial and arboreal. According to Enders the tamandua is encountered more often on the ground than in the trees on Barro Colorado Island. It moves in much the same manner as the ant bear with the long claws of the forefeet curled beneath. Occasionally it breaks into a gallop; but this method of progression is slow and cumbersome, and it is easily overtaken. If possible it will escape by climbing, keeping the bole of the tree between itself and its pursuer until it is lost to sight in the enveloping foliage far overhead. If overtaken on the ground, it will either tumble over and lie supine with its feet in the air awaiting attack, or stand on its hind limbs with the arms striking out at whatever comes within reach. The latter is the more characteristic posture. In this position the body is upright with the hind feet firmly planted on the ground and the long tail stretching behind as a counterbalance. This tripodal attitude is virtually the same as that assumed by the giant anteater. There is one noticeable difference, however. The tamandua can progress while in this erect position, and with considerable celerity, whereas the ant bear invariably flops over on all fours when it attempts to move forward.

The lesser anteater is capable of making severe gashes in the flesh, if a person comes too near. Ordinarily the beast will do its utmost to escape; indeed, the last thing to be expected of the tamandua is an attack. Cherrie once encountered a tamandua in a forest near Ciudad de Bolívar in Venezuela which, within a few brief moments, completely upset all his preconceived notions of its behavior. For instance, he thought the tamandua was strictly arboreal and traveled abroad only at night; furthermore he considered its disposition to be of the mildest. His surprise may be imagined when he found the tamandua not only sauntering along on the ground in the middle of the day but quite ready for a fight. As soon as it saw Cherrie, it showed signs of anger and immediately rushed at him. As it arrived within a few feet of the naturalist, it stood upright and began swinging its forefeet in pugilistic fashion. Cherrie backed away, parrying the thrusts with his rifle barrel. This maneuver served only to enrage the beast further, and as it persisted in its attack Cherrie was forced to shoot it.

The tamandua does not move about in the trees with any great amount of celerity; without its prehensile tail, upon which it depends at all times, it would be severely inconvenienced. Although found active occasionally at all hours of the day, it is essentially nocturnal and spends the day curled up on a limb asleep. If disturbed at such a time its only action, according to Cherrie, is to move slowly farther out on the limb and resume its sleep.

It feeds on ants and termites and may be kept for long periods in captivity if fed on these insects. As much as a pint of ants has been discovered in the stomach of one. With its strong claws it quickly tears apart termite-inhabited wood; and it employs its long tongue in capturing the insects in much the manner described for the ant bear.

The Two-Toed Anteater

The two-toed, or silky, anteater *(Cycloterus didactylus)* is the Lilliputian among existing anteaters. It is a soft-furred creature no larger than a squirrel and spends its life in the trees of tropical America. Its color is a beautiful golden yellow, and the pelage is so extremely thick, shiny, and soft that, according to Miller, were the animal obtainable in quantities large enough to be commercially profitable, it would rival in price the finest furs on the market today.

Bates kept one in captivity for several hours and observed that when excited it reared up on its hind limbs and struck out with its clawed forefeet much like a cat. It made no sound at any time while he had it. The behavior of a closely allied form on Barro Colorado was observed by Enders to be somewhat different. When this species of anteater was irritated it stood upright, maintaining its balance with its specialized hind feet and prehensile tail, placed the forefeet on either side of the nose, and then bowed and swayed to and fro in an oddly amusing manner, at the same time making a peculiar hissing noise. This posture was maintained for as much as a minute or until the creature sensed that all danger was past, when it slowly reverted to its normal position.

The two-toed anteater is strictly arboreal, and its locomotion is generally said to be slow. Its leisurely method of traveling reminded Bates of the sloth. On the contrary Miller stated that "it moves along the branches with great rapidity, either in an upright position or inverted like a sloth, the prehensile tail being used constantly." It spends the day curled up asleep on some limb far above the ground, and consequently is rarely found even though abundant locally.

So far as is known, it feeds entirely on ants and termites, and since these are ubiquitous in the tropical forest, even in treetops, the silky anteater has a perennial supply. In captivity it feeds on termites but does not, as a rule, live long.

THE PUMA

There is no other land mammal alive with such a north-and-south range as that of the puma *(Felis concolor);* originally it inhabited the whole of the western hemisphere from British Columbia and Ontario to the southernmost tip of Patagonia. In this vast territory practically every condition of climate and topography is encountered: bleak, sterile mountainside; hot, stifling jungle; broad, treeless pampa. The altitudinal range of the puma is from sea level to points high in the Rockies and Andes. Darwin found evidence of its presence at an elevation of 10,000 feet in the Chilean Cordillera, and Spruce found its footprints 13,000 feet up in the Andes of Ecuador to the eastward of Riobamba. The puma is eurythermal to an extent approached by few other mammals; it is at home in all conditions of climate from Puget Sound to the Strait of Magellan.

As a result of its extensive distribution it is known by several names: lion, puma, panther, painter, catamount, mountain lion, cougar. As one writer has put it, the puma is a "beast of many aliases but few virtues." In the Appalachian Mountains of West Virginia and Tennessee the natives are familiar with the terms "panther," "painter," and "catamount"; but few of them know that the terms "cougar" and "mountain lion" employed in Arizona apply to the same animal. "Puma" and "lion" are the appellations used in South America. With the diversity of the landscape which makes up the range of the puma a number of distinct, well marked species might logically be expected; certainly it would not be surprising to find the puma of Patagonia easily distinguishable from the mountain lion of Colorado or Arizona. On the contrary, there is a remarkable uniformity in color and size over the entire range. In almost any part of its range the color varies from a deep red to a distinct fawn, and occasionally a melanistic form is found—Miller saw a black puma that had been killed by Indians; but these color phases are so general that none may be said to represent a distinct variety. There is no sure method of determining from the examination of a skin alone whether it came from Patagonia, the Mexican Plateau, the Magdalena valley, or the Bolivian Andes.

A person may live for months, and even years, in a region where the puma is known to be without seeing one. Prichard had as a companion in Patagonia a native who had been living there for eighteen years, and who had yet to see a live puma. Selous, probably the greatest of all African big-game hunters, has pointed out that men have lived in Central Africa for many years at a stretch without meeting a single lion. It is not surprising then that so many of the naturalists who traveled in South America make no reference to the puma. Darwin did not meet with a live one, nor did Wallace. We are also led to believe that Bates, in eleven years of Brazilian travel, did not see one. He stated that the puma was not common along the Amazon and, if he encountered one, he did not write of it. Later naturalists, with considerable experience in the southern continent, also make no reference to the big tawny cat.

Without a reasonable doubt the puma is more abundant in Patagonia than in any other part of South America. Prichard wrote, "The number of pumas in Patagonia is very great, more so than any zoologist has yet given any idea of"; seventy-three had been killed during one winter by two men living near Lake Argentino, and about the same time (1900) fourteen were killed on one farm. During the whole course of his journey in Patagonia, Prichard constantly came upon evidences of the presence of the big cats. At Tandeel, south of the Plata, Darwin was told that within three months three hundred had been killed.

With the coming of settlers into this region the pumas have been gradually killed off, and their number is greatly diminished. However, much of Patagonia is inaccessible, and they will remain there beyond the reach of rifle or bola for many decades to come.

The puma is known to reach a length of eight to nine feet from nose to end of tail and to weigh 150 to 200 pounds, dimensions which approach those of its more dangerous congener, the jaguar. The puma is not so bulky as the jaguar, has a smaller head and a much larger tail. The young when born have spotted bodies and ringed tails. These markings, which are lost before many weeks, indicate that at some remote period in this creature's history the adults were similarly stamped, according to the currently accepted theory that the embryological development of an animal includes a hasty summarization of its phylogeny, or past history.

The puma is a great enemy to livestock everywhere; and, in the absence of calves, pigs, and sheep, its destruction of the native fauna is prodigious. It does not hesitate to attack animals larger than itself and feeds locally on mountain sheep, deer of all kinds, guanaco, and tapir. Whenever these are not available it satisfies its appetite with coyotes, peccaries, capybaras, and lesser fry. The puma is said to kill its prey almost instantly, thus evidencing a great amount of strength, agility, and skill. Its general procedure, as described by Hudson, Darwin, and others, is to mount to a convenient overhead limb or to lie hidden in a convenient clump of vegetation where it can await the approach of its intended victim without detection. Once its prey arrives, the puma leaps for the shoulders, firmly anchors itself with its long retractile claws, and then with one sweep of a muscular paw forces the head back until the cervical vertebrae are dislocated. Hudson declared that on a hunting trip he saw as many as half a dozen deer each day that had been killed by pumas. In each case the neck of the ruminant had been dislocated, proving that the puma had played the role of the lord high executioner. Darwin wrote that he had seen the skeletons of guanacos with their necks thus dislocated.

Although the puma is such a persistent enemy of the larger North and South American mammals it religiously avoids man. Its attitude toward human beings is such that the Indians of both continents endow it with but few virtues, and all agree that it is a pusillanimous creature of the worst possible stripe. This singular attitude of the puma toward man cannot be described as just an "avoiding reaction"; it is much more than that. Most predatory beasts will go out of their way to avoid members of the human race but will, if cornered or wounded, attack rapidly, courageously, and often with serious results. On the contrary, the puma under such conditions—even though badly wounded or held at bay—will not become aggressive. It either submits to being slaughtered or slinks away like a whipped cur.

In support of the cowardly attitude of the cougar, Bates writes that the natives have no fear of the puma and always speak of it in a deprecating manner. Edwards tells a yarn about a puma and a native hunter, named Alexander, whose services he enlisted while at Pará. Alexander was in the habit of making forays into the near-by forests to get specimens for Edwards. Since he usually secured only the smaller indigenous forms he was armed with just a single-barreled gun loaded with nothing but BB shot. On one of his daily trips he met a puma, and the beast incontinently retired to a limb of the nearest tree. The course of events from then on indicated an entire lack of fear on the part of Alexander. With no hesitancy whatever he proceeded to blast away at the puma, with nothing more powerful than BB shot. More than that he poured broadside after broadside into its tawny skin until the beast—having made no effort either at defense or at offense—finally toppled off the limb stone-dead.

When Spruce was botanizing in the Andes a puma was killed by natives within just a few feet of the house in which he was living. It was being chased when he was first apprised of its nearness, and it would have escaped except for a thirty-foot perpendicular bank which it was unable to hurdle. "There he was speedily dispatched with bullets and lances," Spruce wrote. "He made no sign of resistance and seemed stupefied by the savage shrieks and cries of his pursuers."

In spite of this universally held opinion of the puma's lack of prowess among felines Hudson took up the cudgels in its defense. In one chapter of *The Naturalist in La Plata* he attempted to prove that this resident of the pampas was shamefully maligned, there if nowhere else. "To those personally acquainted with the habits of this lesser lion of the New World," he wrote, "it is known to possess a marvelous courage and daring." He went on to admit that it does not attack man and will not even defend itself against man; but this, he declared, is not enough evidence upon which to condemn the puma. At considerable length he pointed out how this "lesser lion" kills, with remarkable courage, all of the larger animals of the southern continent, even the jaguar, and asked, in substance, if this is the action of a cowardly, sniveling cat!

Hudson maintained that the puma is a friend of mankind, and

that on many occasions it had been known to befriend human beings. "In desert places," he wrote, "it is man's only friend among the wild animals. How strange that this most cunning, bold, and bloodthirsty of the Felidae, the persecutor of the jaguar and the scourge of the ruminants in the regions it inhabits, able to kill its prey with the celerity of a rifle bullet, never attacks a human being! Even the cowardly, carrion-feeding dog will attack a man when it can do so with impunity; but in places where the puma is the only large beast of prey, it is notorious that it is there perfectly safe for even a small child to go out and sleep on the plain. At the same time it will not fly from man (though the contrary is always stated in books of natural history) except in places where it is continually persecuted. Nor is this all: it will not, as a rule, even defend itself against man, although in some rare instances it has been known to do so. The mysterious, gentle instinct of this ungentle species, which causes the gauchos of the pampas to name it man's friend—'amigo del cristiano'—has been persistently ignored by all travelers and naturalists who have mentioned the puma. They have thus made it a very incongruous creature strong enough to kill a horse, yet so cowardly withal that it invariably flies from a human being—even from a sleeping child!"

Hudson admitted that this "gentle instinct" may not be had by all the pumas within its range; that those of the Amazon and Arizona may have other less gentle instincts which predominate. Considering the magnitude of its range, with the diversities of climate, it would not be surprising, he declared, if there were some divergence of habit.

The greater part of Hudson's chapter is taken up with anecdotes, most of which were related to him by the gauchos. By means of these stories he attempted to prove that the puma is not cowardly, and that it suspends its predatory instincts toward man not through a lack of courage, but because of an innate sense of camaraderie. One of the anecdotes is as follows: A gaucho was out on the pampas looking for cattle, and a puma was encountered. The big cat did not run but sat up on its haunches against a stone; it did not move even when a lasso was thrown about its neck. The gaucho "then dismounted, and, drawing his knife, advanced to kill it: still the puma made no attempt to free itself from the lasso, but it seemed to know what was coming for it began to tremble, the tears ran from its eyes, and it whined in the most pitiful manner." The gaucho killed it but told Hudson that he afterward felt like a murderer.

Another story concerned a man who, while hunting, broke his leg and was thrown from his horse. The latter immediately ran away, and he had to spend the night on the plains alone. Sometime after dark "a puma appeared and sat near him." It was restless and kept making journeys into the distance from which it returned. Later in the night the gaucho heard a jaguar roaring "and gave himself up for lost." However, to make a long story short—if we accept Hudson's interpretation—the puma fought with the jaguar and prevented it from attacking the man. This it did, not because of an innate predatory disposition but because of this remarkable "instinct of friendliness for man, the origin of which, like that of many other well-known instincts of animals, must remain a mystery." Although this instinct "must remain a mystery" Hudson did attempt to explain it. "We know," he wrote, "that certain sounds, colours, or smells, which are not particularly noticed by most animals, produce an extraordinary effect on some species; and it is possible to believe, I think, that the human form or countenance, or the odor of the human body, may also have the effect on the puma of suspending its predatory instincts and inspiring it with a gentleness towards man, which we are only accustomed to see in our domesticated carnivores or in feral animals toward those of their own species."

The notion that the puma is a friend of man may have arisen from a story of Buenos Aires related by Rui Díaz de Guzmán, a chronicler of the colonization of southern South America in the sixteenth century. In the year 1536 the town of Buenos Aires had some two thousand inhabitants. All went well with them until they began to run short of provisions. Governor Mendoza, going up-river to get food from near-by colonies, left a Captain Ruiz in charge. Soon rations were so low that, it is said, eighteen hundred of the two thousand inhabitants died of hunger. The dead bodies attracted wild beasts, and the remaining inhabitants were forbidden to leave the city because of this danger; but some of them did, and among these was a girl by the name of Maldonado. She strayed too far, became lost, and was captured by the Indians. Months afterwards she was brought back to Buenos Aires where Captain Ruiz charged her with desertion and with having gone to the Indians with the idea of betraying her countrymen. He ordered that she be taken from the town, tied to a tree, and left for the wild beasts to devour. At the expiration of two nights and a day a party was sent to learn her fate and was amazed to find her alive. She said that a puma had kept watch over her and had fought off the animals that might have torn her limb from limb. As to this story, Hudson wrote: "If such a thing were to happen now, in any portion of southern South America, where the puma's disposition is best known, it would not be looked on as a miracle, as it was, and that unavoidably, in the case of Maldonado."

The telling and retelling of this story, and the passing on of it from one generation to another, may conceivably have built up in the minds of the people the belief that the puma is in reality a friend of theirs. Dr. Francisco P. Moreno, the Argentinian scientist, told Roosevelt that Hudson knew nothing from personal experience of the puma, and that he relied entirely upon the gauchos for his information. In spite of Hudson's conviction that this "beast of many aliases" shows a particular friendliness for man derived from some gentle instinct, few scientists agree with him. On the contrary there is good evidence that in a certain region of the Argentine the pumas have attacked man. The region where pumas have dared to test their prowess with that of man is between Lake Argentino and Lake Viedmo. The fact that these attacks occurred is attested by Dr. Moreno. Prichard wrote of them, and many years later they were recounted in considerable detail by Roosevelt after he had had a description of them from Dr. Moreno himself. In 1877 Dr. Moreno was a member of a boundary commission that was working near Lake Viedmo. The region at that time was entirely uninhabited by whites and was only occasionally visited by Indians. One morning early he went out to make a survey of the lake, unarmed and carrying only a compass. Since the morning was cold he threw a poncho over his shoulders. He had not gone far when a puma leapt on his back and knocked him to the ground. His back and mouth were painfully lacerated, but in the struggle that ensued he managed to free himself and to regain his feet. The puma soon rushed at him again, but this time he swirled his poncho in its face and hit it over the head with his compass. This method of defense was effective, for the puma did not rush him again; however, it followed him to the near-by camp, where an Indian came to his aid and killed the beast with his bola. Dr. Moreno was scarred for life, but his wounds were not serious.

In 1898, some twenty years afterwards, Dr. Moreno returned to this same part of his country. Accompanying him were four soldiers. They made camp on the shore of Lake Viedmo, and during the night Dr. Moreno was awakened by a cry from one of the other men. As he struggled hastily to his feet he saw a puma run away into the night. It had attacked one of the sleeping soldiers and had tried to make away with him. The man was not injured, for he had been well wrapped up in heavy blankets against the cold. Not long after this a surveyor attached to Dr. Moreno's party was similarly attacked while he was asleep. This man was not so fortunate as the soldier, for the puma clawed him badly and knocked out some of his teeth. According to Dr. Moreno the Indians inhabiting this remote part of Patagonia forbade their women to go out alone because on occasions some had been killed by pumas.

Roosevelt was much interested in Dr. Moreno's reports, for he had been of the opinion that the puma practically never made an unprovoked attack upon man. He was now forced to admit that this anomalous beast did, in this restricted part of the Argentine, go out of its way to take the offensive against mankind. As he said, "I had often met men who knew other men who had seen other men who said that they had been attacked by pumas, but this was the first time I had ever come across a man who had himself been attacked." For the remainder of its range, however, Roosevelt was in agreement with Dr. Moreno in saying that the puma is "as a general rule, a cowardly animal which not only never attacks man, but rarely makes any efficient defence when attacked."

THE JAGUAR

THE jaguar *(Felis onca),* generally called *el tigre* in South America, is an extremely handsome creature; deep yellow in color, punctuated with black spots and rosettes, it is a much more attractive-looking cat than any of its relatives now living in the western hemisphere. Its every motion is easy and graceful, and it possesses remarkable agility in leaping through the tall grasses of the savannas or the dense undergrowth of the jungle. Distinctly at home either on the ground or in the trees, it exercises the same tyranny over other animals in North and South America as its royal Bengal relative in Asia, and its more powerful cousin, the lion, in Africa.

The jaguar is larger than the puma, being six to eight feet long from nose to tip of tail and weighing 150 to 250 pounds. It is a more formidable animal, too; though Hudson did contend "that whatever may be its status elsewhere the puma is mightier than the jaguar on the pampas." The jaguar has a massive build throughout, a very large head, and a tail that is disproportionately short. At first glance it might be mistaken for a leopard; but the jaguar's body is heavier and more powerful, and the large rosettes are in distinct contrast to the black spots of the leopard.

The strength of the jaguar is amazing. Azara related the story of a jaguar that killed a horse, dragged it several yards to the edge of a river, and then swam with it to the opposite bank; and Roosevelt was told by Rondon of a horse that was pulled a mile, in order that the jaguar might enjoy its meal near a water supply, the Brazilian explorer believed.

The range of the jaguar, while not so great as that of the puma, is extensive. His spotted majesty is to be found all the way from the southwestern United States to the Argentine Republic. Formerly it was found as far north as Colorado and east to the Mississippi; just why it never ventured to cross the "Father of Waters" to make itself a part of the general fauna of the Alleghenies remains a mystery. At the present time jaguars are found only in Texas, New Mexico, and Arizona, whither they occasionally wander from the sultry lowlands of Mexico. The southernmost limit of its range would seem to be the Argentine Río Negro. Prichard was assured that it had not been seen to the south of that river and none of the other explorers of Patagonia—Darwin, Musters, or Beerbohm—makes any reference to it from that region.

The jaguar is a great nomad, and within a very few days it has been known to travel hundreds of miles. It remains *in situ* only while the young are borne and brought to a condition of independence. There is some question as to whether the jaguar prefers the sultry, humid forest regions of Central and South America or the open savannas and pampas. At one time the jaguar was abundant on the Argentine pampas. Azara stated that, during the first years of Spanish settlement in the valley of La Plata, at least two thousand were killed each twelvemonth. No longer ago than 1833, Darwin found them quite common near the mouth of this river, particularly on the wooded banks and in the reeds near the water's edge. At one time they were so abundant on the Venezuelan llanos, Paez said, that it was almost impossible to raise cattle and horses, so frequently were they killed by *el tigre*. That these big felines love the jungle is true beyond a doubt; but they inhabit open country commonly and are found under too many environmental conditions to justify a statement that they have a preference for certain ones. Would it not be nearer the truth, perhaps, to say that they make a perfect adjustment to any and all environmental conditions within their range?

The idea persisted for a long time that there were two species of jaguars, the common spotted variety, and a rarer, more ferocious relative that possessed a black, unpatterned coat. Humboldt inspected some skins of the latter type at Esmeraldas and was convinced that these represented a distinct species. "This animal," he remarked, "is celebrated for its skill and ferocity; it appears to be still larger than the common jaguar. The black spots are scarcely visible on the dark-brown ground of the skin. The Indians assert that these tigers are very rare, that they never mix with the common jaguars, and that they form another race."

Schomburgk also was of the opinion that the black jaguar was distinct from its spotted congener. It was feared more by the

Courtesy of Zoological Society of **Philadelphia**

JAGUARS

Courtesy of N.Y. Zoological Society

GIANT ANTEATER

Courtesy of N.Y. Zoological Society

TAMANDUA OR LESSER ANTEATER

natives than either the ordinary jaguar or the puma, he wrote, "because it will attack human beings by day or night just as blood-thirstily as it will the tapir and cattle."

Even Bates wrote of the black jaguar. He encountered one at Ega and followed it for some distance before it escaped. The famous naturalist had but few experiences with the larger mammals. It is to be regretted that he did not have the opportunity of studying at least a small number of jaguar skins. If he had had, it is more than likely that the riddle of the "black tiger" would have been solved much sooner than it was.

It is now known that the coloration in jaguars varies tremendously. Some have only a small amount of pigment (melanin)—albinos have even been seen—while others, at the opposite extreme, have a large amount. The last, of which the so-called black jaguars are examples, are considered to be "melanic accidents" and differ from other, lighter-colored jaguars only in having a greater quantity of melanin in their coats. There are other animals that furnish similar examples of color variation. For instance, the black and silver foxes are color phases of the red fox; and the black leopard of the Far East is a "sister" of the spotted variety "under the skin."

Just why Schomburgk did not arrive at the conclusion that the black jaguar is a color phase of the common type is difficult to understand. As he said, he had examined a large number of skins and noted that, with scarcely any exceptions, they were of a different pattern and differently colored. "The ground colour of the pelt of some was more russet, of others more pale (greyish), and others again were brownish; the size of the rings also varied, according as some were more or less complete, nearer or farther apart, here lighter or darker, there distinctly or lightly dotted in the centre; indeed, the variation of pattern proceeds to such an extent that only rarely does one side of an animal correspond in exact pattern with the others."

All mammals, even though they lead a serious existence, have periods in their life when they play a little; and the members of the cat family are especially so disposed. Humboldt related the following incident, told to him by a missionary: Two Indian children were at play on the edge of a forest overlooking a small corner of the great savanna region of southern Venezuela. Suddenly a jaguar burst from the woods and began leaping back and forth, making huge bounds as it circled about them. Tiring of these maneuvers, it hid in the grass, playfully arching its back and lowering its head, and then sprang toward them in precisely the same way as a domestic cat would have done. At last it became bolder and began leaping against the children, still in a playful manner, however. In so doing, it clawed one of the youngsters on the forehead and on the top of the head. At this the other child picked up a stick, hit the jaguar over the head, and it ran away. Humboldt saw these children soon after the incident happened, examined the wounds, and verified the details of the occurrence.

The jaguar at times, too, demonstrates considerable curiosity. Waterton asserted that one night one of these beasts came to his camp and sat down on its haunches not more than twenty yards away from his campfire. When his native helper yelled at it, it leaped away into the tropical night and did not return. "Tigers are too few, and too apt to fly before the noble face of man, to require a moment of your attention," Waterton opined. Some other naturalists relate incidents of the lively curiosity which the jaguar possesses. Verrill was followed ten miles or more along a narrow jungle trail, he said. When he sensed that he was being followed he retraced his steps and found the large footprints of the beast superimposed over those of his own.

Schomburgk told of a jaguar that gave his brother, Sir Robert Schomburgk, all sorts of trouble while he was at an Indian village on the Rupununi. One night the purring and roaring of a jaguar announced its presence near the encampment. Everyone was on the alert, but the creature did not come close enough to be seen. Next morning, however, one of the dogs was missing. For several nights following, the beast came again, but no more dogs lost their lives. After each visit, though, some article of the camp equipment was missing. One morning it was discovered that a hammock was not to be found; another morning a cooking utensil could not be located; and still another morning it was a tablecloth that did not turn up. Sir Robert naturally suspected the Indians; they denied any part in the theft, however, and maintained that the jaguar was the culprit. He could not believe that an animal would pilfer hammocks and cooking utensils. Time went on, and other thefts were perpetrated. Feeling against the Indians began to grow rather high among the white members of the party. The jaguar was still coughing out feline oaths at night, and the Indians were still maintaining their innocence in the matter. More than that, they continued to lay all of the blame on the jaguar. Under such circumstances guns were kept within easy reach. Late one night, while working at his table, Schomburgk looked up to see indistinctly an animal at the entrance of his tent. He lifted a light and saw that it was a jaguar; but before he could grab his pistol it had vanished into the darkness. The next night he was awakened by some animal moving about under his hammock. Thinking it was one of the many dogs about the camp he leaned over and gave it a hearty slap. With noises that no canine ever made, the creature bounded out of the tent and disappeared. It was a jaguar. This was too much for comfort, and Schomburgk, next morning, called all hands together and declared war. Within short order all members of the party were in the forest looking for some trace of the jaguar. They searched the jungle thoroughly and vainly for the animal. Scattered here and there through the jungle, however, were found stewpans, hammocks, shirts, and tablecloths that had been missing. Schomburgk was forced to accept the Indians' contention that the jaguar had actually been the guilty party.

Schomburgk stated that the jaguar will, as a rule, avoid man; that when it encounters a human it shows no fear whatever but, with dignity and care, retreats into the jungle; and that it will not run unless there are dogs present or the number of men assumes proportions that are unduly formidable.

While this is essentially true the jaguar is not always such a benign creature. Like the lion of Africa it turns maneater now and then, and once having tasted human flesh it may develop an insatiable craving for the blood of man. Azara said: "It is certain, that since I have been in Paraguay, the few remaining [jaguars] in this country have devoured six men, carrying off two of them from the midst of companies who were warming themselves by the fire." The natives informed him that if a jaguar "comes upon a company of travelers asleep he carries off the dog, if there is one; if not, the negro; afterwards, the Indian; and only pounces on the Spaniard in the absence of all these."

In the midst of his exploration along the lower Paraná, Darwin was informed that many woodcutters of that region had been killed by jaguars, and that these had been known to enter vessels at night. A man was still living at Bajada who had been attacked one night when coming up on deck from the hold of his ship. The sailor escaped, but lost the use of his arm in the encounter. Darwin was also told that two padres had been killed in a church near by and a third had escaped with difficulty. Wallace wrote that "many persons are annually killed or wounded by these animals" in South America.

Colonel Roosevelt averred, "The jaguar has long been known, not only to be a dangerous foe when itself attacked, but also now and then to become a man-eater." He was shown a jaguar in the zoological gardens at Buenos Aires that had been trapped after taking the lives of three people. He was also told of another death. A competent Argentine scientist had been making a survey along the boundary between the Argentine and Brazil. There was quite a bit of dried beef in the camp of the officer to which a jaguar took a liking. In order to prevent any further pilfering the meat was hung up out of reach. This was a disastrous move, for the next night the jaguar returned, and not being able to get at the meat seized a man, killing him instantly, by biting through the wall of his cranium.

The jaguar, like most of the Felidae, is nocturnal. As a result its presence in a neighborhood is rarely suspected until after depredation on livestock. On occasion it is observed abroad during the day.

Whenever jaguars exist in the neighborhood of a farm or ranch, the livestock is certain to suffer. Darwin was told that they destroyed numerous horses and cattle, particularly during flood time when other natural food was limited. Gardner visited a cattle-raiser in the interior of Brazil who had many calves and adult cattle killed each year. Schomburgk stated that the jaguar was "the most dangerous enemy of the cattle-herds, sheep, flocks, and piggeries" in British Guiana. The big cats were more numerous along the coast than they were in the interior, he said. The livestock attracted them from the forest, he believed. Im Thurn said he was informed that on the cattle farms along the Brazilian border of British Guiana hardly a night passed in which the cattle were not attacked by jaguars. Miller told of a large herd of cattle that was stampeded by a jaguar one night when he was collecting in the Andes of Colombia. It took several days to round them up, and many of them were not found at all.

Domesticated animals not being available, the jaguars feed upon the wild life that is most easily procurable. Darwin wrote that their chief food was the capybara, and where it was numerous there was little danger to man. On occasion the jaguar was sufficiently bold, or hungry, to attack a large caiman. Terrific fights resulted in which the cat was usually the victor. Bates found a dead caiman with practically nothing left but bones. There was no doubt about the assassin: jaguar footprints were numerous all about.

Jaguars are said to kill peccaries frequently; but even a jaguar has good reason not to attack a band of peccaries. Instead, the big cat mounts to a limb and waits for the usual straggler, upon which it pounces. If others of the band are apprised of the situation and make an attack the jaguar postpones its feast, quickly regaining its former position in the tree and waiting till the pigs move off again.

Turtles are attacked also upon occasion. André found shells along the Caura that had been emptied, and was greatly impressed with the strength of an animal capable of breaking the bridge which joins the carapace and the plastron. The "tigers" are fond also of turtle eggs and spend much time looking for the nests. Frequently holes in the sand are discovered, with pieces of shells scattered about, where the jaguars have enjoyed a meal.

The tapir, the largest of all South American terrestrials, is occasionally attacked and killed. André shot a tapir that bore the marks of a conflict with his spotted majesty.

Jaguars are hunted in several ways in the southern continent, the method used depending upon the section of the country and upon the hunter. Sometimes they are trapped, sometimes lassoed, sometimes captured with the bola; but as a rule they are hunted with dogs. With the aid of the latter they are sooner or later treed and easily shot. However, a wounded jaguar will show fight; it will not hesitate to attack dogs and men, sometimes with tragic results. Schomburgk knew of such cases. In one a negro shot without killing; the cat attacked quickly and viciously, and seized him before he could get his gun into play again. He would have been torn to pieces if an accompanying Indian had not come to the rescue with a knife.

Now and then a sort of "superman" is to be found in South America who dares to attack the jaguar single-handed. Armed only with a long spear, this enterprising Nimrod travels alone into the jungle, taking death in his own hands, in an attempt to kill *el tigre.* Azara described this method of hunting, which was known in Paraguay in the early part of the nineteenth century. Rusby encountered a native in the cinchona region of Mapiri who had this art down to a fine point. His weapons consisted of a long, straight-edged sword that was wielded by the right arm, and a heavily bandaged left arm that served in the capacity of a shield. Thus prepared, he advanced to the fray. Having located the jaguar in some impenetrable bit of forest, he maddened the creature until it charged. As it did so it leaped onto the end of the sword and was impaled. The most modern exponent of this type of jaguar hunting is the "Tiger Man," Sascha Siemel, who claims to have killed many of these brutes in single-handed combat. He learned his technique from a native of the Guato tribe of Indians. He does not venture alone into the jungle but takes along a pack of dogs. These pick up the trail and eventually tree the cat or bring it to bay in some dense thicket. The spear, which is Siemel's only weapon, is not thrown at the animal: if it missed he would be defenseless. Nor is it jabbed at the huge carnivore: the point of the spear would in all likelihood be diverted by the paw of the cat. The "Tiger Man" provokes the animal to charge and then holds his weapon in such a manner that the jaguar is impaled upon the point when it leaps. Since the beast may not be over ten or fifteen feet away when it makes its charge the hunter must adjust the point of the spear in a fraction of a second. The animal may leap into the air, or it may rush at him like an infuriated rhino, but there must be no indecision on his part. There is really no time to think or to map out a course of action;

every movement must be reflexive. Siemel claims to have developed his skill to such an extent that he is able to kill a jaguar in half a minute.

A. Hyatt Verrill relates one of the most unusual methods of securing a jaguar that have been described—a method which, for its uniqueness and safe-and-sound tactics, recommends itself to any man, whether he is an ambitious hunter or an unarmed pacifist. Verrill was descending a large South American stream in a small boat, making about ten knots an hour, with the help of the current and an outboard motor. Shortly, one of the Indians with him cried out, "*Maipuri* [Tapir]," at the same time pointing to a spot some distance ahead where a large animal could be seen swimming the stream. Verrill was short of meat and, not being averse to laying in a fresh supply of such excellent food as the tapir provides, turned the boat in the direction of the animal. The speed with which they were traveling quickly brought them close, when Verrill suddenly realized that the beast was not a tapir at all but a jaguar. As the boat swept by, some latent, juvenile whim seized Verrill and he reached out and grabbed the jaguar by the tail. Almost yanked from the boat, Verrill yet managed to hold on and drag the cat after him. Because of the speed of the boat the brute was unable to turn in defense; and the more it struggled, the worse it fared. Gradually its efforts to escape grew weaker, and shortly thereafter Verrill was able to pull it into the boat, where no efforts at resuscitation were made. This was probably the only jaguar that was ever captured in this remarkable manner.

THE COATI

THE coati *(Nasua),* also known locally as *coatimondi, pisoti, quashi,* and *kibihie,* is one of tropical America's most interesting contributions to the raccoon family. It is a near relative of our northern "coon," which it resembles not only in size and general proportions but in habit and disposition. Both have the ringed tail, the pointed muzzle, the short legs and plantigrade feet, and both are surprisingly intelligent. They differ markedly on the basis of extremities. The coati has a longer tail that is decidedly conspicuous and is often carried upright; and its long, mobile, almost prehensile nose projects beyond the lower jaw in regular Cyrano de Bergerac fashion, and on occasion seems capable of registering such contrasting emotions as disdain and pleasure in addition to performing its customary olfactory functions.

The forebears of the coati and raccoon had their origin, it is alleged, some fifteen millions of years ago in what is now North America. The present range of this group embraces North America, South America, and Asia. Although of such ancient lineage and wide dispersal, it has but few existing members. In addition to the coati and raccoon there are the kinkajou *(Potos)* and ring-tailed cat, or cacomistle *(Bassariscus),* all American, and the giant and lesser pandas of Asia. The giant panda, much resembling a bear in its general detail, is now considered (by those competent to give opinion) to be a distant relative of the coati and a much modified and overgrown variation of the lesser panda.

There appear to be at least four distinct species of coatis now frequenting tropical America. One of these is Mexican and Central American in distribution, the others are South American. The range is from the Río Grande to Paraguay; and, considering the extent of the dispersal, it is possible that additional species may be discovered in the future.

The Central American species *(Nasua narica)* is distinctly gregarious. Belt reported seeing a pack in the interior of Nicaragua that contained in the neighborhood of fifty individuals, and Chapman has observed many bands on Barro Colorado Island that numbered from fifteen to forty. Singularly enough, these aggregations consist entirely of females and their young. In no instance recorded are there any males in attendance; whether they choose a life of seclusion or are coerced into exile by their former mates has not been determined. Suffice it to say that the males play no important part in the communal existence of coatis, so far as is known. In each family the proportion of young to adult females is roughly six to one.

The South American species are not all gregarious, for according to Im Thurn one of the two species occupying British Guiana *(N. solitaris)* is found only singly or in pairs. The other form *(N. socialis),* as its name implies, is definitely social.

Unlike such highly specialized animals as the giant anteater and three-toed sloth, the coati eats a wide variety of foods. Among these are vegetable products, such as nuts, berries, and bananas, as well as fledgling birds, eggs, small mammals, spiders, and various and sundry reptiles. Belt was much interested in a drove of hungry coatis that were after iguanas in a clump of bushes. It was his opinion that with some of them on the ground and others in the trees the objects of their united search stood small chance of escape.

There is little doubt that these roving bands are extremely destructive to many of the smaller forms of animals. Their special senses of sight and smell, particularly the latter, are highly developed; their method of attack is savage, and their persistence habitual. Any slower or weaker creature is in danger of sudden, violent death. A large pack can cover a huge expanse of the forest floor within a day. Since they have a fondness for eggs, one may well wonder if the ground-nesting birds in a given area are able to hold their own.

These raccoonlike animals are at home both on the ground and in the trees, yet in spite of assertions of the early naturalists to the contrary they are preeminently terrestrial. One has only to watch carefully their behavior to be convinced that they are not completely adapted to an arboreal environment. The most pronounced evidence of this is their action when alarmed. If a pack is disturbed in the trees by some person on the ground they make no attempt to secrete themselves among the leaves or to reach a point of safety higher in the branches, but instead make their way to earth as fast as safety will permit. An observer not acquainted with this behavior would easily be led into the belief that the cause of alarm was somewhere in the trees rather than on terra firma.

Of even more interest is the reaction of these creatures when surprised on the ground. They almost invariably run up the nearest tree to a height of ten or fifteen feet, apparently make a quick survey of their surroundings, and then, instead of climbing higher, jump to earth and make off as fast as their short legs will take them. This action has been noted by Chapman many times on Barro Colorado and by Brown in British Guiana.

Yet the coati is surprisingly well adapted to an arboreal existence. It clambers about in the trees with much of the abandon and assurance that characterize the monkey. Its long tail, although not prehensile, is put to good use as a balancing organ. Although the coatimondi weighs ten to fifteen pounds it climbs to the tops of the tallest jungle trees and travels out to the ends of small branches where ordinarily only the smaller creatures venture. If the food it seeks is still out of reach it demonstrates extraordinary ingenuity by bending the twig toward it until the attached fruit may be grasped.

Nothing is more characteristic of the coati than its willingness to fight. The males fight viciously among themselves, using claws and teeth with deadly effect, and the females protect their young with every ounce of energy and strength at their command. Miller once saw a dog killed by a coati, and Chapman and others have reported witnessing occasional attacks on man. A human being is very likely to experience the wrath of a female coati if he surprises her with her young. While the coatis have their enemies among the large cats—the pumas, ocelots, and jaguars—their worst enemy, according to Chapman, is the coati itself. When two males meet in the silent pathways of the forest a fight is imminent. The loser, if not killed, is generally badly wounded. There is some cause for believing that the females outnumber the males, and this disparity may account for the intensity of the warfare between the males.

Courtesy of Frank M. Chapman

COATI

Courtesy of N.Y. Zoological Society

COLLARED PECCARY

Courtesy of N.Y. Zoological Society

WHITE-LIPPED PECCARY

The Coati

Coatis apparently feel a measure of confidence in their ability to protect themselves, for they make no sensible effort to travel quietly in the jungle. Their presence may be detected by the human ear at a distance of several rods by the noise they make in going through the undergrowth and by their peculiar, harsh, piglike grunts. They are usually so intense in their search for food, and so noisy withal, that a person may approach within a few feet without detection if the wind is toward him.

Like the raccoons, coatis are favorite pets. They have all the mischievous qualities of their northern relatives and at the same time are intelligent, responsive, and inquiring. They are seen more often in the Indian villages where they have been tamed than in the wild. On occasion captured specimens may play havoc with the poultry, destroy fruit, and otherwise disrupt the even tenor of the owner's life. Bigg-Wither had a tame coati that was a constant source of amusement to him and "became adept at everything from cleaning red-hot ashes out of a pipe to standing on its head in a hammock." Whether the coatis are found in the wild or in a state of partial domestication, they add more than a little interest to the life of the great equatorial forest.

PECCARIES

THE peccaries are the true "wild pigs" of America. There are no close relatives in the New World, the domestic swine and wild boars of the eastern hemisphere being their closest living kin.

There are just two living species: the white-lipped peccary *(Dicotyles labiatus)* and the collared peccary *(Dicotyles tajacu)*. Both are relatively small, spindly-legged animals that have four toes on the front feet and three on the hind, a complex ruminant-like stomach, and a functional musk gland adorning the rump. They are clothed in coarse, bristlelike hairs and bear a mane of black bristles extending from between the ears to the region of the musk gland. The head is ill formed with a truncated snout, and the mouth contains razor-sharp tusks in both jaws. The tail is rudimentary, almost wanting. If alarmed, peccaries demonstrate unexpected speed which is put to advantage either in outdistancing an enemy or in rushing to the attack.

The collared peccary is the smaller of the two species, with a total length of about three feet and a weight of sixty to seventy-five pounds. Within its range there are several geographic races in which the color varies from a grizzled gray to black, but all are readily identified by a white collarlike streak on the forequarters at about the point where the neck joins the body.

Until recently the collared peccary was found as far north as the Red River of Arkansas and south to the Río Negro of Patagonia. Only one other American mammal, the puma, has a range exceeding that of this animal. As in the case of the puma the dispersion of the collared peccary is less extensive than it was a few decades ago—its occurrence in the United States is now limited to the southern parts of Arizona, New Mexico, and Texas.

The collared form usually runs in small bands of eight or ten, although there may be as few as three and, infrequently, as many as twenty to thirty. As a rule these porkers, when in wooded country, prefer rank undergrowth to open forest. They make numerous, winding trails through the jungle thickets, all of which tend to be narrow from the circumstance that the collared peccaries, like camels in caravan, have the habit of marching single file. Even when they are crossing open forest-rooms they adhere to this tandem method of progression. While engaged in feeding they deploy, covering considerable ground, as is evidenced by the large rooted-up areas that are found here and there throughout the forest. Sometimes near habitations the presence of a band is entirely unsuspected until these feeding grounds have been discovered.

Peccaries, both collared and white-lipped, are notoriously omnivorous. They eat great quantities of fruits, nuts, tubers, worms, insects, and, when available, salamanders, lizards, snakes, and many other animals.

The collared peccary is, by nature, a diurnal beast and feeds more energetically in the early hours of morning and those of late afternoon. Midday is generally spent lying in wallows or at rest in dense undergrowth. Recent observations indicate, however, that it occasionally feeds at almost any hour of the day and sometimes, especially when the moon is bright, at night. The native hunters say that if the peccary is hunted vigorously, as it is in many localities, it changes its habits and feeds at night.

The musk glands of the peccary are the matter of frequent reference by naturalists; but few have ventured an opinion as to their possible functions. These particular secretory organs, located on the top of the buttocks, are well developed in both male and female. The musk of the collared peccary is a clear, rather amber-colored fluid with a consistency and appearance somewhat like that of melted butter. According to Enders it has a "rather pleasant" odor if not too intensified. The glands secrete only periodically, and just what stimuli are most powerful in provoking their activity does not seem to be known. They become active following excitement, regardless of whether it is agreeable or annoying; but to what purpose is uncertain.

The lasting qualities of the musk are considerable, for, according to Enders, one may determine whether collared peccaries have recently used a runway by smelling the branches and leaves along it. Usually the odor surrounds a band for some distance in each direction.

The South American naturalists are one in saying that if the meat of the peccary is to be eaten, the musk gland must be removed on the spot or the flesh will be tainted. This statement has been so universally made that the observation of Enders is in the nature of a distinct surprise. He killed two collared peccaries from which the musk glands were not removed for considerable time—two and a half hours in one of them—and yet there was not the slightest trace of musk in the flesh when it was eaten.

It is said that the sense of smell is highly developed in peccaries, that hearing is only fair, and eyesight poor. Chapman managed to get within forty feet of a band without detection when the wind was toward him, but could not approach closer than sixty feet with the wind in the opposite direction.

Where man is concerned, the collared peccaries are relatively harmless, inoffensive brutes. Tales of their ferocity have little foundation in fact. There is an occasional authenticated instance of unprovoked attack, but the tendency of the animal is to flee at the approach of man. An exception to the rule was related by Up de Graff. According to this traveler he ran across two collared peccaries when in the unfortunate position of having no gun with him—only an ax. He hurled a club at them to frighten them away, whereupon the larger of the two came at him so viciously he dropped his ax and took to the nearest tree.

When one encounters these pigs in the forest, their action can never be predicted. They may bolt with much teeth clashing and grunting, or they may slip away so quietly that they give no clue to the direction taken. Sometimes they advance toward the intruder, showing more curiosity than anger, and then, after a cursory inspection, flee into the protecting foliage as fast as their spindly legs will carry them. If they were to make a mass attack on man, the results might well be serious, for they have been known to rip large hunting dogs to pieces.

The white-lipped peccary is not marked by the white collar but by a white patch on each lower jaw. It is larger, measuring about forty inches and weighing one hundred pounds or more, and is darker in color. It is not so well turned out as its relative: the coat is inclined to be shaggy, the hair sparse, and there is the general appearance of being ill fed.

The social instinct is highly developed in the white-lipped peccaries. They run together in bands that range from three or four to more than a hundred. Up de Graff saw a herd swimming the Napo at a point where it was a good three hundred yards wide. While the advance guard was climbing the far bank the rear guard was still streaming into the water on the near shore. They were not in single file but "came swarming across in a great black mass." Up de Graff said they occur in bands of two hundred or more, and both Waterton and Cherrie stated that huge roving companies of three to four hundred may be encountered. Aggregations of that magnitude must occur rarely.

The odor of the musk excreted by the white-lip is much stronger than that discharged by the collared form and, as Brown remarks, "is by no means pleasant to one's olfactory nerves." The scent is so powerful that, according to Up de Graff, "a man can track them through the woods by scent as easily as a hound follows a hare." If at any time the stench of a distant herd is wafted to the nose it may be described at once as that from a white-lip band; and if the wind is right this effluvium can be smelled a mile away.

The white-jawed forms are said to prefer open woods to dense undergrowth, and to march in a more or less compact group rather than Indian file.

Always when excited the peccaries clash their teeth together in what one author has termed their "war cry." The jaws work at a terrific speed, and if a large band pool their efforts the volume of sound is amazing and, according to one author, reminiscent of the effect produced by hundreds of castanets.

There is no question that the tusks of the white-lipped peccary are formidable weapons, and that with them these pigs are capable of making short shrift of any animal they attack *en masse,* be it jaguar, puma, or man. It is because of this danger of concerted action that Chapman characterizes the white-lipped peccary as "Public Enemy No. 1" among the mammals of tropical America. Theodore Roosevelt considered the African buffalo the most dangerous beast of the Dark Continent for the same reason. Apparently a man's only chance when attacked by one of these excited bands of pigs is to climb the nearest tree. Whenever one reads of a traveler who has been treed somewhere in the jungle by peccaries, he may be certain that white-lipped peccaries were the cause of the ascent. Up de Graff knew what he was talking about when he advised hunters who were stalking white-lipped peccaries to select a tree before covering the last fifty yards. "The in-and-in fighting ability of these animals," Rice said, "I have witnessed on numerous occasions when they, with jaws shot away, legs broken, and bodies fearfully mutilated, have badly punished big hounds." He considered the white-lipped peccary the most dangerous of all South American land mammals to hunt. No more interesting fact about the white-lipped peccary has come to the attention of the scientist in recent years than the discovery on Barro Colorado Island, Canal Zone, that when these porkers moved into a certain region of the island, other animals moved out. Particularly noteworthy was the fact that the tapir, the largest of tropical American mammals, absconded with other lesser forms. Tracks of this beast were common along the banks of certain streams until the pigs came, and then were encountered no more until the peccaries left for other parts. A captive deer became frantic as soon as it scented the white-lip, although it had shown no fear at all when collared peccaries were in the neighborhood.

Bigg-Wither, an English engineer, told of a jaguar that was killed and eaten by these pugnacious brutes although it disposed of fourteen of the pigs before succumbing to their ferocity and courage. Jaguars and pumas apparently feed upon peccaries—indeed, there are no other mammals in South America strong enough to cope with them—but they mount into trees and then drop onto the stragglers after the rest of the band has gone by.

However, the ability of these pigs to do damage is one thing; their actual behavior is another. What has been the experience of the naturalist with them?

Schomburgk related that one morning in the interior of British Guiana he heard a noise in the distance like the galloping of horses. The natives with him immediately recognized the sound as that of a herd of white-lipped peccaries and made ready their guns and bows and arrows. However, as the pigs came close and caught sight of the men, they did not charge but dashed off at a great rate in another direction.

At La Prisión, while he was making preparations for his ascent of the Caura, André's camp was overrun by a herd of about one hundred peccaries. The appearance of the beasts was unexpected, and the camp was at once in an uproar. The porkers ran wildly about the place, grunting and upsetting the provisions, and the men, women, and children added to the general confusion by shouts and screams. In a little while the peccaries, as though dissatisfied with their inventory, scampered away into the forest. During the few minutes they were present no attempt was made by any of them to attack the members of André's party.

Roosevelt engaged in a peccary hunt on the River of Tapirs (Sepatuba) during the course of which three white-lips were killed. The band was encountered in dense jungle so thick that the hunters could see only a few feet ahead. Although the animals made a lot of noise, groaning and clashing their tusks, they made no attempt to charge.

William M. Mann,* director of the National Zoological Park at Washington, said he had heard of peccaries chasing men up trees, but that he not only shot a female from a band of fifty white-lipped peccaries but caught a young one and held it squealing until he got away. The other peccaries did their usual teeth-clashing but did not charge.

Brown encountered a herd of white-lips on the Quitaro, a secondary tributary of the Essequibo, where he found them rather common. On this occasion he heard their characteristic gruntings but, on account of dense undergrowth, was unable to see any of them. They soon winded him, however, and all clashed their tusks together in the accepted porcine manner. This show of ferocity was followed almost at once by a charge. Brown fired, hitting one in the chest with a charge of BB shot, and the rest, as though deprived of their leader, quickly turned and bolted away into the thick undergrowth.

Cherrie seems to have been the only one of the naturalists who had the fortune, or misfortune, to be driven up a tree by a band

*Smithsonian Scientific Series, Vol. VI, 1930.

of peccaries. This incident occurred in Costa Rica, and the attackers numbered three to four hundred, according to Roosevelt who related this incident. Cherrie was able to carry his gun with him during his ascent, and from a point of vantage killed quite a few of them; but his assailants kept him aloft for several hours before hunger, restlessness, or ennui caused them to depart.

In four of the six specific cases given above that relate the experiences of naturalists with these animals, there was no attempt to charge although in at least two cases there was more than ample provocation. In the remaining two the peccaries charged. One of the onslaughts was stopped by a discharge of BB shot.

From this amount of evidence it is impossible to make any positive statement as to how likely these animals are to become the aggressors where man is concerned. But may it not be true that their pugnacious disposition has been somewhat exaggerated? Perhaps Enders has summed the matter up correctly when he says they usually retreat, but not always. Even though these white-lipped pigs may attack man only on rare occasions, there is no denying their ability to cope with a situation if concerted action is taken. In the presence of a large herd of peccaries all of which rush viciously to the attack, a man, no matter how carefully chosen his arsenal, would have just about as much chance of coming off unscathed as a lightning beetle attacked by a regiment of army ants.

The meat of the peccary, whether collared or white-lipped, is held in high esteem by the Indians, being much like pork. Consequently they kill these beasts on every possible occasion. The natives are particularly pleased when they encounter a band swimming a river. The pigs are indifferent swimmers, and the natives, without hesitation, go after them armed with clubs and other weapons and dispatch many of them. According to Schomburgk the nasal region of a peccary is a very sensitive spot, and one or two well directed blows over it will kill the animal. Spruce encountered a herd of peccaries swimming the Amazon just above Iquitos. He and some of his men launched a canoe and with the aid of guns and cutlasses quickly killed nine of them. Im Thurn wrote that he knew of a native who had administered the death blow to fifty peccaries, which were part of a large band swimming one of the Guiana streams. According to Rice, one of the members of his party with the aid of several *seringueros* killed 130 white-lipped peccaries in a great horde that was crossing the Casiquiare. Just how helpless these beasts are in the water is further attested by Im Thurn: A British Guiana native swam into the midst of a band of peccaries, armed only with a rope. Within a few moments he had tied up six of them, which he subsequently towed to shore and dispatched.

Dickey related a strange story about peccaries that will lose nothing in the retelling. He discovered an anaconda asleep by the side of a jungle stream. Startled at the discovery, he hesitated as to the advisability of shooting it. Apparently there were both pros and cons. While in the midst of his meditations, a strangely familiar odor permeated the atmosphere, and almost at once the grunting and teeth-clashing announced the approach of a band of some forty white-lipped peccaries. Without hesitation, they made straight for the huge serpent, which by this time gave indications of life by raising its head above the folds of the body and moving it back and forth in an excited manner. Before further movements were possible, the peccaries were at it. With unbelievable ferocity they attacked it from all sides. Using their tusks and hoofs with deadly effect, they tore it to shreds. In less than five minutes the ravage was complete; nothing remained but torn fragments of muscle and viscera which the pigs were devouring.

Peccaries will attack poisonous snakes as well as innocuous varieties, and if they are bitten suffer no ill effects. Formerly it was thought they were immune to snake venom, but it is now believed that their thick hides and subcutaneous layers of fascia and fat prevent the toxin from reaching the blood stream.

THE TAPIR

THE tapir (called *anta* by the Portuguese) is the largest animal native to the continent of South America. Like several other peculiar-looking animals which inhabit equatorial America, it is a faunal oddity that seems out of place. Among an assortment of generalized animals from the Miocene or Pliocene eras its appearance would not be heralded as peculiar; but among a grand motley of present-day, highly specialized beasts it is decidedly anachronistic. It has undergone comparatively little change since its earliest recorded appearance.

Taxonomically the tapir belongs to the mammalian order Ungulata—the group which includes all animals having hoofs. The majority of these have an even number of toes—are split-toed, as the deer, cattle, sheep, goats, and buffalo. Only a few—the horse, rhinoceros, and tapir—have an odd number of digits. These three forms, although not possessing a great degree of outward similarity, are related. It is thought that they had a common ancestor in early Tertiary times, and paleontologists are inclined to believe that this primitive forebear was a fair copy of the tapir as we know it today, only smaller. The horse, in particular, has become greatly modified with the passage of centuries, while the tapir has managed to survive with but few alterations.

In the past, tapirs had an almost world-wide distribution. They lived in Asia and Europe, and were common in the United States. The same, of course, may be said for both the rhinoceros and the horse. Is it not a very strange fact then that none of these animals is now found native to the States, and two of them have disappeared from the western hemisphere entirely? Many species of horses were in North America and South America not so long ago, and they were abundant in Europe at the time the Cro-Magnon man was demonstrating his ability at Paleolithic art; but the only wild species remaining today are to be found in Asia. The rhinoceros, too, was once prevalent in North America, but if it is to be found at large today, a visit either to Africa or to the Dutch East Indies is imperative. Likewise, the range of the tapir has atrophied, until this animal is now found only on two spots of the earth's surface. Three species inhabit Central and South America, and one species is found in the Malay Peninsula and the near-by islands of Sumatra and Borneo. Between these two regions there is a distance almost as great as our planet will allow.

There are not so many cases of discontinuous distribution as to be commonplace. On the basis of our modern theory of evolution the case of the tapir's range is explainable in one of two ways: first, there were separate ancestors for the American and the Asiatic tapirs, and the two evolved independently of each other; second, at a remote period tapirs were found the world around, all of which came from a common ancestor. Those inhabiting the intervening land masses between America and Malaysia became extinct, leaving feeble remnants of a once distinguished race in these two widely separated places. Paleontologists consider the first theory as untenable and vigorously espouse the second. Even though there had been no discoveries of fossil material in the intervening land masses to bolster their convictions, they would still support the second theory. But paleontologists have discovered fossil species of tapirs, many of them, and they know that they formerly inhabited the continents which lie between Neotropical America and the Malay Peninsula; namely, Europe, Asia, and North America. More than that, they point with a steady finger to the presence of a land bridge which joined North America to Asia in the days when tapirs were indigenous to northern and eastern Asia and were willing to take advantage of the opportunity to cross from the Siberian steppes to the Alaskan forests.

The *anta,* in structure and in habit, resembles a cross between a pig and a hornless rhinoceros, if such a hybrid is imaginable. While it is a relative of both the horse and the rhinoceros, there is little in the general make-up of the beast to suggest an equine relationship. Its legs are heavy and massive, the neck is short, and the skull is high and abbreviated. The head seems to be long, but this effect is due to the elongation of its nose into a cylindrical proboscis three or four inches in length. This particular member is capable of being moved in all directions and projects over the mouth like a drooping eyelid. Its presence does not seem to be of any particular advantage to the tapir, but it does emphasize its general antiquated appearance more than any other portion of its anatomy. The coloration is dull in the adults—a brownish black. The young are definitely marked with a number of white spots on the legs and feet and several yellowish white longitudinal stripes on the sides and flanks. These markings give some idea, it is believed, of what the color patterns of the ancestral forms must have been like. The hair is short and bristly except on the neck, where a slight mane exists. The tail is only a vestige; a good lengthy appendage would help marvelously "to carry out the symmetry of its form," according to Brown.

The three recognized species of tapir in the western hemisphere are Baird's tapir *(Tapirus bairdii)* of Central America, the rare, hairy tapir *(Tapirus roulini)* of the Ecuadorian Andes, and the American tapir *(Tapirus americanus),* indigenous to most parts of tropical South America east of the cordilleras.

All these forms are terrestrial; but they love water and are generally found near some pool or river, into which they plunge at the least indication of danger. It is probably true as André said that, "were it not for the safety this powerful but defenceless creature can obtain by taking to the water whenever it happens to be attacked by some beast of prey, it is not unlikely that it would be very much rarer, if not actually extinct." Even though the tapir is most often found near water, it appears to be a great traveler and is occasionally encountered some distance from any river or lake, where it lives by browsing.

It is a vigorous swimmer and is as much at home in the water as an animal could possibly be without gills, flippers, or fins. It can remain submerged for surprisingly long periods of time and is extremely clever in eluding an enemy. It may disappear beneath the water at one point and reappear at some totally unexpected place far removed. It is said by the natives that it sinks and then walks on the bottoms of the streams regardless of their depth. There is no definite evidence to support this contention; the idea may have arisen from the fact that the tapir swims with such a small portion of the head above the water that in poor light it is practically invisible.

Several of the naturalists have asserted that the tapir is rarely seen, although common. While this statement is probably true in general, André found this animal particularly abundant on the Caura, one of the large eastern tributaries of the Orinoco; and Bigg-Wither discovered it almost on every hand in the province of Paraná in southern Brazil.

In at least one respect the *anta* is like its distant cousin the rhinoceros: its eyesight is decidedly poor. Both Rusby and Enders have testified to this deficiency, and Up de Graff had two encounters both of which indicated ill developed visual powers.

On the first occasion Up de Graff and his companions were paddling their canoe along a jungle river in western Brazil when need for food caused them to beach their craft and go ashore. They were on the alert for game and had not gone far when they met a tapir face to face. The beast immediately bolted for the river as fast as its short stumpy legs would carry it. At the bank of the stream, it hesitated not a second but dived headfirst for the water, the one and only haven of refuge for tapirs. Apparently a myopic condition prevented the tapir from seeing the canoe, for it landed squarely on top of it and smashed it to bits. Under different circumstances the loss might have been a major catastrophe but, fortunately in this instance, it was possible to get another boat. Up de Graff characteristically remarks, "We gave thanks to providence for endowing the bananas and yams [which were in the canoe] with a specific gravity less than 1.00," and concludes with the statement that the tapir is not a dangerous creature by any stretch of the imagination, but its clumsiness and poor eyesight are potential menaces at totally unexpected times.

Somewhat later he had another experience with a tapir that made him all the more certain it had a serious eye deficiency. On this occasion he and his companions had paddled their canoe close to the bank of a stream and had settled themselves for a brief rest before continuing their journey. Suddenly they heard a commotion in the forest a short distance away, and before they could conjecture as to its cause three tapirs came charging out of the dense undergrowth which bordered the stream. They were headed straight as a poker for their canoe. As one man Up de Graff and his companions arose, waved their arms, and shouted as lustily as they could, but these myopic brutes saw them not at all. One of the three jumped over the prow of the boat just missing it by a nose length, and another almost swamped the canoe when its legs collided with the side in going over. Quite a bit of water was shipped but not enough to send the craft to the bottom of the stream. It was an extremely close shave and Up de Graff had no hesitancy in saying that tapirs should wear spectacles.

Nearsightedness is apparently common to all tapirs, irrespective of the part of South America they frequent. In the course of Bigg-Wither's engineering pursuits in southern Brazil he found it advisable to build himself a shack in which to live. He chose a location near the river Ivahy that seemed to him desirable in all respects and had his man go ahead with the construction. One night, soon after the building was completed and he had moved in, he was awakened by a loud scream that came from the jungle near by. The night was pitch-dark; the only illumination came from the intermittent flashes of fireflies. Bigg-Wither, as soon as he could make the transition from slumber to consciousness, jumped from his bed and reached for his gun. A second he stood in tense silence, and then realized from the crashing of undergrowth that some large animal was desperately running toward the river, closely pursued by a beast of prey. He felt sure that the fleeing animal was a tapir, which rendered it nearly certain that the beast of prey was the jaguar. The pursued and pursuer were apparently coming straight toward the shack, and it was only now that Bigg-Wither realized he had built his present abode right across a tapir "run"—a pathway made and frequently used by these beasts. He made ready to shoot at one or the other of the animals as they passed. However, things did not turn out in just the manner he had anticipated. The tapir, unable to see beyond its nose, did not swerve one inch either to port or to starboard. It ran with full force, head on, into one of the corner posts of the structure, veered off, and plunged madly on toward the river. Within a very few seconds Bigg-Wither heard a tremendous splash as the tapir landed in the water, and then all was still.

The tapir is a recluse, an unsociable "varmint" that has but little use for others of its kind, except during the mating season. More often than not the tapir is found alone. Since it has been able to persist so long on earth relatively unmodified, the conclusion might be drawn that a solitary existence has been of the utmost benefit to it in that respect. The horse, greatly changed, has been gregarious over a long period of time.

Food is never a problem in the life of the *anta;* it eats all kinds of leaves and shoots and succulent vegetable matter. On occasion it invades the natives' gardens, much to the detriment of the cabbages and other plants growing therein. This is the only way, however, in which the tapir is known to be negatively important.

Of all the beasts in South America which are edible, the tapir is said to be most prized by the natives. Since it is the largest animal on that continent, it furnishes much meat and, of perhaps more importance, meat of a very high quality. For these reasons the tapir is a much hunted animal. However, unless the hunters are well equipped with formidable arms the chances are that the tapir will live to run another day.

As examples of what may be considered typical hunts two will be described here: the first by André, and the second by Roosevelt.

André's expedition was paddling slowly along a stream in eastern Venezuela when the notes of a curassow were heard from a tree on the right-hand bank of the stream. One of the men was sent to kill the bird, if possible, since meat was scarce. While waiting for his return they saw a full-grown tapir swimming across the river just a short distance from the boats. At this place the water was swift and deep, and, knowing if the beast were killed in midstream it would sink and in all probability be lost, André held his fire until it came to shore and started to clamber up the bank. He fired twice, both shots apparently taking effect, and the tapir plunged into the forest. As expeditiously as possible one of the men was landed with the dogs, and together they set out in hot pursuit. As was expected the creature soon returned to the river and was able to reach the other side before the dogs and man caught up with it. Soon, however, the barking of the dogs indicated that they were closing in, and a minute afterward the tapir again took to the water. The boat now came close, but the tapir, seeing it, turned quickly into the mouth of a small creek where it dived. Within short order André and the men arrived; but the animal was nowhere to be seen even after a wait of several minutes; they were at a total loss. The beast might still be submerged or it might have taken to the forest again, in which case the chances were that it had escaped. After a short search and considerable speculation, however, one of the Indians grabbed André's arm and pointed to the bank. There, partially protected from sight by a clump of leaves, the tapir's head was just visible. The animal was perfectly motionless, and but for the keen eyesight of the native it might have lived to gambol once more in the swirling waters of the Caura. Another shot from the gun of André, and it was dead. This was the most interesting and exciting hunt that he experienced, and since it is typical of the experiences of many other hunters it has been enlarged upon. It is worth noting that, once attacked, the animal invariably takes to water. This particular tapir made two different plunges into the river after being hit and one dash on land; and it never went far from the stream. The river was straight at this point, and André was at all times in a position to watch every move. He was astonished at the ease and grace of the tapir in swimming and the apparent sagacity employed as it carefully avoided the most dangerous parts of the stream.

André and his men "fared sumptuously on tapir steaks" after the kill. While the men grumbled about most of their tasks there was no lack of enthusiasm when it came to cutting up tapirs. Although there is an enormous amount of flesh on a tapir the men ate it all; none of it went to waste. Long strips of it were stuck on green sticks and roasted over the fire. In every case the men preserved the hoofs, which were marked and carefully apportioned among them. It was explained that the scrapings from the digits have exceptional medicinal powers. However, if a male Indian is to receive any therapeutic benefit from the scrapings they must come from a male tapir. Similarly, an Indian squaw must have her elixir prepared from the scrapings of a female tapir. Brown recorded that the natives he had with him in British Guiana carefully preserved all the tapir hoofs they were able to find. They made remarkable cordials which they said would cure snake bite, alleviate the stings from rays, and bring to an end all sorts of fits. Since there may be some compound in the hoofs which exercises

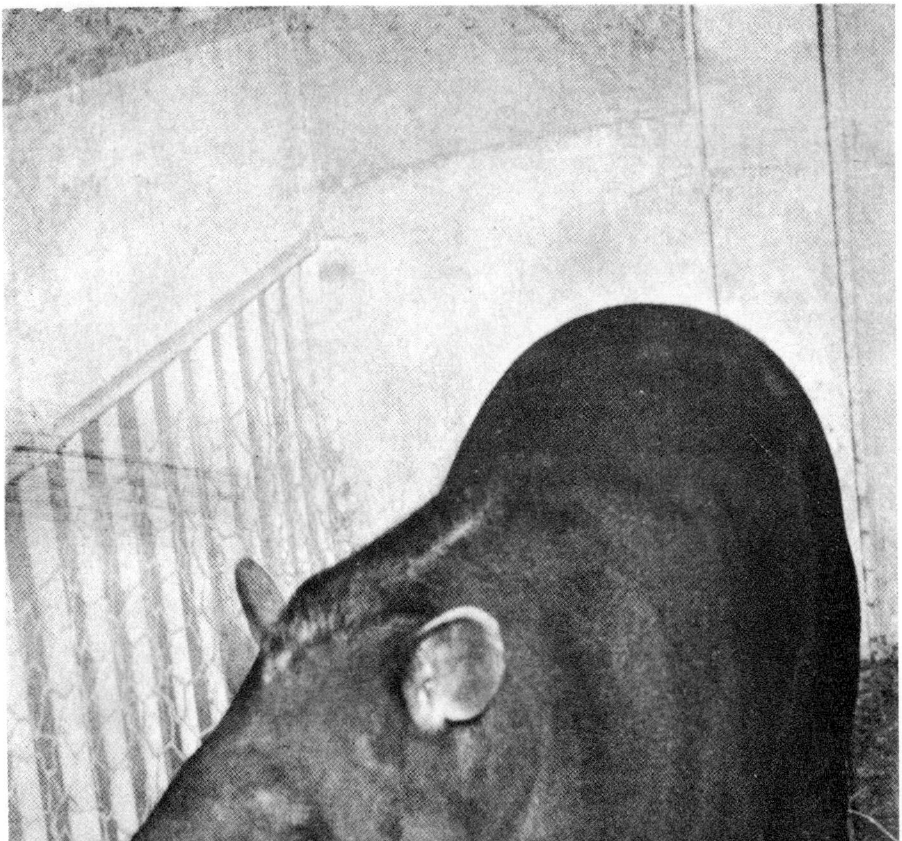

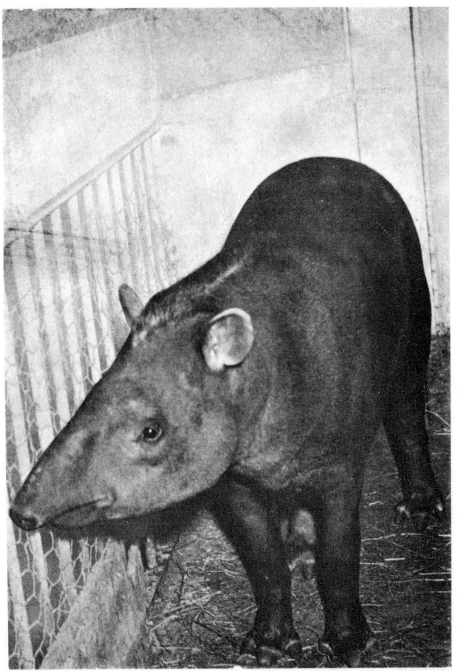

Courtesy of Zoological Society of Philadelphia

TAPIR

Courtesy of Zoological Society of Philadelphia

GUANACO

an effect upon the body, Brown wondered if ammonia might not be present in stimulating quantities.

Several years before Roosevelt went to South America he confided to Father Zahm that he wished particularly to secure specimens of the jaguar and the tapir, if he were ever able to make the trip there. His wish for a tapir was realized in 1913 on a small tributary of the Paraguay, the Sepatuba (that is, River of Tapirs). On the day appointed for a tapir hunt Roosevelt, Colonel Rondon, Fiala, and several of the native inhabitants, provided with a pack of dogs, started upstream in four boats. After several hours of paddling, a tapir was sighted swimming the river. At the time two of the boats were above the beast and in such a position that a shot from Roosevelt's gun would be dangerous. He held his fire, and the tapir, sighting the canoes which were closing in from two sides, dived. It stayed under water for some time but finally was seen climbing the bank under a dense mass of foliage. The target was anything but good, but Roosevelt fired, hitting too far back. Away it lumbered into the forest, which here everywhere came down to the river's edge a solid wall, impenetrable to a man without a machete. Three or four of the dogs soon were on the trail, however, and shortly afterwards the creature returned to the river far upstream. The boats went after it as fast as the paddles could urge them, but they were too far away to head it off. Fortunately some of the dogs appeared on the bank at this point just as the tapir was starting to climb out of the water. They drove it back to the stream, and, the boats now coming near, it dived again. This time it remained under water even longer than before. It swam underneath the boats and came up near the bank on the other side. Roosevelt shot, and the bullet pierced its brain. The body sank almost immediately, and he was apprehensive lest his prize was lost. The natives assured him, however, that it would come up in an hour or two at approximately the place where it went down. It did come up about three hours later when, completely discouraged, Roosevelt was considering giving it up. The body was now lifted into one of the canoes, and the party headed for camp in jovial mood.

It will be noted that the actions of the tapir on this hunt were similar to those already described on André's hunt. If man were not equipped with high-powered rifles the tapir would escape nearly every time. Its perfect adjustment to land and water insures escape from most predaceous enemies. The large carnivores are unable to cope with the tapir in the water, and the caimans and crocodiles are not able to match the speed of the tapir on land.

The real enemy of the tapir is the jaguar, but according to Rusby a certain species of fly on the Beni River causes it much more actual misery. The hide of the *anta* is so thick that the bites of this pest make no impression, but numbers of flies crawl into the delicate nostrils and reduce the mucus linings to a sad state of inflammation.

It is well known that the rhinoceros is assiduously followed by a bird that makes itself welcome by eating the ticks from its back. Rusby states explicitly that the tapir is accompanied by a similarly intentioned bird resembling a small hawk. The bird is fond of feeding upon the flies described above and is therefore on intimate terms with the tapir. Moreover, Rusby affirms, the bird has a note that is quite similar to that of the tapir itself. He thinks that the tapir recognizes the call and responds to it, knowing the bird will relieve it of its tormentors. The Indians, whenever they hear the notes of this bird, are assured that a tapir is also near at hand. This is an observation about which more information is desirable.

Tapirs caught when young are easily tamed. Both Schomburgk and Edwards describe tame tapirs owned by Indians that were quite docile and allowed the run of the place. Edwards even goes so far as to say that they were "taught to return home regularly." At Manáos, Brown and Lidstone visited the president of the province. This dignitary had a fine young tapir in his back yard which "recognized at once the President's voice and whinnied pleasantly in answer to his call."

THE GUANACO

The early history of the camel family, of which the guanaco is a member, is entirely North American. From the Eocene era to the Miocene, a period of millions of years, this distinctive group of animals was found on no other continent. What is now the United States was overrun with great numbers of camel-like animals as late as the middle of the Pleistocene, when disease, predaceous animals, adverse climatic conditions, overspecialization, or some other cause brought about their extinction.

Near the close of the Miocene, or early in the Pliocene, a few of the camel tribe developed the spirit of the nomad. Some of them traveled to the northwest, succeeded in traversing the Alaskan land bridge to Siberia, and then journeyed in a general southwesterly direction to the hotter, more arid regions of central and southern Asia. Those that completed this hegira successfully were destined to become the "ships of the desert" and beasts of burden for untold generations of Tartar, Arab, and Hindu masters.

To others, the south beckoned, and they made the long pilgrimage of jungle and mountain, through what is now Mexico and Central America, to the land of the condor. These forms, the guanacos, became wards and vassals of the "children of the sun" and the only beasts of burden known to the western hemisphere before 1519, when Cortez landed the first shipment of horses in Mexico.

How strange that a large family of animals, once so widely dispersed, should now be found in only two rather restricted areas and should now consist of only two genera! How strange that the camels should be living their lives of complaint in far-away Mongolia and Arabia, thousands of miles from the ancestral stamping grounds in North America, and the guanacos should be inhabiting the cold, barren regions of southern South America, also thousands of miles from their original homes, and even farther from their only kin on earth! Cases of discontinuous distribution such as this are readily explained now, but they never fail to capture our imagination.

Although several species of animals similar to the guanaco are known to have inhabited Peru, Bolivia, and Argentina in the Pleistocene, it seems fairly certain that only two existed when man first made his appearance in South America. These two were the guanaco *(Lama huanacus)* and the vicuña *(Lama vicunia)*. They were the lone survivors of a great array of long-necked quadrupeds that had traversed every square mile of land in the western hemisphere from Baffin Bay to Cape Horn in their long conquest begun millions of years ago in the period which cradled the mammals and ending now in the Holocene epoch, the period fostering the dominance of man.

The pre-Incans, upon their arrival in what is now Peru, probably found the guanacos living there in great abundance. They perhaps found them tractable and easily tamed, for the wild guanacos of today are frequently tamed by the natives. It is the opinion of mammalogists that the llama *(Lama huanacus glama)* and the alpaca *(Lama huanacus paca)* were domesticated from the wild guanaco after centuries of careful selection by the Incas and their ancestors. These two forms, the llama as a beast of burden and the alpaca as a producer of wool, are familiar animals even to persons residing in northern countries; however, the guanaco—the animal responsible for the existence of both llama and alpaca—is seldom heard of outside of South America.

The guanaco's range today extends from Peru and Bolivia to the southernmost tip of the continent. In the past some of the most venturesome swam the Strait of Magellan to Tierra del Fuego, one of the most uninhabitable and inhospitable bits of land known to bird or mammal; and here they are found today. Darwin saw them there in 1832 or 1833 and found them capable of indulging in strange antics in spite of the desolate nature of the country. "On the mountains of Tierra del Fuego," he wrote, "I have more than once seen a guanaco, on being approached not only neigh and squeal, but prance and leap about in the most ridiculous manner, apparently in defiance as a challenge."

The guanaco is most abundant on the plains of Patagonia.

Prichard wrote that during his travels in that land scarcely a day passed that he did not encounter some of them. "They were most numerous," he said, "in the Cañadon Davis, in the neighborhood of Bahía Camerones, and on the high basaltic tablelands to the south of Lake Buenos Aires."

Tschudi said that the guanaco lives in herds of five to seven, rarely exceeding that number. However, the German zoologist's observations were limited to Peru—he did not make a visit to Patagonia. Darwin saw a herd on the Santa Cruz that must have numbered at least five hundred, he declared. Beerbohm saw several herds of two hundred or more, and Hudson said that "Herds numbering several hundreds or even a thousand are occasionally met on the stony, desolate plateaus of Southern Patagonia." Prichard, in one place, found "literally thousands of guanacos on the summits of the surrounding barren ridges," and Musters wrote that he saw a herd "some three thousand strong."

The naturalists have been variously impressed by the appearance of the guanaco. To Darwin it was "an elegant animal in a state of nature, with a long slender neck and fine legs," and "anything more graceful than their actions" he could not imagine. Hudson admired "its finely shaped head and long ears, and its proud and graceful carriage" and said it resembled "an antelope rather than its huge and, from an aesthetic point of view, deformed Asiatic relations." George Simpson, with a slightly different impression, wrote, "A guanaco looks like a small, humpless camel, which it is, and it also looks like a careless mixture of parts intended for other beasts and turned down as below standard." Musters, who lived for several months in the guanaco country, declared that it had "the head of a camel, the body of a deer, the wool of a sheep, and the neigh of a horse."

The sides and back of the guanaco are reddish or dark russet to pale yellow, while the under parts are whitish. The wool is soft and fleecy in the young, but before long it becomes coarse, matted, and often filthy. A full-grown specimen measures six to seven feet from its hoofs to the tips of its elongate ears. The weight of an average specimen is estimated to be about 170 to 200 pounds.

The sexes are said to be remarkably similar although the

males tend to be somewhat larger than the females. They are thought to have a life span of near thirty years.

Their main vocal effort is most frequently compared to the neigh of a horse. Prichard described it as a very unique cry, "something between a bleat, a laugh, and a neigh." To Simpson the noise was a yammer. In elaboration of this he says: "Imagine a tin horse that has been left out in the rain until thoroughly rusty, and then imagine that the tin horse has colic and is trying to whinny, and you will have a faint conception of a guanaco's yammer."

It is unfortunate that a particular observation was made by Darwin while he was exploring along the Santa Cruz River of Patagonia. He found that in certain places at the edge of the river there were great numbers of bones of the guanaco; these were especially abundant, he said, in wooded areas quite close to the stream. In one spot he counted some twenty skulls all close together and remarked that "the ground was actually white with bones." He examined the skeletal parts closely to find whether they had been gnawed or crushed but could find no evidence that the death of the guanacos was due to beasts of prey. Mr. Bynoe informed him that he had seen similar heaps of bones on the Río Gallegos. Darwin admitted that he did not understand the reason for this but said in the same paragraph that "the guanacos appear to have favorite spots for lying down to die." There is no question but that Darwin was hinting at a common burial ground for the guanacos, a certain spot where the aged and the inflicted, the wounded and diseased, made a point of assembling just before death. This was not an original idea, because the same notion had been expressed previously in regard to elephants and other animals. Darwin had in all likelihood heard of these supposed burial grounds and, not finding any other ready explanation, made use of it here as the only solution that came to his mind.

In 1892, sixty years after H.M.S. *Beagle* dropped anchor near the mouth of the Santa Cruz, Hudson's *The Naturalist in La Plata* was published. Of considerably more than passing interest is a chapter in this book entitled "The Dying Huanaco." At the very outset Hudson makes it clear that the chapter heading does not refer to the approaching extinction of the guanaco—he does not consider that likely in the near future—but to the peculiar action of these beasts in seeking out special dying places—the guanaco's Golgothas, he called them. After pointing out the same general facts as those enumerated by Darwin, the author of *Green Mansions* proceeds to spend page after page in an attempted analysis of the instinct responsible for this unprecedented behavior. Although he considers it worthy of note that in northern Argentina, and in the Chilean and Peruvian Andes, there are no known special dying places—only in the southern extremity of the continent and especially along the Santa Cruz—the implications of that truth do not, unfortunately, cause him to think there may be some other explanation.

The true explanation for the death of many guanacos in one place is not in any way sensational. In 1871, eleven years before Hudson published *The Naturalist in La Plata,* Captain Musters wrote of his experiences in Patagonia in *At Home with the Patagonians.* Herein we find the following statement:

"Fitzroy remarked the number of guanaco bones found in his ascent of the river Santa Cruz, which appear to have puzzled him but the cause is not far to seek. During the very severe winters which occur I believe about once in three years these animals, finding no pasture on the highlands, which are covered with snow, are necessarily driven down to the plains fringing the river, where they die from starvation."

In the same connection Prichard says: "These animals come down to live on the lower ground and near unfrozen water during the cold season and there, when the weather is particularly severe, they die in crowds. We saw their skeletons in one or two places literally heaped one upon the other." Farther along in his narrative Prichard is more explicit about the numbers killed. Not far from Lake Argentino along the Santa Cruz he found eighty dead guanacos at one place. At another, there were over five hundred. To quote verbatim: "There cannot have been less than five hundred lying there in positions as forced and ungainly as the most ill-taken snapshot photograph could produce. Their long necks were outstretched, the rime of weather upon their decaying hides, and their bone-joints glistening through the wounds made by the beaks of carrion-birds. They had died during the severities of the previous winter, and lay literally piled one upon another. The mortality among guanaco in a really hard winter is tremendous. They die in batches, absolutely in hundreds."

A very curious habit of the guanaco has been described by several observers. At the sound of a gunshot or some other loud noise, they plunge, and irrespective of how many may be in the herd all dip their heads in unison almost to the ground. When shooting at a single animal the hunter is often misled into thinking that he has hit the beast, because of this odd manner in which it plunges and appears to stumble.

Another characteristic of the guanaco is the posting of a sentinel. With every herd there always seems to be one animal, apparently a male, that takes a position on some eminence where a good view is procured. From that point of vantage it is able to warn the other animals of the approach of any danger.

The guanacos have no trouble in adjusting themselves to a life of domesticity, and as a result it is not unusual to find them in Patagonian homes as pets. Like their Asiatic relatives and the llamas, they have the habit (objected to by some humans) of spitting directly and unerringly into the face of human friend or foe alike without any advance notice of their intention.

The guanaco may have led directly to the invention and development of the bola. This ingenious weapon was in use by the Indians of Patagonia when the whites first reached that part of the continent, and has its counterpart in no other country. It was used principally in the chase of the guanaco and rhea, so that its origin must have been intimately associated with the hunting of these two animals.

The first bola was probably a single stone, with a thong of indeterminate length tied around a groove in it. Holding on to the end of the thong the natives swung this around their head and then discharged it at the fleeing animal. This single-ball bola was used by the Tehuelches at the time Musters lived among them and was called the *bola perdida,* since, once thrown, it was not picked up and was therefore lost. The Indians probably found that it was difficult to hold onto the thong with a heavy ball at the opposite end, and the result was a second ball, a smaller one, at the opposite end which they could grasp with the hand. This ball is not only smaller, but usually made of a lighter substance, such as the vesicular lava, which is abundant in that region. Still later the bola was made more efficient by the addition of a third ball; all three in this form are tied to a common center. The two-ball bola is used more in hunting rheas, and the three-ball in hunting guanacos.

At first the thong connecting the balls was tied around a groove in the center. Later it was the practice to cover the balls with leather and to tie the thong to the overlapping edges of the leather. A special quality leather secured from the hocks of the guanaco was used for the covers; the thongs were made of leather from the neck of the same animal—four cords, seven to eight feet in length, were plaited together. The bolas were originally of wood or stone. They are now made of copper, iron, lead, and other metals of various kinds. Simpson tells of a rich Patagonian who had some gold bolas made for himself.

It requires no little skill to handle the bola effectively, yet the natives are remarkably accurate with them. With their mounts going at breakneck speed the riders whirl the bola above their heads until the desired force is attained, and then hurl it. They invariably ride toward the prey from behind, and, in hunting rhea and guanaco, the bola is thrown at the neck. If it reaches the mark the missile wraps itself around the animal, which either comes to a dead stop or is slowed up so that there is no difficulty in riding alongside and giving the *coup de grâce*. The natives are able to strike the animals from a distance of fifty to seventy yards.

The Indians would find existence extremely precarious, if not impossible, without the guanacos. They have learned to rely upon them for so many of the necessities of life that it is difficult to see how they could continue living in Patagonia without them. They practice no agriculture to speak of, and most of their food is guanaco and, to a lesser extent, rhea. In addition to food, they depend upon the hide of the guanacos for practically all of their clothing. More than that the hides are indispensable as covering for the rude shelters which they make, and for practically all of the accouterments of their horses. Even the bones of the guanaco are utilized; from these they make needles, dice, certain primitive musical instruments, and various articles of adornment.

Although the guanacos were extremely abundant a half-century ago, it was inevitable that their extinction would be threatened as civilization encroached farther and farther upon their domain. The natural enemy of the guanaco is the puma; and after man invaded Patagonia the pumas found the sheep, which the settlers had brought with them, a much more desirable type of food. The result of this was soon evident—the guanacos increased in numbers and continued to increase steadily year after year. The flesh of the adult guanaco is not especially palatable to a Caucasian, and its hide is not worth much, so that they were hunted only by the Indians. A very good quality leather may be made from the hides of the young *(chulengos)*, however. According to Simpson many of the new inhabitants of the country, finding it difficult to make a living, resorted to all sorts of odd professions in an effort to earn enough to keep body and soul together. Among these professions was the hunting of *chulengos*. Since no preliminary outlay was necessary and the profits were found to be considerable, this kind of hunting became increasingly popular. It finally reached the point where a young guanaco had about as much chance of escaping the bola or gun as the average child has of escaping mumps or measles. The life span of the guanaco is probably twenty-five to thirty years, and the death of a great number of *chulengos* did not at once reduce the total number since the bulk of the adult population continued to live on. It was perfectly clear, however, that before many years there would suddenly be a great decrease in numbers, and there was. Fortunately the Argentine government recognized the situation in time and ordered that no guanacos of any age be killed for a period of years. Because of this foresight it now appears that the species is not in any immediate danger of extinction.

If the guanaco does become extinct in the future it will probably be due to the presence of numerous fences erected by farmers. These will prevent the guanacos from reaching the warmer valleys in extremely severe winters.

THE RODENTS

The rodents, those prolific creatures with such pronounced gnawing ability, are the most successful group of mammals on the earth today. In the number of strikingly contrasted species, the sum total of individuals, diversity of body structure, and adaptation to environment they excel all other mammalian orders. Only the whales, the range of which embraces all oceans, surpass the rodents in dispersal. None of the gnawing mammals are marine, but they inhabit practically every portion of land surface that is capable of supporting life. Even deserts and the arctic wastes far beyond the limits of our northern forests sustain a normal rodent population. Most rodents are found on or near the ground, but some live high in the trees, and others, like the prairie dog, dig deep into the earth. Some climb with the facility of a monkey, others are adept at swimming and diving, and still others have the ability to volplane from tree to tree.

To the casual observer the rodents appear an inconsequential group. Only the scientist who has made a special study of the rats, mice, prairie dogs, rabbits, *et al.* knows how numerous they are and what a destructive force they have become. Although man has reduced the numbers of carnivores, ungulates, marsupials, and other mammalian orders, he has had no success in diminishing the size of the enormous battalions of rodents found everywhere.

In South America the numerical superiority of rodents is just as pronounced as on the other continents, but there is an entirely different mammalian apportionment. The southern continent is noticeably deficient in the large mammals that are so conspicuous on other land masses. For instance there are no great herds of antelopes, zebras, giraffes, and buffalo, such as are found in Africa; there are no elephants, hippopotamuses, or rhinoceroses. Furthermore there is not an indigenous population of bison, elk, moose, mountain goat, or wild sheep, such as obtains in North America. The species of mammals in South America large enough to be included under the heading of "big-game animals" may be counted on the fingers of two hands, and none of these are appreciably larger than a moderate-sized brown bear of the Allegheny Mountains. If we exclude a few species of small deer there remain only the guanaco, vicuña, tapir, the spectacled bear, the puma, and the jaguar. As a result of this scarcity of great mammals the rodents enjoy an exalted position in South America. In the same manner that Australia may be referred to as the home of marsupials, and Africa as the land of ungulates, South America may justly be called the home of rodents.

The history of the rodents in South America is imperfectly known, but it dates from the very beginning of the age of mammals. The rodents could probably trace their lineage as far back as any other existing order of mammals. Because of the isolation of South America from the rest of the world quite early in the Cenozoic era—a separation that existed for many millions of years—the evolution of rodent stock was entirely independent from that on the other continents. In that pristine epoch many of these gnawing mammals had their origin, prospered, fell from their high estate, and then went the way of the ground sloths and glyptodonts. A great amount of fossil material unearthed by the paleontologist testifies to this fact. On the other hand certain relatives of these extinct beasts managed to persist through subsequent ages of travail and dilemma, and are now plentifully distributed in forest and on pampa from the Caribbean to the Strait of Magellan. These particular forms now comprehend a group of rodents that is in many respects different from that evolved on other continents. These animals, comprising one of four existing suborders, are the hystricoids, or porcupinelike animals. After connections were reestablished between North and South America there was considerable migration of rodents south across the Isthmus of Panama. Mice, rabbits, squirrels, rats and other forms occupied the territory formerly inhabited only by the hystricoids and made their home among them. However, there are more porcupinelike rodents than all the immigrants; the southern continent is still headquarters for the hystricoids as it was in ages long past. Even though the southerly migration of North American rodents was considerable, there are still in South

America no beavers, muskrats, pocket gophers, ground squirrels, prairie dogs, or marmots so familiar to the inhabitants of the United States.

These porcupinelike rodents, of which the Canada porcupine is an example, form a large assemblage; there have been recognized six families and at least twenty-nine genera. The representatives of this peculiarly South American group of rodents rarely resemble porcupines to the extent of having a covering of quills. The more pronounced similarities are to be sought for elsewhere in the anatomy of the beasts. However, they are all sufficiently alike to warrant their inclusion in a single group.

A complete list of the described species of rodents in South America would cover several pages. Very little more than name and habitat is known about most of them. As is generally the case the life histories of only the largest, the most interesting, the most abundant, or the most important economically are a matter of record. A list of a very few of these includes such species as the cavies, one of which is the guinea pig *(Cavia porcellus)*, the tropical, prehensile-tailed porcupines, the chinchillas, the tucotucos, the coypus, the agoutis, the pacas, the viscachas, and the capybaras.

To judge by the fullness of their comment, the naturalists have found the capybara, paca, and viscacha of more interest than the others. Since exigencies of time and space will not permit a consideration of all the above-mentioned forms, only these three will be discussed in detail.

The Capybara

The fame of the capybara *(Hydrochoerus capybara)* rests primarily on its size since it is the largest existing rodent. It is not especially large compared with certain other mammals, but it is a giant among rodents. Darwin killed one near the mouth of the Río de La Plata which tipped the scales at ninety-eight pounds, and Cherrie wrote that the capybara may weigh as much as one hundred fifty pounds. Even though this is a titan among modern rodents, it is just a pocket edition of one of its Miocene ancestors. In that Cenozoic period there was a South American rodent—*Megamys* by name—that was about the size of an African rhinoceros.

The Rodents

The capybara (known also as carpincho, water hog, and water haas) is frequently described as a "huge aquatic guinea pig." This comparison is apropos, for the capybara is, in reality, a close relative of the guinea pig. The latter had its origin in South America, probably from Cutler's cavy. It was first domesticated by the Incans or their predecessors, and belongs to the same family as the capybara.

Darwin wrote that the carpincho at some distance reminded him of a pig, although, when squatted on the ground, it had the appearance of a rabbit, or cavy. "Both the front and side view of their head," he declared, "has quite a ludicrous aspect, from the depth of their jaw." It must have been this feature of the jaw which caused Theodore Roosevelt to write that the capybara looked like a blunt-nosed pig.

Its range is extensive. Practically everywhere from Venezuela and the Guianas on the north to northern Argentina on the south it is a common animal; and in many parts of this territory it is abundant. Im Thurn wrote that the paca, agouti, and capybara are the most prominent animals in British Guiana. Roosevelt frequently came across ponds in western Brazil tenanted by capybaras; Up de Graff saw them daily on the Yasuni, one of the secondary tributaries of the Napo; and Darwin observed that "in the Río Paraná they are exceedingly abundant."

Their abundance may be due in part to the circumstance that they are gregarious. In no place do they run in such large herds as do the white-lipped peccaries, but Gardner saw "upward of fifty individuals" together in Brazil, and Azara reported troops of fifty to sixty on the banks of the Plata near Buenos Aires. However, these herds may have been exceptional, for no other naturalist has reported seeing so many at one time. The capybaras Darwin saw near Maldonado, Uruguay, consorted together in groups of only three to four, and Schomburgk mentioned aggregations of only six to eight in the Guianas.

The capybara is perfectly at home in the water, is never found far from it, and retreats to it at the first indication of danger. According to Roosevelt it usually goes ashore to feed, and it has well beaten paths in the immediate vicinity of ponds and streams. He saw none on these rodential highways, however, and concluded that they must travel only at night. When frightened, these hypertrophied guinea pigs dive into the nearest pond or stream and quickly disappear. Dogs that chase them to their submarine retreats pull up hurriedly at the edge of the water and are at a total loss as to which way to turn next. Humboldt declared the capybaras were able to "remain eight or ten minutes under water." Schomburgk wrote, "Like otters, they are good swimmers and yet cleverer divers, and only very seldom betake themselves inland far from the waterside."

Out of the water they are described as ungainly. When pursued on land, they travel at a heavy, lumbering gallop and may be overtaken and caught without much difficulty. Some of their excursions in search of food take them into the gardens of the natives, where they do considerable damage.

The Indians of certain tribes eat the capybara, but the naturalists are almost unanimous in saying the flesh is not good.

Roosevelt was told by the natives that the water hog is very shy and retiring, but he found it quite tame. Darwin wrote that, approaching carefully, he was able to come within three yards of a group of four old ones at Maldonado.

Paca

The paca, or labba *(Coelogenys paca)*, is an extremely common rodent found over the most of northern South America. It is about the size of a hare, being some two feet in length, but has a stouter body and a head like a rat's. The body is covered with a brown fur spotted with white. Brown said: "It is nocturnal in its habits, spending the day in its burrow under tree roots near the edges of rivers. These sleeping chambers are not very long, and have two entrances. The huntsman rams a thin pole in at one end, which startles the occupant, causing it to fly precipitately from the other, like a ball from a cannon, closely followed by the dog. The labba, when close pressed, takes to the water, and while swimming is hunted down by the Indian sportsman in his woodskin. Sometimes the animal escapes by diving, and hiding amongst fallen brushwood on the river's edge but more frequently falls a victim to the arrow of the Indian."

In the daytime, the paca's vision is defective and it cannot see its way about. Brown and Lidstone, on an excursion near Santarem, disturbed a beast which had been sleeping under the top of a fallen tree. It created quite a furor in the underbrush, and all sorts of conjectures were made as to just what animal it was. As the men stood trying to get a glimpse of the creature, it suddenly came straight toward them, collided with Brown's shins, and then ran into a small tree with great force. However, it veered off and escaped into the brush. After Brown and Lidstone had recovered from their surprise and confusion they realized that the animal was nothing but a labba completely blinded by the bright sunlight.

Although the paca is little known to residents north of the Caribbean it is one of South America's most famous animals. On all sides its praises are sung, for its flesh when properly prepared is said to be the fulfillment of an epicure's fondest dream.

Brown asserted that "the flesh of the labba is considered the most delicate of all bush animals and is, therefore, much sought after," and Im Thurn vowed: "Its flesh is more esteemed than that of any other animal, not only by Indians, but also by the colonists; indeed the latter have a proverb that 'the man who has eaten labba and drunk creek water will never die out of the colony.'" After McGovern had eaten the meat of the paca he declared that he knew of no flesh more appetizing and concluded, with unmistakable fervor, "I would trade all the beefsteaks and roast chickens in the world in order to banquet off one once more." The demand for it is so great that it is vigorously hunted. Enders reported that in Panama the hunters are offered as much as forty cents a pound for the undressed animals.

Viscacha

The viscacha *(Lagostomus trichodactylus)* is the characteristic animal of the Argentine pampas, where it abounds. It is a close relative of the chinchilla *(Chinchilla laniger),* its soft-furred Andean congener, the skin of which is so highly esteemed by furriers. The vischacha is one of the larger rodents, weighing as much as fifteen pounds, and to Darwin it resembled "a large rabbit, but with bigger gnawing teeth and a long tail."

While the viscacha ranges over a large territory it is not found

Courtesy of Zoological Society of Philadelphia

PACA

Courtesy of N.Y. Zoological Society

VISCACHA

Courtesy of Zoological Society of Philadelphia

CAPYBARA

south of the Río Negro, or east of the river Uruguay. It lives a communal life and, for that and other reasons, has been compared to the beaver, one of the most interesting and intelligent of North American rodents. As many as twenty or thirty of these creatures are found living together in an extensive subterranean retreat *(vizcachera)* of their own construction. By bringing the earth up from their burrows, as they dig, they form a mound a foot or a foot and a half high. There are several burrows beneath the ground, perhaps one for each animal, some of them extending to a depth of five or six feet. The entire underworld covers as much as a hundred to two hundred square feet. The communal life extends beyond the confines of any one particular mound. There are always others in the immediate vicinity, and in sections of the pampas these mounds closely spot the landscape for miles in every direction. Hudson wrote: "It will afford some conception of the numbers of these vizcacheras on the settled pampas when I say that, in some directions, a person might ride five hundred miles and never advance half a mile without seeing one or more of them. In some places they are so near together that a person on horseback may count a hundred of them from one point of view."

Animals that live in the ground occasionally attract other creatures, and some perfectly amazing relationships are established. Who would believe, for instance, that an armadillo, a cottontail rabbit, and a rattlesnake would live together in the same burrow! It is not surprising then to learn that the *vizcacheras* have certain inhabitants in addition to the viscachas themselves. It is surprising, though, to learn the number and variety of these guests. Birds, reptiles, mammals, and insects are all known to hobnob with the viscachas; and they do not exhaust the list. Among birds, owls and swallows are very common, while the mammals are represented by the fox and the weasel. Snakes find these underground passageways a safe retreat in summer and a luxurious hide-away for hibernation in winter. Leo Miller found a boa constrictor near a *vizcachera* which glided into one of the burrows after he had frightened it. In addition to these vertebrates innumerable species of insects and spiders make their homes in the darkness of these caverns. "It would be no mere fancy to say," Hudson wrote, "that probably hundreds of species are either directly or indirectly affected in their struggle for existence by the vizcacheras so abundantly sprinkled over the pampas."

Some animals, armadillos for example, build underground homes which they inhabit for only a short period of time. According to Hudson, that is not true of the viscachas. They inhabit them many years at a stretch. He said that people had told him of *vizcacheras* that had been occupied for as many years as they could remember.

The viscacha has one remarkable instinct that should appeal to many human beings, for it is a collecting instinct. This habit was recorded by Darwin over a century ago. "Around each group of holes," he wrote, "many bones of cattle, stones, thistle-stalks, hard lumps of earth, etc., are collected into an irregular heap, which frequently amounts to as much as a wheelbarrow could contain." These mounds are frequently quite close to human habitations, and when an article has disappeared it can generally be found at the nearest viscacha mound.

Darwin related the story of a gentleman who lost his watch one night when riding on the pampas. The next morning he retraced his course, made an examination of neighboring *vizcacheras,* and found that the watch had been picked up by an observant viscacha and placed on the top of a mound with an odd assortment of bones, sticks, and what not. Darwin was unable to explain this instinct, but Hudson thought that it was "a part of the instinct of clearing the ground about the village." For a distance of several yards in each direction they customarily tear away all vegetation and anything else that may be present. They do this, it is believed, in order that they may have an unobstructed view of the approach of an enemy.

THE MANATEE

A TRAVELER making his first voyage up the Amazon on one of the boats running regularly from Pará (Belém) to Obidos, Manáos, Iquitos, and other ports of call along the river sometimes notes a large aquatic animal as it breaks the surface of the water close to the ship. Although it has a certain resemblance to a fish, and again to a seal or porpoise, he is convinced that it is none of these animals. As he watches its appearance once more he observes that the animal has a very peculiar head with mouth parts suggesting somewhat those of a cow, that the body is grayish, seven or eight feet long and definitely seal-like in shape, that there is only one pair of appendages—flipperlike—anteriorly located, and that the tail is flat, rounded, and paddlelike.

After some investigation the traveler learns that the animal is the Amazonian manatee or sea cow *(Manatus inunguis)* called *peixe boi* by the Portuguese and *vaca marina* by the Spaniards. Also that there is another species in the Americas, the Florida manatee *(Trichechus latirostris)* found along the coasts of Florida and other southern states, Mexico, Central America, and certain islands in the West Indies; and still another form *(Manatus senegalensis)* occurring along the west coast and in some of the rivers and lakes of equatorial Africa. Steller's sea cow *(Rhytina)*, a very large species that reached a length of twenty to thirty feet, once frequented the shores of Bering Strait; but it became extinct about 1768, because of the persistent hunting by man for its flesh and oil. There are three other species closely related, all inhabitants of the eastern world. These go by the name of dugong.

In some respects both the manatee and dugong resemble whales. They were for a time placed in the same mammalian order *(Cetacea)*—for these beasts are true mammals—but they are included now in an order of their own, Sirenia. It is considered that their likenesses to whales are adaptive and have arisen from a similar mode of existence.

The Amazonian manatee is not restricted to the Amazon but

occurs in the Orinoco, Essequibo, and other streams of central and northern South America east of the Andes. Its range, therefore, is extensive. The general impression seems to be that it ascends these streams until it is stopped by the cataracts. However, it occurs in the Napo, where Orton reported seeing "numerous sea-cows" and in the Marañon where Up de Graff saw it near Barranca. Both of these observations were made in Ecuador not far from the eastern slopes of the Andes and, as the crow flies, almost two thousand miles from the vicinity of Pará, where it is also found. Wallace observed it in the Rio Negro, Rusby in the Madeira, and Im Thurn on the British Guiana border in the Tacutú, a stream joining the Cotinga to form the Rio Branco. And Brown wrote of seeing a sea cow in the Pirara River, a small tributary of the Ireng which, in turn, is a tributary of the Tacutú. It seems then, that the manatee has been able to overcome the rapids of certain streams and to reach their headwaters.

The Amazonian manatee is not so large as its Florida congener. Wallace studied several, both in the Amazon and in the Rio Negro, and was inclined to the belief that they did not exceed seven or eight feet in length. On the contrary both Bates and Edwards saw specimens that were about ten feet long.

The manatee has been called "sea cow," because of a fancied resemblance in the head to that of a cow. The bovine expression, if it exists at all, does not extend beyond the upper lip. The head as a whole is shapeless and is similar to that of no other known animal. Both upper and lower lips are covered with bristles, and the upper labium is divided by a cleft into two lobes, each of which is independent of the other in its movements. There are no external ears on the head, only two comparatively small openings leading to the internal ear. The eyes, too, are small, but both vision and hearing are well developed, according to Wallace.

Although the head is not like that of any other mammal the body is definitely seal-like. Wallace described the color of the Amazonian manatee as "a dusky lead, with some large pinkish-white, marbled blotches on the belly." This coloration tends to make it almost invisible in smooth water, according to Im Thurn. The skin is quite thick and very sparsely covered with hairs (the embryo is said to be thickly covered with hair, suggesting a prototype with full pelage); beneath it is a thick layer of fat containing much oil. The only limbs are a pair of anterior flippers. At the ends of these in the Florida manatee are three nails; however, they are not present in the Amazonian form—hence the name, *inunguis.* There are no posterior limbs, even internally, although there is a vestige of a pelvis to which, it is believed, posterior limbs were once attached. Mammalogists are convinced, as a result of embryological and paleontological studies, that all Cetaceans and Sirenians were terrestrial animals at one time.

The manatee reminded Bates "of those Egyptian tombs which are made of dark, smooth stone and shaped to the human figure." Edwards, on the other hand, thought the *peixe boi* was "much like that of a fine old English gentleman whose legs were developed into a broad flat tail." Both Orton and Wickham had a like notion—that the manatee resembles "a hippopotamus without tusks or legs."

Just one young is generally produced at a time by the manatee, and it is held to the pectorally located breasts by one of the flippers of the female while it feeds. This habit is thought by some to be responsible for the mermaid legend. According to Bates the manatee is perplexing to the Indians, even though they are familiar with it. They cannot understand why an animal living in water and bearing a resemblance to a fish suckles its young.

The sea cow is herbivorous, just as much so as its namesake, subsisting on grass and other juicy vegetation which is found growing along the shores and bottoms of river and lake. The stomach is large, being partitioned off into several chambers, something after the fashion of the camel stomach; and the intestine, according to Humboldt, is over one hundred feet in length. Humboldt stated that in one specimen which Bonpland dissected on the Orinoco the exact length was 108 feet.

The South American Indian is always on the alert for the manatee. It is a real acquisition to him; he eats the flesh, of which there is an abundance, uses the oil as a substitute for lard or butter and for lighting purposes, and employs the hide in various ways. He has several methods of capturing this beast but generally depends on one of two procedures. Quite frequently he drives it into large nets (one of the specimens Wallace had for study was captured in this fashion). Just as often, he harpoons it. Since the larger manatees weigh several hundred pounds, it might be thought the natives would have considerable difficulty in transporting them. On the contrary, a lone Indian can bring in a manatee with comparative ease, by sinking his boat, bringing it under the sea cow, bailing out the water; then he paddles home in triumph.

A surprising amount of oil is yielded by the manatee; from five to twenty-five gallons, according to Wallace. Most of this comes from the thick layer of blubber just beneath the skin.

The natives, with few exceptions, are fond of the flesh. It tasted to Wallace like a cross between beef and pork, and to Bates like coarse pork. Wickham thought its flesh was "superlatively delicate." Brown and Lidstone found the meat a pleasant relief from salt beef and fish but added that, "when critically reviewed as an article of diet and its toughness, indigestibility and utter want of distinct flavour are taken into account, it must be confessed that the entire absence of *peixe-boi* from bills of fare in England is not a matter for keen regret."

MONKEYS

About 500 species of monkeys disport themselves throughout the tropical and semitropical forest regions of the world. They are native to all the continents except Australia, although in Europe they are found only in Gibraltar, and in North America only in Central America and Mexico. The monkeys inhabiting the eastern hemisphere are known simply as the old-world monkeys and those in the western hemisphere as the new-world monkeys. The two groups are much alike and differ chiefly on the basis of noses. The new-world monkeys have evolved nostrils that are separated by a wide nasal septum *(platyrrhine)* and are directed forward, whereas, the old-world monkeys have nostrils that are separated by a narrow septum *(catarrhine)* and are pointed downward. The former are smaller on the whole; have thirty-six teeth as compared with the thirty-two of the latter, and do not display the flamboyantly colored skin on the buttocks known as ischial callosities, or "peripatetic sofa cushions." Quite a few of the new-world monkeys have tails with prehensibility, a condition not obtaining in any of the catarrhine forms. The high development of the new-world monkeys is emphasized by their large, well formed brain and by their custom of giving birth to just one baby at a time.

The platyrrhine monkeys number in the neighborhood of one hundred species and are readily divided into two families. One *(Hapalidae),* a small group, contains only the marmosets; the other *(Cebidae),* a very large group, includes the capuchins, the spider monkeys, the howlers, and a number of less known forms such as the night monkeys, the sakis, ouakaris, the squirrel monkeys, and the woolly monkeys.

Marmosets

The marmosets *(Hapale* and *Midas)* form a group of twenty or more species which must be placed near the bottom in the order Primates. They resemble the lemurs of Africa and Madagascar in some respects more than they do other monkeys. Their primitive condition is evidenced by the clawlike nails on all the digits except the great toes, which have true nails, by the structure of their brain, and by the lack of thumb opposability. They give birth, too, to litters of two and three, which is a low-class habit, according to E. A. Hooton.*

All the marmosets are small; they average about eight to nine inches in length exclusive of the tail, which is generally longer than the body. The pygmy marmoset *(Hapale pygmaeus)* is the smallest monkey in the world. Full-grown, it stands not over two and one-half inches high and weighs only four or five ounces. Bates secured three specimens of this diminutive species near São Paulo. The face of each was covered with long brown whiskers, and the body was brownish-tawny with a tail conspicuously barred with black. Bates said he was surprised to learn later that this diminutive form had a very wide dispersal, being found as far north as Mexico. Ditmars, however, gives its range as western Brazil and eastern Ecuador.

Marmosets resemble squirrels more than they do monkeys, especially in their jumpy manner of scampering through a tree. The bodies are slender, covered heavily with a very soft hair, and the hind limbs are longer than the fore. Their tails are not prehensile. Like the old-world monkeys, they have thirty-two teeth. They are gentle and delicate, and the sounds they make resemble the chirps of birds. All are arboreal and very much at home in the trees although Bates saw one lose its footing and fall at least fifty feet headlong to the ground. It landed on its feet and ran off as though that were an everyday occurrence in its life.

The brain of the marmoset is as free of convolutions as the brain of the squirrel. For that reason it is not accorded much more intelligence by the anatomists than that rodent. With this criterion for judging mental capabilities Bates would not have agreed, at least in so far as marmosets were concerned. He believed that in facial expression, general alertness, and curiosity they were much more like the higher monkeys than the squirrel, or any rodent he knew. On the contrary it was Beebe's notion that marmosets are undiscerning creatures that think only of their stomachs and their safety.

* *Up from the Ape,* Macmillan, 1931.

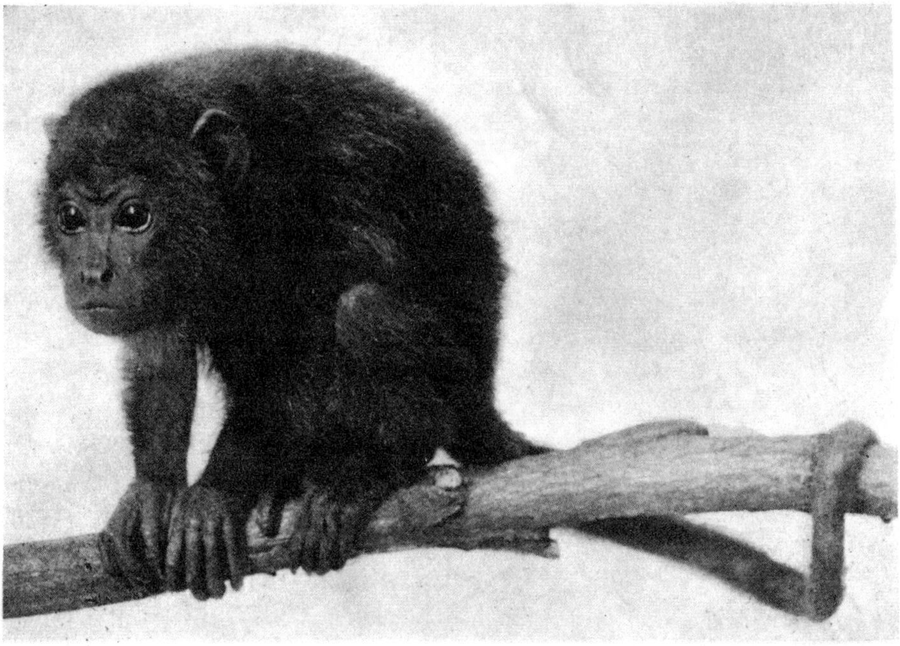

Courtesy of N.Y. Zoological Society

HOWLING MONKEY

Courtesy of N.Y. Zoological Society

SPIDER MONKEY

Courtesy of Julius Johnson

NIGHT MONKEY

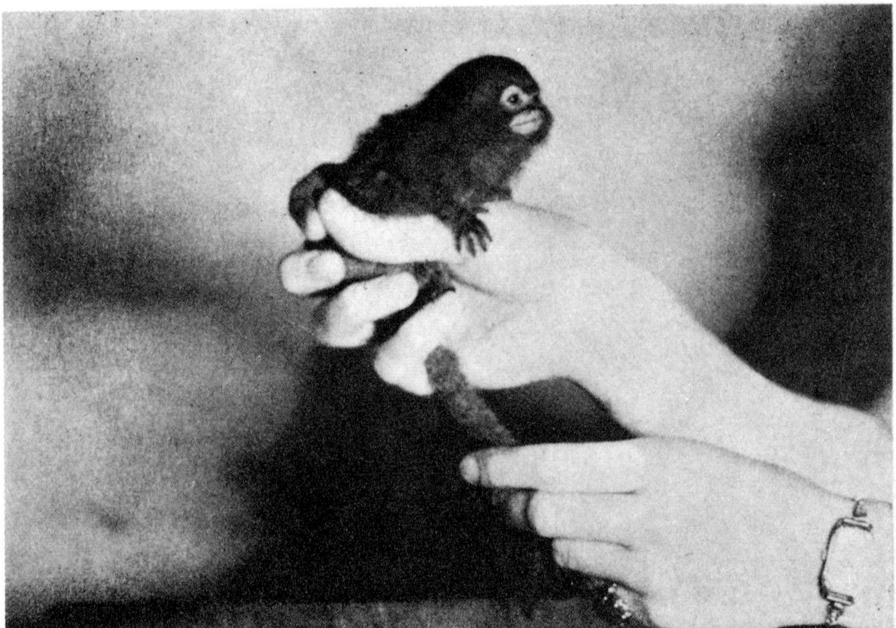

Courtesy of N.Y. Zoological Society

PYGMY MARMOSET

They make attractive pets, and many of them are captured in South America each year for that purpose. Since in captivity they do not get the habitual amount of exercise, they frequently suffer from stiffness of the legs and live only a few months at the most.

Perhaps the most attractive of all the marmosets is the beautifully colored golden marmoset, a dainty creature from the upper Amazon whose appearance is enhanced by the presence of a conspicuous, lionlike mane of lustrous, golden hair.

Howlers

The howling monkeys *(Mycetes),* called baboons by the colonists of British Guiana, are the largest and most formidable of the American monkeys. In at least one respect they are the most remarkable of all monkeys—they can make more noise than a score of other jungle animals, and do it with comparative ease. If contests were held among the beasts of the world to determine the one with the most powerful voice, the howling monkey would surely be acclaimed champion on every occasion—the roar of the lion, the howl of the wolf, even the wail of a banshee dwindling to a mere whisper beside the efforts of the great, bearded vocalist of the South American forests.

None of the six or more species is very large; the biggest probably does not exceed thirty pounds. Bates measured the largest one he saw along the Amazon, and it was twenty-eight inches long. There is considerable variation in color: one is entirely black, another brownish black, and the well known form of the Guianas *(M. seniculus)* is yellowish red. Im Thurn, who knew this species intimately, said that it might well be called the "red roarer."

The face of the howler has more resemblance to the human countenance than that of almost any other monkey, according to some authors. Lopez de Gaumana, a writer of the sixteenth century whom Humboldt quoted, opined that it "has the face of a man, the beard of a goat, and a grave demeanor." In commenting on this human resemblance Humboldt remarked that "monkeys are more melancholy in proportion as they have more resemblance to man. Their sprightliness diminishes as their intellectual faculties appear to increase." However that may be, the howler has the disparaging reputation of being sullen, morose, intractable. According to Bates it is the only simian the Indians have failed to tame; and that is saying a great deal, for the natives have tamed practically every other animal in the jungle. Paez has said that it is very taciturn and retiring, and not at all mischievous like most of its relatives. It is very frequently caught but, on account of its unyielding disposition, does not live long in captivity. The howlers live on buds and leaves, and monkeys that are such specialized vegetarians are notoriously difficult to keep in captivity. With careful treatment Ditmars managed to keep one alive two years, which broke all records.

The howlers have a pair of jaws that might be the envy of a carnivore. Up de Graff related that a common joke among the Indians was to throw a fatally wounded howler into the bottom of a boat. The reflexes of the wounded monkey would still be active, and the jaws would snap viciously at anything with which they came in contact. The moment the howler landed in a boat, its occupants would bail out, taking no chance of being severely and painfully bitten. That this could happen was not doubted by Up de Graff, for on one occasion a wounded howler attacked him. Rather than shoot it, he tried to keep it away from him with the barrel of his gun. The infuriated creature grabbed the point of the rifle in its jaws and closed the bore before Up de Graff could pull it away.

An experience such as this, coupled with the ferocious appearance and remarkable voice of the howler might lead one to believe that it is a vicious and altogether dangerous beast. Recent studies by C. R. Carpenter* on Barro Colorado Island have shown that it has a mild disposition, rarely attacks its mates, shows little or no sexual jealousy, and for the most part lives in perfect equanimity, not only with the members of its family but with most other animals. Even though possessed of a capable pair of jaws it feeds on vegetable matter, and its entire mode of living suggests that its bark is far worse than its bite.

The vocal organs responsible for the roar are unique and are

* *A Field Study of the Behavior and Social Relations of Howling Monkeys* (Comparative Psychology Monographs, Vol. X, No. 2, May 1934), Johns Hopkins Press.

present only in this particular group of American monkeys. Humboldt was probably the first scientist to make a careful dissection of the howler's voice box. In regard to it the eminent German naturalist had this to say: "Their superior larynx has six pouches, in which the voice loses itself; and two of which, shaped like pigeons' nests, resemble the inferior larynx of birds. The air driven with force into the bony drum produces the mournful sound which characterizes the *Araguatoes* [native name for howler]." He sketched on the spot these organs, which were at that time imperfectly known to anatomists, and published his description of them on his return to Europe. The bony drum of which he wrote is the hyoid bone. This protrudes from the neck like an exaggerated Adam's apple to form a thin-walled bony cup or reservoir, wherein is a sac connecting with the larynx. When the air is expelled from the voice box it is blown over the mouth of the reservoir, producing the extravagant volume of sound so disturbing to the jungle novice. The principle involved is much the same as that in blowing across the mouth of a bottle. In this day of radio one might refer to the howler's voice apparatus as a built-in loud speaker.

When breaking into "song" the howlers prefer a position in the topmost boughs of the trees, Bates said. Up de Graff called them the "evening and morning songsters" since they are most actively vocal at those times. Waterton stated, however, that from eleven o'clock at night till near dawn they howl at intervals, and that "in dark and cloudy weather, and just before a squall, the monkey will howl in the daytime." Im Thurn, also, commented on the continuance of the howlings at intervals throughout the day. Wallace wrote, "A full-grown male alone makes the howling." In this assertion he was wrong, for the howlers, large and small, young and old, male and female, join in the concert.

The naturalists who have heard the howlers when they were at their best are unanimous in describing the roar as appalling, deafening, startling, sleep-dispelling. They have difficulty, however, in conveying to the reader just what the unearthly din really sounds like. Waterton said: "You would suppose that half the wild beasts of the forest were collecting for the work of carnage. Now, it is the tremendous roar of the jaguar, as he springs on his prey; now it changes to his terrible and deep-toned growlings as he is pressed on all sides by superior force; and now, you hear his last dying moan, beneath a mortal wound." To Im Thurn it was almost incredible that such an infernal noise could be produced by such a small beast as the howler: "Though not bigger than a setter, it roars like any jaguar, tiger, or lion." To him the sound was like that heard in the zoological gardens when the great carnivores are being fed. Up de Graff declared that the first time he heard the howler he was so startled he thought all the jaguars on the Amazon were "engaged in a death struggle." Beebe gives the most impressive description of the vocal efforts of these animals. "They do not howl, they roar," he says, "and the sound is perfectly suited to such a wilderness as this. Before the first signs of day light up the east, a low, soft moaning comes through the forest, like the forewarning of a storm through pine trees. This gains in volume and depth until it becomes a roar. It is no wind now, nor like anything one ever hears in the north; it is a deep, grating, rumbling roar—a voice of the tropics; a hint of the long-past ages when speech was yet unformed."

Such vocal outbursts as these are often so appalling and so long drawn-out that they become almost unendurable. Chapman wrote of one outbreak that lasted without intermission for four solid hours—from seven in the morning until eleven. The sound is of such volume that it can be clearly heard at a distance of three miles.

What is the explanation of these periodical outbursts? Do the monkeys have in mind the intimidation of their enemies? Or do they shout just for the sheer joy of hearing themselves? Hooton,* in commenting on the howler's vocal ability, asks, "Why is it that loud voices go with meager wits, even in monkeys?" His conclusion is that these primates must bluff their way through life by bellowing and roaring. Bates thought it probable that the roar of the howler served to frighten away whatever foes were near at hand. It is well known that the howlers make themselves heard on a great many occasions. A clap of thunder, strong wind, an airplane, an enemy, a human being, the proximity of another clan of howlers, a fallen young monkey, any one of these

* *Op. cit.*

disturbing elements will produce violent vocalizations, day or night. It is Hingston's notion that these responses have an intimidating function. None of the roars can have any mating significance, it is thought, because members of both sexes, as well as the immature young, join in the concerts.

What about the impressive deep-toned roars that occur regularly at daybreak? As the first streaks of dawn light up the east the early morning silence will be shattered by the howls of some clan. These roars will shortly be followed by similar ones from tribes in contiguous parts of the forest. Carpenter * believes these noises are very important (1) in determining the location of the various clans, (2) in determining the direction of tribe movements, and (3) in regulating the territorial ranges. With this viewpoint Hingston is apparently in accord; moreover it is his belief that each clan keeps its area defined by its vocalizations, and that this "is the sole reason for the complicated apparatus and the tremendous powers of voice possessed by this particular species."

Capuchins

The capuchin, also called white-faced monkey, ring-tailed monkey, and sapajou *(Cebus)*, is the best known, the most intelligent, and at the same time the most characteristic monkey of the tropical American forests. It is the hand-organ monkey common in captivity the world over. The name, capuchin, arises from the dark patch of hair on the top of the head that suggests the cowl worn by Capuchin monks. There are twenty or more species inhabiting Central and South America, and all are small, not much more than a foot in length. The tail is prehensile but not nearly so well developed as in the spider, woolly, and howler monkeys. The capuchins employ their hands in a great variety of ways. This manual dexterity generally suggests a large brain and high intelligence.

No other monkeys appear to be so restlessly active. Perhaps they are responsible for the definition of a monkey formulated by Beebe: "An animal which never wants to be where it is."

They are gregarious, and sometimes two species consort together. Schomburgk told of seeing a flock of four or five hundred

* *Op. cit.*

which consisted of two species—*Cebus capucinus* and *C. apella.* Whenever he saw *C. capucinus, C. apella* was associated with it; and several individuals were evidently hybrids of the two, differing from both species in the color of the hair.

Capuchins excel all other monkeys in the prodigious leaps they make from one tree to another. Bates, who was extremely well informed on South American monkeys, watched several troops of thirty or more individuals leaping through the trees in single file on the upper Amazon, and wrote: "When the foremost of the flock reaches the outermost branch of an unusually lofty tree, he springs forth into the air without a moment's hesitation and alights on the dome of yielding foliage belonging to the neighbouring tree, maybe fifty feet beneath; all the rest following the example. They grasp, on falling, with hands and tails, right themselves in a moment, and then away they go along branch and bough to the next tree."

With their pensive faces, cowled heads, and energetic movements they make attractive and intelligent pets. Most monkeys do not breed well in captivity, and the capuchins are no exception. They are the hardiest in captivity, though, of all American monkeys, and a few have lived as long as twenty-five years in zoological gardens.

Spider Monkeys

None of the monkeys now inhabiting the Americas is so much at home in the trees as the spider monkey or coaita *(Ateles)*. This is so called because of its wiry, elongate limbs and remarkably slender body. The arms are longer than the legs, and the tail has greater length than either. One look at this animal is enough to prove that streamlining is not a modern innovation. Of particular note is the fact that the thumbs are rudimentary, and in some instances entirely absent. Whether this condition is to be associated with the highly specialized arboreal existence of the animals is difficult to say; but some authors consider that the thumbs would be an impediment to their peculiar manner of locomotion in the trees. The spider monkey is a gymnast of the first order and has reached a higher state of arboreal specialization than any other mammal except the gibbon of the old world.

Courtesy of Zoological Society of Philadelphia

SQUIRREL MONKEY

Courtesy of Zoological Society of Philadelphia

CAPUCHIN MONKEY

"The tendency of Nature here has been, to all appearances," wrote Bates, "simply to perfect those organs which adapt the species more and more completely to a purely arboreal life." In this monkey the observer may see the prehensile tail perfected to a point unequaled in any other creature. As a "fifth hand" it is extremely long, naked on the ventral side where it is covered with ridges, and constantly in motion like the tentacle of a giant squid.

The natives are very eager to capture the spider monkeys on all occasions. They make excellent pets, and their flesh is most tasty. Their appearance, though, is not a compliment to the species. "The face is pinched and drawn," wrote Miller, "with a long-suffering expression about the eyes, while a long, stiff hair extending over the forehead like a ragged cap gives it a greater look of misery and grotesqueness." In still another way they are unattractive, as they are alleged to be the most smelly of all monkeys.

To capture these and other monkeys alive, the Indians shoot them with darts covered with curare poison. The poison soon renders them unconscious, after which the natives restore them to life by placing a small amount of salt in their mouths, salt being the specific antidote for the much publicized curare.

Schomburgk wrote that spider monkeys, when followed, break off branches and hurl them at their pursuers. Just how many of the American monkeys have this manner of defense is not definitely known. Carpenter reported that the howling monkeys on Barro Colorado broke off dead limbs and dropped them toward him. The monkeys rarely carried a branch, but broke it off at a point nearest the pursuer and then dropped it.

The stories of monkeys forming bridges of their connected bodies across streams and forest avenues over which others of their kind scramble are without foundation.

Prehensile tails are characteristically new-world in origin and occurrence. Monkeys do not have a monopoly on prehensile tails, however, since the opossums, kinkajous, and the Australian phalangers, among other forms, have them.

In enumerating the characteristics pertaining to the Platyrrhine monkeys it is customary to include a prehensile tail. The truth is that of all the new-world monkeys only the spider, woolly, and howler monkeys have it well developed. In the capuchin it is only partially developed, as the occurrence of hair on the underside testifies. The squirrel, night, saki, and ouakari monkeys lack it entirely, and so do the marmosets. That being the case, only the spider, woolly, and howler monkeys can boast of a dependable fifth grasping member. The number of species in each genus is not known, but even if we allow for a few that have not been described, the fact remains that fewer than a third of all new-world primates have highly developed prehensile tails.

In these select few the underside of the tail is as bare as the palm of the hand, and like that organ is covered with friction ridges that aid the animal in grasping. Prehensile tails serve a variety of functions: they are of signal value to their owners as they travel through the trees, just as five hands are better than four; they counteract any inclination to fall and are invariably held ready for action; they are used for conveying food and other objects to the mouth; they enable the young ones to hold on to the mothers; they help in frightening away insects; they are extremely important in mooring the body to a limb while asleep; they are useful in brushing and otherwise grooming the hair. Hunters sometimes shoot a prehensile-tailed monkey in the top of a tree; as it loses consciousness its tail sometimes wraps about a limb from which it hangs for many hours after death. The prehensile tail must not be considered essential among mammals for arboreal life; in most monkeys it is altogether wanting, and the gibbon, one of the most active of all primates in the trees, has no tail at all. However, among the American simians those having tails with grasping ability are the super-aerialists.

The extreme development of the tail in new-world monkeys is thought to indicate an arboreal existence lasting over a long period of time; and, since it is limited chiefly to those creatures in Central and South American woods it is considered that these forests must have persisted since remote times. Another factor that may have aided in the development of the prehensile tail is the periodical flooding of much of the lowlands in South America. This, of necessity, forced the tree-living forms into arboreal exile during several months of the year and tended to increase adaptations for that particular type of existence. However that may be, the monkeys of South America, according to Bates, "are the most intensely arboreal animals in the world." They spend no more of their life in the trees than some other animals—the sloth, for example; but they are much more adequately equipped for that kind of existence.

Night Monkeys

The night, or owl, monkey *(Nyctipithecus)*, also called durukuli, is the only nocturnal primate inhabiting the Americas. Throughout the day it sleeps curled up in hollow trees and only ventures forth after nightfall in search of food, which consists chiefly of fruits and insects. It is said to be a light sleeper and to awake at any unaccustomed noise. If a person passes by a tree in which night monkeys are sleeping he may suddenly be delighted at the appearance of a group of tiny faces with large, closely approximated eyes peering forth from a hole in the tree trunk to see what the disturbance is about.

There are a half-dozen species, and all are small with a body length of about twelve inches and a nonprehensile tail somewhat longer. Bates gives an excellent description of one of the species familiar to him. "Their physiognomy," he wrote, "reminds one of an owl, or tiger-cat; the face is round and encircled by a ruff of whitish fur; the muzzle is not at all prominent; the mouth and chin are small; the ears are very short, scarcely appearing above the hair of the head; and the eyes are large and yellowish in colour, imparting the staring expression of nocturnal animals of prey."

The nose is more prominent than in any of the other American monkeys. Perhaps as a result of their night life they have developed the sense of smell more highly than their diurnal relatives. Miller found night monkeys plentiful at a certain camp in the Bolivian highlands. One night they chose a tree above his tent for their playground. He was kept awake much of the night by their low grunting notes and by the leaves and twigs they dropped onto the tent fly.

They make agreeable pets and are commonly found with the Indians of Brazil. Since they sleep all day long, they are not very popular in zoological gardens.

Sakis

The saki, or couxio *(Pithecia)*, is a medium-sized monkey that is covered with long, loose fur and sometimes has a long, black beard. "The hair of the head sits on it like a cap," wrote Bates, "and looks as if it had been carefully combed." The tail is an aid to identification as it is long and bushy and nonprehensile. Sometimes sakis are mistaken for howling monkeys. They are delicate and do not live long in captivity; for that reason they are not so well known. They have the reputation of being inoffensive, and quiet. There are at least five species, the largest and best known of which is the black saki *(P. satanas)*.

Ouakari Monkeys

The ouakari, or yarke, monkeys *(Brachyurus)*, of which there are three species known to science, are easily distinguished from other American monkeys by their short tails. When these monkeys first reached Europe the scientists were convinced that their tails had been docked by somebody.

The bald yarke of the upper Amazon, one of the rarest of all American monkeys, has a length of about eighteen inches, is covered from nape to tail with long, shaggy hair, and has a bright vermilion-colored face. Bates referred to these as the "scarlet-faced monkeys."

The ouakari monkeys live in forest that is covered with flood waters for more than half of the year, so that they cannot come to ground. Their rudimentary tails are therefore no indication of terrestrial life. In fact, there are no terrestrial primates in the Americas comparable to the land-dwelling baboons of the old world.

Woolly Monkeys

The woolly monkeys *(Lagothrix)*, also called barrigudos because of their prominent abdomens, are closely related to the spider monkeys and, like them, have exceedingly long, active

Courtesy of Zoological Society of Philadelphia

GEOFFREY'S MARMOSET

Photo by Newton H. Hartman

WOOLLY MONKEY

Courtesy of N.Y. Zoological Society

OUAKARI MONKEY

tails that are naked underneath. They are almost as large as the howlers. Bates measured one with a body twenty-seven inches long and a tail twenty-six inches. The body is somewhat bulky and is covered with a fine woolly coat of hair which is usually silvery gray. "The skin of the face in the Barrigudo," wrote Bates, "is black and wrinkled, the forehead is low, with the eyebrows projecting, and, in short, the features altogether resemble in a striking manner those of an old negro." The tail is very sensitive and almost, if not quite, as efficient as that of the spider monkey. The woolly monkeys are not so agile in the trees as the spider monkeys, though Miller tells of seeing them racing "through the tree-tops at great speed, making long jumps from branch to branch." In the mornings and evenings, he states, they were vocal, emitting notes that resembled a series of quickly repated *oh's*.

According to Mann,* the barrigudo has the gentlest disposition of all the American monkeys and makes the best pet. Dr. Mann has a thorough acquaintance with monkeys, and he says without hesitation that in general they do not make good pets. Their disposition is too unreliable, and they tend to become ugly with age. It is his experience that the woolly monkeys, even when old, have mild tempers and are the most dependable of all.

Unfortunately they are quite delicate and rarely live long away from their native haunts. There are just two described species, both of which are much in favor with the natives for food.

Squirrel Monkeys

The squirrel monkeys, or saimiris *(Chrysothrix)*, are diminutive, arboreal forms that are so called because of a certain resemblance to squirrels. There are some half-dozen species, all brightly colored. The best known form *(C. sciureus)* has a body about ten inches long and a fourteen-inch tail that is nonprehensile. One author states that these petite creatures are "brainy" but not very bright. It is a singular fact that the proportion of brain to body is greater in the squirrel monkeys than in human beings. The cerebrum is only slightly convoluted, but it extends far to the back of the cranium.

The squirrel monkeys live in the trees in fairly large flocks—

* Smithsonian Scientific Series, Vol. VI, 1930.

twenty to fifty, Miller said—and their movements are easy and graceful. Im Thurn wrote that they usually follow one another through the trees in single file and seem to delight in hurling themselves through space for extraordinary distances as they pass from tree to tree.

They feed largely on insects and will devour young birds and eggs. Miller had for a pet a squirrel monkey whose chief delight was in hunting and catching mosquitoes; it demonstrated unbelievable patience in searching through decks of cards for mosquitoes that might be sandwiched between them. A squirrel monkey that Humboldt had in his possession tried its best to eat figures of wasps from books when the illustrations were shown to it. The German scientist thought the face of this monkey had certain qualities usually noted in the countenance of a child. He and later observers have discerned a certain amount of innocence in its expression and have commented on the rapid change from joy to sorrow.

* * *

"The gastronomical possibilities of a monkey probably occur to only a very few of the millions who gaze at him through iron bars," Up de Graff averred. Yet the natives of South America consider the flesh of certain species of monkeys to be superior to that of almost any other animal. The meat of the larger forms, the howling, spider, and woolly monkeys, is especially sapid.

After eating monkey meat for the first time (a spider monkey) Bates declared, "I thought the meat the best flavoured I had ever tasted. It resembled beef, but had a richer and sweeter taste." The marked resemblance of the flesh of the larger forms to beef is probably responsible for its almost universal popularity among the inhabitants of the jungle. Up de Graff said that it is the only meat of the jungle that can be eaten regularly over a considerable period of time. The South American explorers complain repeatedly about the intolerableness of turtle meat and the flesh of certain birds and fish after subsisting on it for only a few days. This complaint is made very infrequently in regard to monkey meat. After becoming accustomed to it, the traveler discovers to his great pleasure and surprise that it is extremely palatable and easily digested, and eats it with relish at every future opportunity. The Indians are greatly elated when one or more of the large monkeys is killed. They eat everything but the skin and break open the bones for the marrow they contain. Some tribes go so far as to wash out the contents of the stomach, which, with the addition of water, is said to make a palatable drink. This consists for the most part of only leaves and fruits that have been acted upon by the enzyme pepsin, so that the idea of swallowing such a beverage is not so nauseating as it seems on first thought.

Food is difficult to obtain in parts of the great South American rain forest, and monkey flesh has been the means of preventing many a jungle inhabitant from starving. When food ran dangerously short during Roosevelt's expedition down the River of Doubt the men were only too glad to eat the monkeys Cherrie and Kermit Roosevelt shot.

Although most travelers would feel that a trip to the jungle was complete without a taste of monkey flesh, few would be willing to leave without hearing the incomparable ululations of the howler or seeing the friend of the organ grinder in its native habitat.

BIRD MIGRANTS TO SOUTH AMERICA

In the early part of the year 1914 a remarkable meeting occurred in the far western part of Brazil, in Nhambiquara land, a region inhabited by the tribe of primitive savages known by that name. It is one of the most inaccessible spots in the whole of South America, and a singularly strange place for a meeting; yet two parties, which had traveled thousands of miles by different routes, found that their paths crossed in this remote section of the southern hemisphere. The better known of the two individuals was Theodore Roosevelt, one of the greatest of our Presidents; the lesser known was a veery—one of the sweetest songsters among American birds.

At about the time of Roosevelt's departure from the United States for South America, the first of October, 1913, the veery had left its summer home, which might well have been Roosevelt's home state of New York, and had started its autumnal flight in a southwesterly direction, probably following the general trend of the Alleghenies, until it came to the Gulf of Mexico. Across this it made a flight of five to six hundred miles to the Yucatan peninsula, the one-time home of the Maya Indians, and then leisurely flew across the jungles, savannas, and mountain ranges of Central and South America until it came to the equator and the Amazon basin. Certainly there was an abundance of food in most of these regions, but some powerful inward force winged the bird onward until it finally made a halt in Nhambiquara land, fifteen degrees below the equatorial line. Roosevelt had traveled by boat to the Argentine and had then ascended the Paraná and Paraguay rivers until he reached the same general region.

The veery is only one of a great number of birds that migrate year after year to South America. Of nearly eight hundred birds listed in Chapman's *Handbook of Birds of Eastern North America,* well over one hundred extend their winter pilgrimages to some portion of the southern continent. It is sufficiently striking that our birds start south each fall and travel as far as Cuba or Mexico; but that they withstand the further dangers entailed by a trip over water, or over jungle, to the mainland of South America is beyond human explanation. Even that is far from being the whole story, for of some one hundred twenty-five species that travel to South America, at least two-thirds fly past the Caribbean countries of Venezuela and Colombia and the Guianas, and beyond the equator in Brazil and Peru. And of the thirty or more species, endowed with an amazing zeal for travel, that push their fragile bodies beyond the Tropic of Capricorn in far-away Chile and Argentina, a few extend their flights to the inhospitable regions of Patagonia, Tierra del Fuego, and the Falkland Islands.

The American naturalists visiting South America have been cheered on many occasions by suddenly encountering a familiar bird that had traveled thousands of miles under its own power to reach the same remote destination. Almost a century ago, Edwards wrote of seeing herons, ibises, gallinules and other birds on the island of Marajó at the mouth of the Amazon, some of which were old acquaintances of his in the Catskills.

During a stay at Bartica in British Guiana from March to August, 1916, Beebe saw the barn swallow, purple martin, Eskimo curlew, yellowlegs, solitary and spotted sandpipers, and the yellow warbler.

Father Zahm identified several shore birds familiar to him in the United States as he ascended the Orinoco and Meta in 1907. Among these were the pintail, baldpate, goldeneye, and the blue-winged teal.

Murphy, while he was visiting the Chincha Islands in the winter of 1919–20, had a wonderful opportunity for observing shore birds that migrate to points below the equatorial line. Of the winter visitors from the United States, and farther north, there were Hudsonian curlews; semipalmated, spotted, and western sandpipers; ringneck and black-bellied plovers; snipes; ruddy turnstones; northern phalaropes; surf birds; wandering tattlers; Franklin's gulls; ospreys; and, last but not least, our own familiar barn swallows.

Of these the Hudsonian curlews may well have come from the north coast of Alaska, the plovers from Coronation Gulf or Melville Peninsula, the Franklin's gulls from Hudson Bay, and the northern phalaropes from James Bay or Greenland. Murphy found the phalaropes "aggregating tens of thousands." This was an important observation because the species had not previously been recorded from the southern hemisphere. Later on Murphy found them to be common all along the coast of Peru.

In 1916, while hunting the region in the north of the Argentine Republic known as the Chaco, Miller discovered a wintering place of bobolinks—an eventful find, for the extent of the bobolink's migration was not known. "We found them in flocks of thousands, perched in the top of the tall grass or picking up seeds from the ground," Miller wrote. "Their cheery song was conspicuously absent. They were in spotted plumage."

In the southern part of Colombia at an elevation of four thousand feet Chapman saw redstarts, olive-backed thrushes, and golden-winged, Tennessee, Blackburnian, cerulean, and Canadian warblers.

We have alluded to the fact that Hudson lived in the Argentine for the first twenty-seven years of his life. He was especially intrigued by the arrival each spring of the bird migrants from North America. In *Birds of La Plata* we find references to at least a dozen of these migrants that each year came to his beloved pampas from the United States or Canada. There were the pectoral, Baird's, Bonaparte's, buff-breasted, and solitary sandpipers; the upland plover, the greater and lesser yellowlegs, the Hudsonian godwit, Eskimo curlew, yellow-billed cuckoo, golden plover, and blue-winged teal.

Each and every one of these birds had traveled seven or eight thousand miles before its instinct for southerly migration was satisfied. These amazing performances were just as mysterious and inexplicable to Hudson then, as they are to us today.

In writing of the yellow-billed cuckoo Hudson said that he encountered it frequently on the pampas from February to April; but these are summer and autumn months in the Argentine, and he was not able to determine whether it nested there. He recognized the possibility that this bird migrated from North America to the pampas but thought it "hardly believable that any Cuckoo could make this journey."

His astonishment is expressed again when writing of the journeys performed by the pectoral sandpiper. This bird, he said, began to arrive in La Plata near the end of August, usually in small flocks. Some of the young birds had bits of down still clinging to the plumage and were otherwise so immature that it was hard to believe that they had been able to complete the journey from near the Arctic circle to the Argentinian pampas so soon after hatching.

The large numbers of certain species added still more fuel to Hudson's incredulity. He wrote of the buff-breasted sandpipers that he had noted these birds in April and May, "in flocks of two to five hundred, traveling north, flock succeeding flock at intervals of about fifteen minutes and continuing to pass for several days."

Hudson's descriptions of the North American migrants are of special interest to us and, as always, charmingly worded. With pleasant anticipation such as might have preceded the visit of distinguished and admired persons to his home, Hudson looked forward to the coming of these birds. Some of them stayed near him on the pampas for several weeks; others he saw only as they were passing overhead. We are particularly interested in his descriptions of some of the species, then numerous, but now exterminated or doomed to extinction in the near future. In Hudson's day the Eskimo curlew was abundant. It nested on the Barren Grounds of the northern Mackenzie River and later migrated to the Argentine, using the over-water route from Nova Scotia to the Guianas or Brazil. Since 1900 not more than a dozen specimens have been seen anywhere. It is possible that a few of these birds may still be in existence, but the great flocks that once were common in Canada and the Argentine pampas are gone forever. Hudson wrote that the Eskimo curlew "was common enough in its season on the pampas in my day, appearing in September to October in small flocks of thirty or forty or a hundred or more, and often associating with the Golden Plover."

Another American species nearing extermination is the charming upland plover, or Bartram's sandpiper. Hudson wrote that the inhabitants of the United States had recently become more interested in the upland plover, not so much because it was a charming bird, as because their hunters had almost exterminated it. "They fear," he concluded, "that it is going the way of the Passenger Pigeon, the Pinnated Grouse, the Carolina Parrokeet, the Ivory-billed Woodpecker, and, I believe we must now add, the Esquimo Whimbrel."

One of the most celebrated bird migrants of the world is the golden plover. Each year this bird, whose nesting ground is near the arctic circle, makes a flight due south across the Atlantic Ocean to northern South America and then on to the Argentine. The total mileage of this journey from the arctic circle to the latitude of Buenos Aires must be in the neighborhood of eight thousand miles, making a round trip of sixteen thousand miles. Equally interesting is the fact that the golden plovers which nest in western Alaska and northeastern Siberia do not migrate to South America but go, for the most part, to the Hawaiian Islands. Some follow the eastern coast of Asia and eventually reach Australia, New Zealand, or Tasmania.

In *Far Away and Long Ago* Hudson tells of a sudden hail storm on the pampas in which the stones were as big as "fowl's eggs," soon after the golden plovers arrived. Great numbers of these birds were scattered here and there in large flocks. Immediately following the storm a native boy took Hudson on horseback, and, riding out a little way, they found dozens of golden plovers lying on the ground dead. Instead of picking up these, however, Hudson's companion let them lie and went after the ones that were running about with broken wings. Within a few minutes they had a score or more, enough for the table, and they rode home.

In *Birds of La Plata* Hudson has more to say about this remarkable avian nomad. Everyone is well acquainted with it on the pampas, he writes, where it is abundant. The first arrivals are heard during the latter part of August, and at that time they are very thin as a result of their long journey from North America. Later they become quite fat and are then much sought after by hunters. The time of their arrival is regular each year, but they do not necessarily visit the same regions. In some parts of the country they may be abundant one season and entirely absent the next. Sometimes they are in such numbers that "they blacken the ground over an area of several acres in extent; and at a distance of a quarter of a mile the din of their united voices resembles the roar of a cataract. As population increases on the pampas these stupendous gatherings are becoming more and more rare." At such times, Hudson goes on to say, if a native boy wants golden plovers he takes a cord about three feet long to one end of which is attached a lead ball and goes out and kills as many as he wants.

The arctic tern, recognized as the bird with the longest migratory route known to man, frequently follows portions of the South American coast line in its extended flight to and from the polar regions. Although scientific data about its route in migrating north or south are still limited, competent ornithologists have noted its movements in both Atlantic and Pacific waters on several occasions. Murphy, in his comprehensive and masterful work entitled *Oceanic Birds of South America,* cites several references to the occurrence of arctic terns in waters south of the equator. According to him Beck saw them frequently off the west coast of Peru in June, 1913. These observations were made in about 10 to 15 degrees South Latitude, some close to shore and others three or four days' sailing to the west. Some of the birds were seen in groups of six and seven, and others were solitary. In the same year Beck saw arctic terns in considerable numbers while on a voyage from the Chilean city of Valparaiso to the purported location of Robinson Crusoe's involuntary exile, the Juan Fernández Islands. These insular possessions of Chile are in about 35 degrees South Latitude. In October of the following year Beck was in Atlantic waters east of the Argentinian town of Mar del Plata in about 38 degrees South Latitude. Here he collected an arctic tern and "noted the presence of hundreds, presumably of the same species." On November 9, 1912, Murphy himself shot a specimen in the Atlantic east of the Río de la Plata estuary.

These observations are not extensive, but others have been made of the same bird in tropical and north temperate waters of the Atlantic and elsewhere. These, taken together, suggest that most arctic terns fly from New England across the Atlantic and then down the west coast of Africa.

The contention that the arctic tern migrates annually beyond the antarctic circle to a latitude of 73 to 75 degrees South is apparently based on questionable evidence. In the words of Murphy it is a "legend which may yet prove to be a far-reaching ornithological illusion."

The exact point indicated by Cooke where the arctic tern winters is the Weddell Sea, a body of water of undefined limits, but a part of the Antarctic Ocean just south of the antarctic circle and east of North Graham and South Graham islands. These islands are about ten degrees due south of Tierra del Fuego. This general region is inhabited, in considerable numbers, by the antarctic tern *(Sterna vittata)*, a species which differs from its arctic congener only in minor details.

The first reports of the arctic tern in Antarctica date from the very beginning of this century, when two scientific cruises were made beyond the antarctic circle. The ornithological reports, subsequently made, tell of the presence of the arctic tern. In 1913 the report from the later *Scotia* cruise tells of finding arctic terns in Weddell Sea by the thousands. Some of these supposed forms were seen in latitude 74° 1′ South.

Without going into further detail, suffice it to say that Murphy inclines to the opinion that these reports are based on observations of the antarctic tern, the quite similar, normal habitué of those waters, and not on the arctic tern.

Even if that be true, the winter home of the arctic tern is not definitely known; chiefly because it is apparently in seas which are very infrequently visited by man. It is thought to be somewhere between West Africa and the Argentine Republic and south to some indeterminate point north of the antarctic circle. Alexander Wetmore says it spends its winters "off the shores of the great Antarctic continent, south and east of the Falkland Islands."

To summarize the case in as few words as possible: it is thought by some that the arctic tern does not go to the antarctic ice-pack zone beyond the circle, as was formerly believed; that the species observed by early scientists in Antarctica in great numbers was not the arctic tern at all, but the antarctic tern; and that the winter home of the arctic tern is probably nearer 50 degrees South Latitude than 70 or 75 degrees.

Even though this does prove to be the case, the arctic tern still remains the champion globe-trotter of them all. As Beebe points out, "It would seem that this obsession of migration sometimes acquires such an impetus that only the whole long length of the planet itself can dissipate it."

Having paid tribute to some of the chief personages in the world of bird migration, let us discuss a few of the perplexing questions which inevitably arise whenever the subject of bird migration to South America is raised. Considerable light has been thrown on certain aspects of the phenomenon within recent years, but many phases of it remain just as enigmatical and unilluminated as they were a century ago, when Audubon and Wilson were scratching their heads and seeking answers to the same questions.

How fast do birds fly while they are making these long, antipodal journeys, and how long does it take them to complete their migrations from Canada, or the United States, to South America?

Several methods are used in determining just how fast birds can travel. For instance, ornithologists traveling in automobiles have clocked the speed of birds flying parallel to their machines. Investigators have utilized the airplane in like manner. The theodolite, an instrument employed by anti-aircraft stations for determining the speed of planes, has proved itself of signal value in determining the speed of birds on the wing. It has also been possible to time the flight of birds over prescribed courses with stop watches. By one or another of these methods a sizable amount of evidence has been accumulated within recent years which concerns the rapidity of flight in birds.

One point definitely established is that birds have two speeds of flight: one is the rate in normal, everyday flying from one point to another, and in migration; the other is the rate in fleeing from an enemy or in pursuit of prey. The latter is much more rapid, and can be maintained only for short distances. Birds do not have the speeds frequently attributed to them, but there are a few that can—if the occasion demands—get up and go with the wind. An aviator in Mesopotamia was cruising at eighty-eight miles an hour when, to his amazement, he saw a species of swift which was flying circles about his ship; time and again it circled his plane with apparent ease. In order to accomplish this feat the bird must have been flying at least one hundred miles an hour. But some Eurasian swifts can fly even faster than this. According to Alexander Wetmore,* E. C. Stuart Baker timed two small species of swifts *(Chaetura nudipes* and *C. cochinchinensis)* as they flew over a two-mile course. According to the stop watches these avian bullets traversed the two miles in from thirty-six to forty-two seconds, or at the lightninglike speed of 171.4 to 200 miles an hour.

Probably the fastest speed merchant among American birds is the peregrine falcon, or duck hawk, made immortal by the art of falconry. One of these was once timed with a stop watch, and its speed was placed at 165 to 180 miles an hour.†

In spite of these records there are only a few species of birds anywhere in the world that can fly faster than sixty miles an hour. According to Lincoln, "It has been found that the common flying speed of ducks and geese is between forty and fifty miles an hour. Herons, hawks, horned larks, ravens, and shrikes, timed with the speedometer of an automobile, have been found to fly twenty-two to twenty-eight miles an hour, while some of the flycatchers are such slow fliers that they attain only ten to seventeen miles an hour."

It is probably safe to say then that the average speed of most birds is from fifteen to thirty-five miles an hour. This is the speed that these birds employ while they are migrating. They are capable of greater speeds, but there is no evidence of haste in these long journeys. Even though a certain species is to fly from Hudson Bay to Patagonia, it seems to be in no hurry whatsoever to arrive at that remote destination. It may fly several hours one day, but the next will probably be spent in feeding and resting. As a matter of fact it may spend several days in one locality before continuing the journey.

The North American birds that winter in South America travel each year from six thousand to eighteen thousand miles, or more. From New York to British Guiana "as the crow flies" is approximately two thousand miles, but the birds making that trip fol-

* *Warm-Blooded Vertebrates,* Smithsonian Scientific Series, Vol. IX, Pt. 1, 1931.

† Lincoln, *The Migration of North American Birds,* U.S. Dept. of Agr. Circular No. 363, 1935.

low such a serpentine and zigzag course that they travel at least three thousand miles before arriving in the British colony; and by the time they have returned to New York they have completed a round trip of six thousand miles. Those that fly from the arctic circle to Patagonia (roughly, 45° South Latitude) must cover close to nine thousand miles each way, for the air-line distance is more than seventy-five hundred miles. Their round-trip distance must be close to eighteen thousand miles.

The great blue heron, Baltimore oriole, redstart, ovenbird, and Kentucky warbler spend the winter in northern South America. They travel at least six thousand miles each year.

The broad-winged hawk, osprey, wood pewee, scarlet tanager, and Canadian warbler are known to winter as far south as Peru. These birds must traverse at least eight to ten thousand miles of forest and sea each year.

The barn swallow, nighthawk, killdeer, Swainson's hawk, pied-billed grebe, bobolink, and many others journey as far each winter as southern Brazil. Upon the return of these birds to their respective breeding grounds they must have successfully completed a journey of at least ten to twelve thousand miles.

And then there are the birds that nest in the summer around the arctic circle—the golden plover, Hudsonian curlew, Franklin's gull, Hudsonian godwit, and Eskimo curlew, to name a few—and fly south at the approach of winter to Patagonia or the southern part of Chile. Incomprehensible though it may seem these birds must fly a distance of sixteen to eighteen thousand miles, and this they do each and every year of their existence. The urge to make these journeys is just as strong within them as the urge to mate, to build nests, and to rear the young.

The amount of time consumed in these journeys varies tremendously, even among the members of a given species. As a result only broad generalizations are possible. No one has been able to follow a bird from the time it left its home in the north until it reached its southernmost objective in Colombia or Uruguay. However, by bird banding, additional data are collected right along, and we may expect to have much more information on this important question in the not too distant future. From the evidence at hand we know that these long pilgrimages are taken in leisurely fashion. We are therefore probably safe in saying that they cover periods ranging from six weeks to three months. Some of the birds spend almost as much time touring the western hemisphere each year as they do at their respective northern and southern homes.

What routes are employed by the birds as they journey toward the equator each year?

There are many routes, but certain highways have much more traffic on them than others. Seven of these avian roads are outstanding. The great majority of the birds flying south congregate in Louisiana, Mississippi, Alabama, and Florida and then fly across the Gulf of Mexico to Yucatan along what may be called bird highway No. 1. From there they travel over the forests and morasses of Guatemala and the other Central American republics until they reach South America. At the height of the migration season millions of birds make this hop over the Gulf from the United States to Mexico. Most of them fly at night; and for a distance of five hundred to seven hundred miles they wing their way through darkness toward an unseen destination with no landmarks to guide them. This route across the Gulf has no terrors even for the ruby-throated hummingbird, the smallest of all our birds.

A second, more direct route carries the birds from Florida to South America by way of Cuba. This entails a long over-water hop across the Caribbean, and only a few birds use it. Since the bobolink migrates this way, it is sometimes called the "bobolink route."

A third route is to the east and follows the numerous islands composing the Greater and Lesser Antilles, which extend from Florida to South America like stepping-stones. This is comparatively safe and direct, but, for some unknown reason, only a few birds follow it.

A fourth route is to the west of route No. 1 and consists of a relatively short over-water road from Texas to eastern Mexico in the vicinity of Vera Cruz.

Of the remaining routes, two are to the west and one to the east. The two western routes are entirely over land through Mexico and Central America. These routes are used by the birds of the Rocky Mountain and Pacific coast regions. The eastern

Courtesy of Zoological Society of Philadelphia

SAKI MONKEY

Courtesy of American Museum of Natural History

GOLDEN PLOVER

route is entirely over water and stretches interminably from Nova Scotia due south to the South American mainland, approximately twenty-five hundred miles.

How do the birds find their way on these prodigious intercontinental journeys?

Birds not only find their way from Manitoba or Pennsylvania to some remote spot in one of the South American republics, but may return in the spring to the very doorstep from which they departed in the fall.

That they have a sense of direction which is beyond the ability of man to understand, is definitely recognized. But the nature of this sense remains a complete mystery, although many theories have been proposed to explain it.

One theory has it that birds set their course by the position of the sun just as the navigators of old did. Another is based on heredity—the birds have a hereditary memory which enables the young birds to follow the routes as well as old ones. Still other theories suppose that birds are influenced by wind currents, by the magnetic pole, by the direction of the sun's rays, by telepathy, and so forth. The nature and diversity of these theories emphasize the fact that little or nothing is known about how birds are able to find their way while migrating.

Why do birds migrate at all? Why do they undertake such stupendous trips yearly when each and every mile of travel is fraught with danger and uncertainty?

The reasons are apparently bound up with the satisfaction of two requirements: ample food supply and suitable nesting grounds. The urge to travel is so firmly established in birds that we may be certain that it had its origin in some remote period.

By some authorities it is believed that the ancestral home of birds was in the north where there was an abundance of food and of satisfactory nesting sites. Then came the first of the Pleistocene glacial periods, to be followed later by at least three more. Huge ice packs advanced to the south, as far as the present Pittsburgh and Cincinnati. Herein lies the major cause of migration, according to these authorities. The birds were driven by the glaciers from their northern ancestral homes, and their only escape was to the tropics. They could not stay in the north because the food supply was destroyed. Each year the glaciers receded, and the birds returned as far north as the ice would permit to build their nests and to rear their young. Each fall, though, the increasing cold forced them to the south again. The first ice age, geologists say, began in the early Pleistocene, perhaps five hundred thousand or more years ago; the last glacial period ended some fifteen to twenty thousand years ago. We have here, then, a period of some half-million years in which the birds have been chasing the ice in spring and fleeing from it in the fall. Each spring they went north to their ancestral breeding grounds, each fall they left for lack of food: the only way of satisfying that need was by migrating south. These northward and southward flights after a period of time became a definite hereditary habit.

The exact antithesis of this theory is advanced by other scholars who presuppose that the ancestral home of birds was in the tropics. Migration came as a result of overpopulation, which brought a scarcity not only of food but of safe nesting grounds. The birds ultimately found both of these requirements eminently satisfied in the north, to which region they repaired each spring. However, their love of home, and scarcity of food in winter, demanded a return to the tropics each fall.

It is well known that birds are very regular in their migratory travels: they generally leave a given region on a definite date and return on a day which can be specified. As a result of their clock-like regularity the theory of photoperiodism has been advanced. The exponents of this hypothesis base their views entirely on the amount of light and length of day at different times of the year. Since birds leave a given region at a definite time year after year it is pointed out that the only environmental factor that corresponds with this regularity is the amount of light.

Light may be a very important factor in the migration of birds; however, biologists agree that these flights are initiated each year through the activity of the sexual glands. Just once each year the ovaries and testes in birds become active and throw off into the blood stream certain chemical messengers known as hormones. These agents awaken in the birds the desire to mate, to build nests, and to rear the young. With this awakening their first impulse is to start north to the breeding grounds. North American birds are sometimes found in South America in May, June, or July when they should be in the north. When the sexual glands of these are examined it is found that they are inactive; the birds have not experienced the cyclic enlargement of the gonads incident to migration, and consequently have received no inner promptings to fly north.

What does the future hold for migrating birds? If we had followed the birds to South America while Hudson was living in Argentina, and could again follow them now, we should find that some of the species present on our first trip have entirely disappeared, still others have become very rare, and the outlook for many others is somber at the best. This reduction in members has been due to a combination of evil practices, some originating in North America, some in South America. Many of these evils have been corrected in the northern continent, but not in the southern. South America is doing just about as much toward protecting her bird life today as we did in the United States prior to the Spanish American War. But the South American republics are finally coming to life in this respect. They are beginning to realize the value of their birds and are sponsoring educational campaigns whereby beneficial laws will be passed.

With uniform legislation existing in all of the countries from Canada to Chile—a dream which should be realized before so many years—the future of migration in the western hemisphere will be brighter than at any time since man began the wholesale slaughter of birds to further his own selfish ends.

THE RHEA

THE rhea, or South American ostrich, was characterized by Hudson as the "greatest and most unbirdlike bird of our continent." Our usual conception of a bird is as an animal with well developed wings capable of carrying it into a world of three dimensions, with a body of graceful outline, a specialized vocal organ that creates a song particularly appealing to our auditory sense, a protective coat of feathers, strikingly if not beautifully colored, an artistically constructed nest of leaves and grass and feathers cleverly hidden away from the casual glance of the human eye. If we are to stick to ordinary prerequisites, the most that can be said for the rhea is that it has a coat of feathers. It is unable to fly; it cannot raise itself as far from the earth as a modern well trained high jumper; its body is ungainly; it has no notes that could by any stretch of the imagination be called a song; the feathers are not attractively colored; and it builds no nest at all, unless the crudest kind of hole scraped in the ground can be so called.

On the other hand it is one of the "greatest" of birds. There is something indefinably regal about the carriage of the rhea as it stands alone on the flat surface of the pampas calmly surveying the distances which stretch away toward an uncertain horizon. Darwin was impressed by his first view of the rhea. "When standing on any little eminence," he says, "and seen against the clear sky, [it] presented a very noble appearance." Its height, five feet or more, is impressive, and its movements are graceful. When pursued, it demonstrates a fleetness usually capable of outdistancing the enemy and a cleverness in side-stepping, if pursued too closely, that calls for a round of enthusiastic applause.

The rhea bears a strong resemblance to its African relative the ostrich, and for that reason is frequently, though incorrectly, referred to as the ostrich. The African bird is much larger, and has two toes on each foot; the rhea has three.

There are three species of rhea in South America, although the presence of two of these was entirely unsuspected before Darwin.

The Rhea

The better and longer known species, *Rhea americana,* is distributed over all of the Argentine north of the Río Negro and is common in Uruguay, Paraguay, and the southern parts of Bolivia and Brazil. This species was common within forty miles of Buenos Aires, when Hudson was a boy. A second form, *Rhea macrorhyncha,* much smaller than the others, is found high in the Andes from the province of Mendoza (Argentina) to Bolivia.

The third species, *Rhea Darwinii,* with a somewhat limited range, is found south of the Río Negro in that portion of the Argentine known as Patagonia. The Río Negro, although not a river of any great size, appears to serve as an efficient barrier against the free northerly and southerly dispersal of animals.* This is particularly true in the case of two of the species of rheas.

Darwin's discovery of the southern rhea, now known by his name, was made at Port Desire. At the Río Negro he had heard the natives refer to a bird they called *avestruz pelise* that was quite simlar to the "ostrich" although smaller and with a dark, mottled color and shorter legs. However, when a rhea was shot at Port Desire he forgot entirely about the *pelise* until after the bird had been cooked and eaten. Fortunately several parts of the body were still intact and these were collected and sent to England, where a reconstruction was made. Mr. Gould, who described the new species, did Darwin the honor of naming it after him.

Rhea americana is said to average about two feet taller than its more southerly congener. It is brownish gray with black crown, white thighs and abdomen, and yellowish cheek. Hudson observed that the eggs of *Rhea americana* are golden yellow when first laid, while those of Darwin's rhea are a deep, rich green. The eggs of both species tend to whiten with age.

The habits of the two appear to be quite similar. While individuals may be seen alone on the pampas, the birds are by nature gregarious. The first ones seen by Darwin were at Maldonado (1832) on the northern bank of the Plata. They were in flocks of twenty to thirty. Prichard saw forty-two in a group on one occasion, but this included several small and immature birds.

The eggs are laid in September, October, and November, the

* Noted by Musters in *At Home with the Patagonians. Rhea americana,* in his experience, was never found south of it.

season which corresponds to our northern spring. The bird's efforts at nest-making are rather ineffective. According to Musters, a hole about two feet and a half in diameter is scooped in the ground, and in this are placed a few bits of grass which serve as a lining.

The number of eggs in a nest varies a great deal; twenty to thirty would seem to be a common range. Beerbohm asserts that the number to be found in a single nest is from ten to forty, usually about twenty. Musters writes that the number is twenty to forty, or more. Cherrie discovered thirty-seven in one nest. Hudson states that nests containing thirty to sixty eggs are common, and that he had heard of as many as a hundred and twenty in a single nest. Darwin found four nests near Bahía Blanca. Three of these contained twenty-two eggs each, and the other, twenty-seven. Each egg is, by weight, the equivalent of eleven hen's eggs, Darwin computes, "so that we obtained from this one nest [the one of twenty-seven eggs] as much food as 297 hens' eggs would have given."

The mating season begins in July. The young cocks are driven off by the old ones ,and if two old males are left they fight for the hens. Hudson describes one of these fights as follows: "Their battles are conducted in a rather curious manner, the combatants twisting their long necks together like a couple of serpents, and then viciously biting at each other's heads with their beaks; meanwhile they turn round and round in a circle, pounding the earth with their feet, so that where the soil is wet they make a circular trench where they trod."

The mating call of the male rhea is a deep, booming sound, deceptive because it frequently seems as loud at a distance as near at hand, so that it is difficult to tell the location of the performer.

The laying of the eggs is a kind of community project. The twenty to sixty or more eggs are not laid by just one hen. It may be seen that if forty eggs were laid by a single hen the first ones would be decidedly "off color" by the time the last ones had arrived. This is particularly evident when we are told that just one egg is forthcoming every two or three days. At that rate forty eggs by one hen would necessitate a period of three to four months of laying. Not all of the eggs are laid in nests. Very frequently solitary eggs are found here and there on the pampas. These are called *hauchos* by the natives and are never hatched. This odd fact, coupled with the additional one that a large number of eggs are laid in a single nest, caused Darwin a considerable amount of speculation. Apparently, to paraphrase his comments, several females lay in the same nest. A certain female, so it would appear, scoops out a nest and makes the initial contribution. Other females may or may not recognize the right of this particular bird to start proceedings. If the first egg is ignored, it become an *haucho*. Moreover, if the number of eggs in any one nest does not exceed on an average the number laid by a single female in one season, "then there must be as many nests as females."

Darwin was only partly correct in his assumptions. All the females of a flock do lay in a single nest. The number of eggs laid by each hen is a dozen or more, according to Hudson. These go into one nest, and not into a dozen or more as Darwin intimated. If there are several females the cocks become tired of waiting—a not unusual masculine trait—and furiously drive them away so that they may start the brooding of the eggs. In this case the hens, not having finished their egg-laying, drop their eggs here and there on the bare floor of the pampas. These are the *hauchos*. There are, of course, not as many nests as females; but rather just one to each flock.

After the eggs are laid, the males sit on the eggs till they hatch and then look after the young. Hudson says that after the young rheas hatch the males look after them so assiduously that it is dangerous to come near on horseback. With wings spread wide and neck outstretched they charge so suddenly and make such a grotesque appearance "that the tamest horse becomes ungovernable with terror."

According to Beerbohm the period of incubation is twenty to twenty-four days. This is incorrect, both the rhea and the ostrich require about forty-two days. The emu, a relative, incubates fifty-six to sixty-three days, a period longer than that of any other bird. If the weather is inclement, the male may not move from the nest for six to seven days at a time, Beerbohm asserts. In fine weather he grazes for an hour or two each evening. If an egg is broken, or abstracted, in the absence of the male, Beerbohm avers, he becomes very irate and vents his spleen by destroying all the others. "The young run immediately, or shortly after emerging from the shell," Musters writes, "and are covered with a down of greyish black colour on the back, and whitish on the breast and neck. Their cry resembles the syllables *pi, pi, pi,* uttered in a sharp, quick manner. The old male, when any danger appears, feigns to be hurt, like other birds endeavouring to distract the attention of the hunter, in order that his brood may escape by hiding in the grass." How remarkable that this instinctive action customarily inherent in the females of many birds should be just as natural in the male in this case!

Rheas are hunted on every possible occasion by the Indians. Prichard says that the natives of Patagonia kill no other bird at all, in spite of the fact that many others—upland geese, for instance—are abundant. To them, the rheas are invaluable. In addition to "furnishing their most valuable food," Musters points out, "from the sinews of the legs thongs for bolas are constructed; the neck is used as a pouch for salt or tobacco; the feathers are exchanged for tobacco and other necessaries; the grease from the breast and back is tried out and secured in bags formed of the skin (taken off during the spring season, when the females, like all the Patagonian animals except the puma, are thin); the meat is more nourishing and more relished by the Indians than that of any other animal in the country, and the eggs form a staple commodity of food during the months of September, October, and November." The age of the eggs does not matter to the Indians, who eat them in all stages of freshness or staleness.

Dinners on the pampas would frequently be quite meager if the rhea were not at hand to fill the pots. Beerbohm took the pains of setting down the exact menu for a meal, perhaps not typical, yet indicative of the food that was available:

Pot-au-feu (rice, rhea meat, etc.)
Boiled Rhea wings
Rhea steak
Cold Guanaco head
Roast Rhea gizzard, à l'Indienne
Rhea eggs
Custard (rhea eggs, sugar, gin)

Courtesy of Zoological Society of Philadelphia

RHEA

Courtesy of William Beebe

YOUNG HOATZIN

Courtesy of William Beebe

ADULT HOATZINS

Of the items listed, Beerbohm was of the opinion that the "rhea wings were the greatest delicacy, tasting something like turkey." The gizzard, too, had an appeal for him. The thighs were coarser than other parts, being something like horse meat, he concluded. A very fat rhea is a treat to the Indians. Fat is more than a luxury with them—it is a necessary article of diet. This is due, Musters thought, to a complete lack of any farinaceous food. The rhea is always preferred to the guanaco.

The rhea is hunted with dogs and, on horseback, with the bola. The latter method, in the opinion of Hudson, when the horse is fast and well trained, "is unquestionably one of the most fascinating forms of sport ever invented by man." It appealed to Hudson particularly because the rhea has more than an even chance to make good its escape. It is surprisingly fast and, when almost within the reach of the hunter, has a unique method of changing its course very suddenly, much to the chagrin and bewilderment of the pursuer. If the bird is caught at all the hunter must be familiar with its side-stepping tactics and must have unusual dexterity in whirling the bola. The rhea is unusually well adapted to its environment. Its height enables it to detect enemies at a great distance, and its brownish gray color harmonizes admirably with its surroundings. To quote Hudson, "There are few more strangely fascinating sights in nature than that of the old black-necked cock bird, standing with raised agitated wings among the tall plumed grasses and calling together his scattered hens with hollow boomings and long mysterious suspirations, as if a wind high up in the void sky had found a voice."

Cherrie found rheas very common at Descalvados on the Paraguay, sometimes not more than twenty-five yards from his camp. One day he ran across a proud male that was displaying his family of twenty to thirty youngsters. The mother, as is customary, was conspicuous by her absence. Cherrie wanted some chicks to complete a museum group. He thought this a good opportunity to capture some by riding after them. Very soon he came up with the flock, but suddenly, as though by some prearranged signal, they vanished from his sight. Search as he would he could not find a trace of a single one of them. The young had flattened themselves on the ground with outstretched necks, and their color harmonized perfectly with the floor of the pampa, so that it was impossible to find them. After a long search Cherrie had to give it up as a bad job.

Hudson speaks of a unique habit that the rhea has when closely pursued; that of raising one of its wings "vertically, like a great sail—a veritable ship of the wilderness." According to Prichard, Darwin's rhea does not have this custom. Prichard observes, also, that this rhea does not have the curiosity of most of the Patagonian animals. It straightway travels out of sight as soon as it catches a glimpse of man, while most other animals will stand for a brief while, at least, seemingly in no great rush to make their getaway.

Hudson very positively affirms that the rhea chicks show no fear of man. In spite of the fact that the rhea is a very ancient bird that has been hunted for a considerable period of time by the South American savages, he was unable to detect any sign of fear in it. "They would follow me about as if they took me for their parent," he said. As a matter of fact they became so tame that on occasion they were a nuisance. Hudson tells of an old cock that was as tame as any of the domestic animals at a certain estancia. But, by some perverse streak in its mental make-up, it could not tolerate the sight of a "human figure in petticoats." As a result the women of the place could not set foot outside of the house unless they were protected by some of the men.

Hudson expressed the view that the rhea would soon become extinct like the dodo, the auk, and the passenger pigeon. Certainly he was right if the enormous quantity of feathers sold in the South American markets is any indication. Miller told of seeing sixty tons of rhea feathers (plucked chiefly for feather dusters) in a single warehouse in Buenos Aires.

Father Zahm states that in 1909 more than fifty thousand pounds were exported from Uruguay to the United States and Europe. The rhea feathers are in general not nearly so valuable as those of the African ostrich. The price at the time of Beerbohm's visit to South America (1877) was only one to two dollars per pound. At that rate he considered the work of the rhea hunter very nonlucrative.

In certain South American countries the rhea is now protected, and it is not unusual to find native homes in which the bird has become domesticated. As a consequence the rhea may not be exterminated. At least it has a chance of survival, in domestication if not in a wild state. The tame ones are valuable as egg layers, if in no other capacity. Miller spoke of seeing eggs for sale in a small town in the northern Argentine, at forty centavos each. These particular ones came from the nests of wild birds in the Chaco, and not from domesticated birds, he was told.

THE CONDOR

As the condor with ebon pinions extended to their limit soars effortlessly high above the Andean passes, making one huge circle after another, it is to the human eye in every respect a magnificent creature, a true "winged symbol of the Andes." As it is seen seated in majestic solitude on the shelf of a towering cliff, looking down on the world spread out below it "like a priest from a pulpit," the condor appears one of the noblest of birds. Viewed close at hand it cannot be described as either magnificent or noble. It is not attractively garbed; its demeanor is unprepossessing, and its form ungainly. Distance lends enchantment to a far greater degree than with any other bird. The plumage is almost entirely black, as though the bird were in perpetual mourning for the dead over which it performs the last mortal rites each time it feeds. There is a ruff of white feathers which almost surrounds the base of the neck and, in the male in particular, there are a few white feathers on each wing. The head and neck are naked and colored a blood-red which might be symbolic of the gruesome, sanguinary feasts these scavengers enjoy.

The condor *(Vultur gryphus)* is nothing more than an overgrown vulture and, with the possible exception of the California condor, is the largest flying bird in the western hemisphere. It has a magnificent spread of wings said by both Humboldt and Tschudi to measure in the neighborhood of fourteen feet. Tschudi wrote that he measured one which, "from the tip of one wing to the tip of the other was fourteen English feet and two inches." If the German zoologist's measurements were correct this was an exceptionally large one. Estimates of the wing spread usually given by ornithologists at the present time range from eight to ten feet. Murphy shot a huge one on San Gallan, a guano island off the coast of Peru, that measured a fraction of an inch over ten feet from tip to tip and weighed 26½ pounds.

The range of the condor is coextensive with the Andean cordilleras. It is seen from Colombia in the north to the Strait of Magellan in the south. The great forests where heavy rainfalls occur do not attract the condor; it prefers the treeless, barren plateaus, and for that reason is not found along the Pacific coast either in the north or in the south. Only in the desert, coastal regions of Ecuador, Peru, and Chile does this giant among vultures descend from the Andes to seek its provender from the animals associated with the Humboldt Current. To the east of the Andes the condor is unknown except in the Argentine and even there only south of the Rio Negro. So it may be said that the condor strays from its Andean home in two regions only: to the west in Peru and adjacent countries, and to the east in Patagonia; but in neither instance has it strayed far.

The altitudinal range of *Vultur gryphus* is perhaps more interesting than the latitudinal. Climbers of Mt. Everest in the Himalayas have witnessed the lammergeier (a Eurasian bird of prey) sailing through the heavens at an estimated elevation of 25,000 feet. Just what dizzy height the condor reaches in its mountain home is a moot question. The first studies of this bird's excursions toward the stratosphere were made by Humboldt early in the last century. The condor, according to the Baron, "embraces atmospheric strata which are from 10,000 to 19,000 feet above the level of the sea." In another place in his *Views* he stated, in regard to a particular bird he observed, that "the absolute height which the condor reached must therefore be 23,273 feet." The highest peak in the Andes is Mt. Aconcagua, 23,081 feet high. Whether the condors which live in the proximity of this peak ever delight in volplaning in the rarefied atmosphere which exists above it, or whether they ever reach such heights anywhere in the Andes, is uncertain. It is incontestable that they fly higher than any other birds in the western hemisphere.

In Colombia and Ecuador, where heavy rainfalls prevail on the Pacific coast and luxuriant forests cover the western slopes of the Andes, the condors do not descend below an altitude of about 10,000 feet. The altitudinal range here is not exceptional. Farther south on the coast of Peru, though, where the Humboldt Current exerts a desiccating influence and desert conditions obtain, the condors extend their range to sea level. Granted that the condor inhabits the Peruvian Andes to an elevation no higher than 16,000 feet, it still has a perpendicular range of over three miles. The puma probably comes closer to equaling this range than any other American animal, since its footprints have been seen in the snow of the Andes at an elevation between 14,000 and 15,000 feet, and it is known to descend to sea level. The puma, however, would take considerable time in going from the altitude of 15,000 feet to sea level. The condor is able to do this in a relatively short time. Its indifference to altitude and the associated atmospheric pressure is phenomenal when compared with the reaction of other animals to these conditions. Many humans feel uncomfortable at elevations no greater than 7,000 or 8,000 feet, and others suffer intensely at a height of 10,000 feet. An abrupt change from the pressure at sea level to that which exists at 16,000 feet, or vice versa, would prove fatal to a great many animals. And yet the condor can mount from sea level to heights beyond the reach of the human eye, or can drop from above the Peruvian snow line to the level of the pounding surf without evidencing any vertigo, nausea, or *soroche*. Few birds are so much the masters of the air as this superb aeronaut. No one, having seen the effortless grace with which the condor shapes its course, can fail to be impressed with the supremacy it exerts over its aerial environment.

Darwin's description of the flight of the condor is just one of many tributes paid by the naturalists to this wizard of the air. His words are as follows: "Except when rising from the ground, I do not recollect ever having seen one of these birds flap its wings. Near Lima, I watched several for nearly half an hour without once taking off my eyes; they moved in large curves, sweeping in circles, descending and ascending without giving a single flap. If the bird wished to descend, the wings for a moment collapsed; and when expanded with an altered inclination the momentum gained by the rapid descent seemed to urge the bird upwards with the even and steady movement of a paper kite. In the case of any bird soaring, its motion must be sufficiently rapid, so that the action of the inclined surface of its body on the atmosphere may counter-balance its gravity. The force to keep up the momentum of a body cannot be great, and this force is all that is wanted. The movement of the neck and body of the condor, we must suppose, is sufficient for this."

Another champion of the airways is the wandering albatross, and it is only natural that a comparison should be made between it and the condor. This has been done in admirable fashion by Murphy. According to him the albatross is a much swifter flyer than the condor because the latter is almost twice as heavy and has much bulkier flight muscles. On the other hand, the condor with its very broad wings and fanlike tail is much better able to fly with steadiness in a stiff breeze. The albatross, with narrow planes and a tail that is used little in either steering or balancing, has to flap its wings and to bank continuously in a strong breeze. This results in a weaving, interrupted manner of flight.

Vultures are scavengers, "dead-game birds," but the condors do not confine their aliment to carrion. The early Peruvians learned long ago that, in the domestication of the llama and alpaca, they had to contend with these harpies of the Andes; and, centuries later, the white man was to find that the condors on occasion kill lambs, kids, calves, and other young domesticated animals. Many of the yarns about the condor are gross exaggerations. The condor does not kill adult animals of the size of sheep or alpaca and may not attack young ones unless they are helpless or diseased. It never carries away in its talons any animal, unless it be very small, for the feet lack the necessary strength.

Within comparatively recent years the government of Peru has taken an unexpected interest in the condor. One of that republic's chief sources of revenue is guano, a fertilizer of high nitrogen content, produced by the innumerable birds occupying a chain of desert islands off the coast. The government officials have discovered that one of the chief enemies of these guano-producing birds is the condor. Of the birds that contribute to the production of guano, the three outstanding, in the order of their economic importance, are: the *guanay (Phalacrocorax bougainvillei)*, a cormorant; the *piquero (Sula variegata)*, a booby; the *alcatraz (Pelecanus thagus)*, a pelican. The problem confronting the government is the protection of these millions of birds scattered over many islands along a thousand-mile front. To that end war has been declared against all enemies of these birds and against the condor in particular, now considered one of the chief offenders.

The case against the condor is summed up in the observations made by Murphy on several of the guano islands. He found that the condors did their greatest damage by eating the eggs of the cormorants, boobies, and pelicans. He was of the opinion that they sucked the eggs by means of their troughlike tongues since pieces of shell were not mixed with the yolks and albumen in the stomach. On one island (Asia) Murphy found that half of the entire western coast, normally covered by a host of *guanayes,* "had become a waste of empty nests and broken shells, and had been deserted for the season by the parent birds." Many condors were seen here: Murphy counted eighteen in the air at one time. Some of these alighted in the center of a colony, and Murphy was close enough to see that their "bare distended crops hung down like goiters from the weight of stolen eggs within them." The depredations on this island were so severe that he estimated the season's normal increase of *guanayes* had been reduced by some tens of thousands. As a result of the destruction here and elsewhere the guards appointed by the guano commission were ordered to kill all condors that came within gunshot.

Not only are the condors egg-eating, but they kill and eat some birds, diving petrels in particular. In one place Murphy found bloody breast bones and tips of petrel wings scattered far and wide. Later two condors' stomachs were found to contain the bodies of diving petrels; this was only a confirmation of earlier suspicions.

The question whether vultures have a sense of smell has been responsible for a considerable amount of argument, some of it heated, that has covered a period of more than a century. The discussion started in 1826, when a comparatively unknown ornithologist by the name of John James Audubon presented a paper before the Wernerian Society in Edinburgh on the se se of smell in the turkey buzzard *(Vultur aura).* Audubon described his researches on the common American vulture which led him to believe that it had a poorly developed sense of smell, and that this sense played little or no part in the location of food, the eyes being the all-important factor in that connection.

This presentation, which launched Audubon into the world of

controversy, was well received by the Scottish scientists; but not many days were to pass before certain naturalists, who claimed to know their vultures, began taking issue with Audubon's findings. Among these dissenters the most caustic of all was none other than Charles Waterton. In unmistakable phraseology he made it known to the world at large that Audubon's discoveries were at decided variance with what he knew to be the truth about the olfactory powers of vultures. He had lived with these feathered scavengers in British Guiana for many years and he knew, even if Audubon did not, that vultures could smell, and did smell. Waterton was supported in his views by the eminent English anatomist of that time, Professor Owen. After carefully dissecting the nasal region of the American vulture Owen declared that the olfactory centers and associated nerves were well developed, indicating that the bird must have the ability to smell.

Audubon, somewhat bewildered by the debate he had stirred up abroad, returned to America deeming it advisable to repeat his experiments. This time he determined not to rely on his own findings but to enlist the services of some other well-known scientist. To that end he was fortunate in gaining the assistance of Reverend John Bachman, a South Carolinian naturalist of recognized merit. Bachman, before proceeding with his experiments, secured six gentlemen as witnesses, and they stood by to watch the proceedings.

The experiment was a very simple one. Bachman covered some highly odoriferous flesh with a thin canvas cloth and then strewed some fresh pieces of meat over the top. The vultures immediately ate the meat on top of the canvas; but the offal underneath it, only an eighth of an inch from their noses, they seemed unable to detect. A small hole was next torn in the covering, following which the vultures immediately discovered the decaying flesh under it. The same experiment was repeated with identical results.

A written statement was now prepared by Bachman with the affixed signatures of the six spectators, which was to settle this matter for a full century at least, and to vindicate Audubon completely.

Only a few years were now to elapse before another naturalist became interested in this subject. This naturalist was at the time in Valparaiso, Chile; his name was Charles Darwin, and his subject was the great vulture of that region, the condor. Darwin discovered in Valparaiso a certain garden where there were kept alive some twenty or thirty condors; and, being familiar with the heated argument which had followed Audubon's pronouncement, he determined to try similar experiments with these birds. The condors were all tied in a row along a stone wall and Darwin took a piece of meat, after wrapping it well with paper, and paraded back and forth before the condors with the parcel in his hand. The birds showed no interest whatsoever in either Darwin or the package of meat. Next, Darwin threw the flesh onto the ground in front of a large male condor. The bird threw a casual glance in the direction of the parcel but paid no more attention to it. Darwin then pushed the meat closer to the bird, "until at last he touched it with his beak; the paper was then instantly torn off with fury, at the same moment, every bird in the long row began struggling and flapping its wings." Although this experiment would tend to show that the condor has, at the best, a very poorly developed sense of smell, Darwin concluded by writing: "The evidence in favor of and against the acute smelling powers of carrion-vultures is singularly balanced."

Even though the evidence was considered "singularly balanced" by Darwin, the majority of biologists continued to consider it conclusive. They did not believe the vulture could locate its food by smell. And that was the way the matter stood for a hundred years. It is true that now and then a naturalist came forth with an article tending to show that the vultures really had a well developed olfactory sense, but these publications caused little or no stir in ornithological circles. The consensus was that the experiments of Audubon, confirmed by those of Bachman, settled the matter once and for all. In a recent work, *Birds of America* (1936), edited by T. Gilbert Pearson, we find that the turkey vulture *(Cathartes aura septentrionalis)* "exists on all forms of carrion, being guided to its food by a sense of sight—not smell."

The most recent experiments on the sense of smell in vultures were performed by no less an authority on birds than Frank M. Chapman, curator of birds in the American Museum of Natural History. For several years Chapman has been spending two or three of the winter months on Barro Colorado Island, in the Canal Zone. On one of his first visits there, he discovered a dead monkey in the dense forest which covers most of the island. The vultures had found the monkey first, and under conditions which made Chapman suspicious that they had found it through their sense of smell. There were two main reasons for thinking so: first, the body of the monkey harmonized so well with the ground on which it lay that Chapman did not think the vultures flying far above the island could see it, however keen their eyesight; second, there was such a dense canopy of leaves overhead that it was difficult for the sun to look through, much less the vultures. Yet, there undoubtedly was a chance that the vultures had discovered the body without the aid of an olfactory sense.

On top of this discovery there soon was another. A vulture found a small bit of meat in the dead of night which had been used as bait for a camera-trap. The evidence for this discovery is a picture of the vulture in the act of taking the meat; a picture which the vulture took of itself. But in this case, as well as the foregoing, Chapman couldn't possibly be positive that the food hadn't been discovered through a sense of sight rather than smell.

Sometime after this photographic event a coati died, and Chapman determined to revive with it the series of experiments started by Audubon a century before. He took the body to a small shack on the island that had no windows and only one door, tied it up near the roof where there was no chance of its being seen, and then left the shack, closing the door. Before the day ended four or five vultures had landed on the roof of the shack and others had circled low over the building, apparently unable to locate the source of the scent.

The next morning the body of the coati was taken from the house, placed on the ground near by, and covered with several thicknesses of mosquito netting. Some of the vultures showed an interest by circling about, but not nearly so much as they had shown the day before. None of the birds landed on the ground, and the hidden body was unmolested, even though the odor was more apparent to human nostrils than on the day before. The results, then, for these two days were contradictory.

A year later another coati was found dead, and Chapman placed it under a covering of dead grass. The first day the body was unmolested. The next day, though, the vultures discovered it, and when Chapman arrived on the scene one bird was pulling the grass away while another stood close by. The remainder of this day Chapman spent in moving the carcass from one point to another. Each time it was moved, the body was well covered; but the buzzards persisted in finding it.

"The positive results obtained by these tests," Chapman wrote, "call for little comment. No one who saw the Buzzards coursing to and fro in increasingly short turns, alighting and going on foot direct to the invisible object, the odor from which had attracted them, could doubt that they were led only by their nose. It is the negative results that call for explanation."

The above evidence was published in *My Tropical Air Castle* quite a few years ago. In Chapman's most recent book, *Life in an Air Castle,* he describes additional experiments that were performed on Barro Colorado Island with the vultures. These tend to prove even more conclusively than his earlier experiments that the buzzards on that island depend more upon their nostrils than upon their eyes in locating the dead carcasses of animals.

The location of a dead animal, either by smell or by vision, often leads to the undoing of the condor. This bird is much sought for its feathers, which go to foreign countries for the adornment of Vanity Fair. Since man cannot follow the condor into its aerial abode he must fall back upon subterfuge in order to capture it; he must induce the bird to leave its home in the air, or on some inaccessible crag, and come to a carefully chosen location on the ground. To do this the native condor hunter may build a palisade of stakes, on the inside of which he leaves the carcass of some large animal. The dead body is soon found by the condors, which drop onto it from a high elevation. After they have surfeited themselves they attempt to fly away but cannot, for in order to launch themselves into the air they, like an airplane, need a runway of some length. The hunter, who has been watching the progress of events from a hidden retreat near by, now runs into the enclosure and either clubs the birds to death or catches them alive with a lasso.

A clever variant of the above procedure is to spread a net about the dead animal. After the condors forgather the hunter pulls a cord and ensnares them. That the condor is far from being rare in certain Andean regions is proved by the fact that a hunter known to Chapman captured sixty-four in one throw of the net. He was an Italian from Mendoza, and laid claim to being the champion of all condor hunters. He told Chapman that he had killed more than sixteen thousand of these vultures in his life. The birds were destroyed for the large wing and tail feathers, which were shipped, for the most part, to France. The price had been as high as twenty dollars for each set of eighty feathers but, because of the World War, had dropped about 50 per cent; and he told Chapman, with commendable spirit, that he refused to hunt such magnificent birds for such meager emolument.

Just what laws, if any, the South American countries will formulate for the protection of the condor remains to be seen. As we have noted, it destroys the guano-producing birds and occasionally kills small domesticated animals. But it is first and foremost a scavenger, and should be protected. As is the case with many birds, its good qualities outweigh its bad ones. If it should be exterminated, the South American people would live to mourn its passing.

THE HOATZIN

AMONG the bird oddities of this planet the hoatzin *(Opisthocomus hoazin)* stands alone, a singularly strange uncomely form about which little was known beyond ornithological circles until the significant researches and writings of Beebe introduced it to the world at large.

The hoatzin is an antique. On the surface of things it should be a fossil; but some strange sequence of events has seen to it that this bird still survives. In its case evolution has been at a standstill for untold centuries. The hoatzin is a relic of the past when birds were only partly birds and reptiles were in their heyday; when mammals were struggling for ascendancy and the genus Homo was not yet. There is no bird living that is such a synthesis of contrasts. It bears a covering of feathers, as all birds do, yet its wings are armed with curved claws, strangely reptilian; it spends most of its life in trees, where it secures its food and builds its nests, like other birds, yet it is practically incapable of progression on the ground; it would have been appropriate as a contemporary of Archaeopteryx, of ancient Mesozoic times, yet it is now a part of the modern fauna, millions of years removed from the Age of Reptiles; in some respects it is the most unattractive of birds, yet it compels attention and has become internationally famous among ornithologists.

The hoatzin, inelegantly called stinkbird, is about the size of a carrier pigeon. The body in both sexes is olive-colored above and yellowish below, with a long tail tipped with saffron. The head bears a high comblike crest of loose, yellowish feathers, an ornament that is of aid in quick identification. The crest is not erectile and retains the same position whether the bird is at rest or alarmed.

The nests are platforms of sticks and twigs loosely fastened together and are almost invariably located over water; and several nests may be found within a small acreage. It is thought that these are occupied, with little or no repair, year after year. Most of them are located only a few feet above the surface of the water, but an occasional one may be up thirty or forty feet. Both male and female help in the construction of the nest, in which most often just two eggs are laid. Sometimes there are three, and rarely four. The eggs are cream-colored with reddish brown spots. In British Guiana, according to Beebe, there are two nesting seasons —April and November.

The hoatzins are said to be most active at sunrise and sunset, when they are inordinately noisy, announcing their presence to the world by loud screeching or raucous notes unpleasant to the human ear. In the hotter parts of the day they withdraw to the cooler, protected regions and, like most tropical birds, are quiet. Frequently they are vocal at night, especially moonlit nights, when they even come out to feed.

Although helpless on the ground, these strange birds are perfectly at home in the water and can dive and swim with the facility of a grebe. They prefer the bushes and trees that border streams and lagoons. In British Guiana they are found most commonly inhabiting an arum known locally as mucka-mucka and a thorn called bundurí pimpler. These plants form a narrow ribbon of growth along the streams and have their bases covered, at least part of the day, by water.

Hoatzins are among the most sedentary of birds. In fact they are found where they had nested the season before, and seasons before that. Their flight is so feeble that they have been seen to fail miserably while trying to negotiate distances as short as fifty to sixty feet. In such cases they made forced landings on the ground and resumed their flight after resting. Sometimes after flying from one tree to another they are too exhausted to balance themselves; they fall over and hang suspended by the toes. In scrambling through the trees from limb to limb they flutter awkwardly as if one wing were fractured, advancing with the aid of both feet and wings. The flight feathers are said to be employed in somewhat the same manner as the wing claws in the young. As a result these wing feathers, and the tail feathers too, become definitely frayed and broken off. Schomburgk noted the soiled condition of the feathers but was in error when he stated that it came from the birds' trailing them on the ground.

Although unable to fly long distances these lizard birds are well adapted to life in the trees. One adaptation was early recognized by Bates. Whereas the hind toe in most birds is placed above the level of the front ones, it is situated on the same plane in the hoatzin, thus enabling the bird to grasp the branches more firmly.

It might be only natural to assume, from the persistence of these birds through the centuries, that they are admirably fitted to their environment. This does not seem to be the case. As a result of their inadequate powers of flight and lack of physical prowess they have a severe struggle for existence. Their enemies are not numerous; but there are caimans in the waters beneath them all too ready for a feathered collation, and various aquatic snakes and fish occasionally exact a free meal. Now and then predaceous birds drop into their midst and depart with one of their number. They are so tame that man can approach within a few feet before they take alarm.

One important factor, perhaps the most important one, in their perpetuation, is the preternaturally strong odor that the bodies of these avians exude. This was compared by Bates to musk combined with the smell of wet hides. It is on account of this pervading effluvium that the natives call the hoatzin "stinkbird." The exhalation from a flock may be detected at a considerable distance if the wind is right; and according to Schomburgk it remains with museum specimens for several years. The odor reminded Beebe of a circus. As he analyzed it, it is a compound of sawdust, peanuts, elephants and other strange animals found under the canvas tops.

Because of this unusually potent emanation the natives never eat the hoatzin, and it may well be that other animals are similarly repelled by its flesh. As Bates once suggested, "If it be as unpalatable to carnivorous animals as it is to man the immunity from persecution which it would thereby enjoy would account for its existing in such great numbers throughout the country."

Whether it exists in "such great numbers throughout the country" may be open to question. It is fairly common in places near the coast in Venezuela and the Guianas and is found sporadically south to the Amazon valley and Bolivia. André and others observed it in the Orinoco delta; Schomburgk saw it on the Takutú in southern British Guiana, where there was a flock of several hundred, and Bates along the Tocantins at Vista Alegre. Miller found it on the upper Orinoco not far from Esmeraldas, again on the Gy-Paraná in northwestern Brazil and still again on the Río Chaparé in Bolivia. In every case the hoatzin has been found in proximity to water. It may be that it is more abundant near New Amsterdam on the Berbice and along the lower reaches of the Abary River, in both of which places it has been found commonly. However, without information as to its prevalence in the interior, a definite statement cannot be made. The discovery of the hoatzin by naturalists in such widely separated places suggests that the bird is not uniformly scattered over its range; that there are many conspicuous gaps in its dispersal.

Even more noteworthy is the extent of the range. How is it possible for such a sedentary creature, of feeble powers of flight, to be distributed over such a great territory? It has not only a lack of aerial ability but an inherent disinclination to travel. In the face of these facts it is a matter of surprise to find its range extending from ten degrees north of the line to twenty degrees south. The hoatzin might conceivably travel short distances downstream on grass islands that break their moorings and float away toward the sea; but grass islands do not float upstream. Furthermore, close to two thousand miles separate the Guiana hoatzins from the Bolivia hoatzins. Is it to be presumed that the hoatzins at one time had strong powers of flight that enabled them to spread over nearly all of northern South America, and that they have managed to persist here and there in this vast area even though their flying ability has been subsequently lost?

It is through a study of the young, not the adult, hoatzin that the species has come into prominence. After hatching, the nestling is revealed as an ugly, featherless, long-necked creature that is almost helpless. In these respects it differs not at all from numerous other altricial birds. It does differ decidedly in certain of its habits, and particularly in the possession of three saurian-like claws on each wing that are sufficiently developed for use in locomotion. Within a very short time after it is hatched, even before it puts on its first coat of feathers, it is able to clamber slowly through the trees, using the claws as locomotor organs.

After a while these lizardlike claws are covered by feathers; but they are not lost in the adult. It is said that they are shed from time to time, just as the feathers are, to be replaced by new ones.

Hoatzins, young and old, feed chiefly on the vegetation nearest at hand. The young leaves of the bundurí pimpler and the mucka-mucka appear to be highly relished by hoatzins in northern British Guiana. Before the mother bird feeds the young she eats an unusually large supply of leaves that pass into a copious rumen or false stomach. When this is full she flies to the nest and proceeds to feed the young in a very singular manner. She opens her mouth wide, and the partially digested leaves rise from the depths below by regurgitation. The young now introduces its beak into the expanded oral orifice of the mother and pecks away at the food as it comes up, lavalike, to the pharyngeal crater, until the feeding period, of some ten to twenty minutes' duration, is over.

It has already been pointed out that the hoatzin nest is almost without exception over water. If the young are disturbed at any time the reason for this location becomes apparent. On one occasion Beebe discovered a nest containing a young bird, some twelve feet above the water, and sent his colored helper to get it. As the negro approached closer and closer the baby hoatzin was seen to clamber onto the rim of its nest, where it perched, swaying awkwardly back and forth on legs that were far from steady. It then climbed slowly, using toes and wing claws, until it occupied a perch a short distance from the nest. It was very young, its feathers not over half an inch in length; and its experience of the world till now must have been quite meager. Certainly this large ebony creature slowly approaching was the first object it had seen that could be catalogued under the heading of foe. The hoarse calls shrieked at the intruder by the fledgling's parents probably informed it that danger was near, but there was nothing in their notes of alarm to tell it how to act. As the colored boy came almost within reach the young hoatzin suddenly leaned forward for an instant and then with ease and assurance dived straight into the water twelve feet below, as gracefully as a booby drops from the air high above into the cold waters of the Humboldt Current for its matutinal meal of fish. There had been no visible manifestation of fear on the part of the youthful hoatzin;

as danger approached it climbed from its nest and dived as skillfully and fearlessly as though the act had been rehearsed thousands of times. And the act had been rehearsed before; of this we feel confident. But—the actors were those of its kin that had gone before, the stage was another tropical stream, and the enemy was probably some animal known now, if at all, by petrified bones. How many thousands of years have passed since the first of the hoatzins evaded an enemy by diving from its nest into the comparative safety of the water below? How many dives were necessary, how many years were to pass, how many generations were involved before this habit became a part of the bird itself, became instinctive? Or did the instinctive maneuver originate in this manner? Perhaps it arose suddenly through some chemical changes in the genes and time was not an element to be considered at all. In any event the swan dive of the baby hoatzin adds one more puzzle to the already long list of animal reactions which we evade explaining by calling them instinctive.

After making the leap the hoatzin swam under water, using not its feet but its wings, until it came to the shore several feet away. Again it dived and came up twenty feet away. It then slowly climbed out of the water and methodically made its way back to the tree and the nest from which it had made its escape.

Although practically all of the nests are over the water, Beebe found two or three so located that at low tide there was only mud below. In one of these was a single young hoatzin. What would this bird do if an enemy approached? Once again the negro was sent on his mission. As he came close the fledgling climbed to the edge of the nest, exhorted no doubt by the cries of its parent, and unhesitatingly dived into the ooze below. Its head sank into the mud, and for a few brief minutes it fought to release itself with legs wildly kicking in all directions. Finally it wriggled free and struggled to the water a short distance away, where it promptly disappeared, apparently none the worse for its experience. What an unbelievably perfect example of the impelling power of an age-old instinct! From this episode we are led to believe that nothing could have prevented this earthward plunge; that if a yawning caiman muzzle had been below the bird it would have dived just as promptly and as inevitably.

Thus these nestlings, hardly out of their swaddling clothes, are able to climb trees with the claws on their wings, to dive with skill, and to swim with agility and grace. On the ground their toes curl up, the body pitches forward, and their movements are awkward and ineffective. In the trees the toes fasten around limbs, anchoring the birds securely, while the claws on the wings pull them farther along toward their destination.

In diving they invariably hit the water headfirst. In swimming, if the head is above the water, the feet become the agents of propulsion. If the body is entirely submerged the wings take over the locomotor duties, sweeping the creature forward with strong, regular strokes.

What a story might be told if it were only possible to relate how this strange bird, which is not even closely related to any other existing species, has managed to persist throughout the centuries!

TOUCANS

THE average person is accustomed to birds with extremely long legs, vermiform necks, and bills of varying shapes and dimensions, but is never quite prepared for the first look at a toucan with its perfectly enormous bananalike beak. This mandibular structure is so large, so out of proportion to the rest of the body, that at first glance nothing is visible but beak. It projects from the head like the snout on a proboscis monkey and adorns each of the seventy existing species. The only bird comparable to the toucan in its beak is the hornbill of the old world. The latter, however, is confined to the eastern hemisphere while the toucan is found only in tropical America. It is no wonder that the bill on a toucan is such an impelling structure, for it is sometimes as long as the body of the bird itself. If the toucan were five or six times as large as it really is, this oral member would not be proportionately small. In one form *(Rhamphastos toco),* described by Bates, the bill is approximately seven inches long and more than two inches wide; in both form and size it resembles a banana so much that the natives call the bird *tocano pacova—pacova* being their name for banana.

Although the size of the beak exposes the toucan to considerable ridicule, the remarkable coloration makes partial amends. The predominant colors in the various forms are red, blue, yellow, orange, and black; and none of these is subdued. Some idea of this elaborate, oral embellishment is given us by Waterton, describing the beak of one of the Guiana toucans as follows: "On the ridge of the upper mandible a broad stripe of most lovely yellow extends from the head to the point; a stripe of the same breadth though somewhat deeper yellow, falls from it at right angles next the head down to the edge of the mandible; then follows a black stripe, half as broad, falling at right angles from the ridge, and running narrower along the edge to within half an inch of the point. The rest of the mandible is a deep bright red. The lower mandible has no yellow, its black and red are distributed in the same manner as on the upper one, with the difference, that there is black about an inch from the point. The stripe corresponding to the deep yellow stripe on the upper mandible is sky blue."

Although the bill is inordinately large, it is not heavy. From appearances, one might wonder how the bird could support its head. In that there is no difficulty, however, for the structure of this organ combines size with both strength and lightness. The distal parts are very thin, and those nearest the head, while thick, are full of air-filled cavities.

The purpose of any bird's bill nearly always becomes evident after an examination of its habits. The recurved beak of the hawk is for tearing flesh, the capacious bill of the pelican for a dip net or scoop with which to capture fish, the daggerlike beak of the heron for spearing fish, and the massive bill of the parrot for cracking nuts. However, the function of the toucan's bill is not definitely known. Waterton could not think of any useful function at all it might have. He contended that it could not be a defensive organ because the toucan is not preyed upon by any of the South American birds; and even if it were, the beak is of such texture that it would be of little service. Neither, he thought, could it be an offensive organ because the toucan has such an abundant food supply throughout the seasons that it never has to dispute its rights with other animals.

Rusby was of the opinion that the principal use of the bill is to protect it against its many enemies, especially when the bird is on its nest. "Any predatory animal must face this formidable beak if seeking to force an entrance to the nest," Rusby declared, "and I know by experience that the toucan can use it with great quickness and effect." Rusby kept one as a pet for some time. It would invariably strike his hand if he was careless, and the force of the blow was sufficient to bring blood. He said that the bird preferred fruit to any other food but was fond of cockroaches and other insect life, and that the bill was serviceable in picking them out of corners and crevices.

Bates wrote that if the function of the beak is for killing small birds, as some writers had claimed, it is poorly constructed for the purpose. Its ill contrived shape, spongy structure, and want of power in seizing objects, all indicated to him a lack of fitness for

Courtesy of Zoological Society of Philadelphia

RED-BILLED TOUCAN

Courtesy of Zoological Society of Philadelphia

COCK-OF-THE-ROCK

such a function. It was his opinion, on the contrary, that fruit is the chief food of toucans and any use that the bill has must be in connection with its mode of obtaining it. Chapman wrote that, regardless of the purpose for which the bill was devised, its size and length increase the radius of the toucan's reach.

Although the exact function of the beak is still obscure, ornithologists are inclined to believe that it is long in order that the bird may reach food from small branches too light to support its weight. And that it is large instead of slender as a result of the kind of food it eats.

Both Humboldt and Edwards were told by the natives that toucans habitually throw their food into the air and then catch it in their wide-open beaks as it falls. They thought this peculiar mode of ingestion necessary because of the shape and weight of the bill. Neither of the two naturalists just mentioned observed this practice; nor did Waterton, Schomburgk, Bates, or any of the other naturalists observe it so far as we know. It was actually witnessed, though, by one writer—Guise, the author of *Six Years in Bolivia.* Guise had a tame toucan which he kept for a period of some weeks, and he was much interested in its actions, some of which were, for a time at least, quite inexplicable. To quote:

"He had an uncanny aptitude for catching in his large and gaily-colored beak any small object that was thrown at him. I would toss a box of matches to him when he was, apparently, engrossed in some other matter, but I never knew him to miss. The reason for this knack puzzled me for a long time until one day I suddenly turned the corner of the fowl-house, and found, in front of the open door, Mr. Toucan, with a hen's egg, which he was throwing up into the air and catching, until at last it broke and the contents slid down his throat. So absorbed was he in his juggling that it was not until he had thrown away the empty eggshell and had smacked his beak appreciatively, that he became aware of my presence. The speed with which he immediately took his departure indicated that he was aware that his action might be viewed unfavorably.

"A few days later the toucan was making a tour of inspection of the yard. Wishing to see how he would behave, I placed an egg on the ground, where he was sure to find it, and hid myself.

He came hopping along jauntily, until, rounding a corner, he perceived the egg lying a few feet away. The bird stopped dead, cocked his head on one side, looked here and there and then up in the air, in a detached manner, as though he were studying the weather. The coast was apparently clear, so he hopped right up to the egg, gazed at it speculatively, passed on for a short distance, and again surveyed the neighborhood. No one in sight! Good! His air of indifference was now cast off, and briskly and boldly he retraced his steps and picked up the treasure-trove. Up into the air he threw it and caught it, without cracking the shell; a second time he made the attempt, without success. I now thought the experiment had gone far enough, for eggs were scarce. I emerged from my hiding place and confronted the villain, who, egg in bill, looked at me for a moment in astonishment, then unceremoniously dropped his booty, and bolted."

The toucan is not a strong flier; it "travels with heavy laborious flight from bough to bough," according to Bates. The other naturalists who have expressed an opinion (with one exception) speak of the flight of the toucan as being feeble, or jerky, or ungainly. Rusby, however, described one species which "flew with an oscillatory up-and-down movement, but with intense velocity; so rapidly, indeed, as to give origin to a peculiar humming or whistling sound as it passed through the air." Unfortunately Rusby did not mention the name of this particular form. Bigg-Wither states that the toucans scream only when sitting; that because of their feeble flight they endanger themselves if they advertise their presence while in the air. Parrots act in exactly the opposite way, he added.

Even though toucans may not be vocal when flying, they are very noisy birds and have a variety of calls. A Guianan form *(Rhamphastos erythrorhynchus)* described by Waterton, made a sound "like the clear yelping of a puppy dog." This note must be a common one, for Bates, Beebe, and others have written of it in like manner. The rare curl-crested toucan emits a peculiar call that to Bates' ear resembled the croaking of frogs. The name "toucan" is apparently onomatopoetic; Edwards and others wrote of toucans that were persistent in their loud cry of *Tucáno*. Apparently none of these cries fall upon the ears any too pleasantly;

at least they were not at all pleasing to Friel, who contended that the toucans "screeched with the harmony of a rusty gate."

Whitney found that nothing was more incongruous to him in the Amazon forests than the many highly colored birds with notes so unmusical. He wrote that he could never get over his bewilderment that in a country "where there is so much to please the eye there should be so little agreeable to the ear."

Waterton asserted that the toucans are social, but not gregarious. They do apparently lack the provocation that actuates most social birds to fly in close formation, although many of them are often seen together. Their general method of flying is one after another. If a toucan puts in an appearance one may be reasonably certain that another will follow in about a second, until several have passed.

The rarest and most beautiful of the toucans, according to Wallace, is the curl-crested toucan *(Beauharnaisia)*. It is seldom seen by the traveler or naturalist, Miller stated, and he considered himself fortunate when he located a flock on the Bolivian Río Chaparé. They kept to the tops of the trees and were constantly on the alert. Bates was more fortunate. He found them in large flocks at Ega. He thought them the most curious of all the toucans with the head feathers modified into black, horny plates that were "curled up at the ends, resembling shavings of steel or ebony wood: the curly crest being arranged on the crown in the form of a wig." One day Bates shot one of these from the top of a tall tree. It fell to the ground, and as he started to pick it up it began to scream loudly. "In an instant, as if by magic," Bates wrote, "the shady nook seemed alive with these birds, although there was certainly none visible when I entered the thicket. They descended towards me, hopping from bough to bough, some of them swinging on the loops and cables of woody lianas, and all croaking and fluttering their wings like so many furies. Had I had a long stick in my hand I could have knocked several of them over. After killing the wounded one I rushed out to fetch my gun, but, the screaming of their companion having ceased, they remounted the trees, and before I could reload, every one of them had disappeared."

It is generally stated that the nests of the toucans are found in holes in hollow trees, although Edwards wrote that the only one he saw "was in the fork of a large tree over the water upon the Amazon." Rusby wrote, "The bird nests in cavities of tree trunks, and when the time comes for the female to sit on her eggs, the male carefully masons her in with clay, leaving an opening just large enough for him to pass in her food."

When Beebe made his first trip to South America in 1908 he noticed, on several occasions, that the toucans were in threes. After careful observation through a pair of binoculars, he became convinced that the three consisted always of two adults and one young, and that just one young one is raised. A few years later, after the establishment of the Tropical Research Station at Kartabo under the auspices of the New York Zoological Society, Beebe continued his studies of the toucan. Up to March 30, 1916, "no definite account existed of the finding of the nests or the eggs and young of any species of these birds," Beebe wrote in *Tropical Wild Life*. On that date he, assisted by Hartley and Howes, cut down a tall forest tree in which they suspected the red-billed toucan *(Rhamphastos monilis)* of having a nest. They were right in their suspicions—there was a nest in the tree and it yielded two pinkish white eggs. This was the first discovery of a nest of which there is a definite record, according to Beebe. Two weeks later, April 16, they cut another suspected tree and in it were two young of the black-necked araçari *(Pteroglossus aracari)* and these were, Beebe said, the first young toucans ever in the hands of an ornithologist.

Toucans are readily tamed and make very amusing pets. Edwards wrote that they "are exceedingly familiar, playful birds, capable of learning as many feats as any of the parrots, with the exception of talking." Bigg-Wither kept one as a pet, and it became quite companionable. It, like the one Guise had, was very adept in catching in its beak food or anything else thrown within its reach. It was so intelligent it learned the hours of his meals and appeared with a punctuality that was a constant surprise to him.

"Its powers of digestion were abnormally rapid," he wrote, "and it was consequently always hungry. Though it quickly became friendly and even intimate with any person that took notice of it, and was kind to it, yet it was very easily offended, and the offence used to rankle in its little bosom for many hours after its committal. Once I threw a bit of charred wood at it at breakfast time, which it caught as usual, but when it tasted the gritty flavor of the charcoal it screamed angrily, hopped quickly out of the rancho, and did not reappear till roosting-time, when it went sulkily up to its perch on one of the cross timbers of the hut, without uttering its customary salutations.

"The manner in which it prepared itself to go to sleep was worth observing. Having first arranged itself comfortably on its perch, with feathers well puffed out, its next operation was to throw up its tail with a sudden jerk into a perpendicular position. This feat being accomplished, it would pause for a few moments to take a last look round the rancho, and then, if all was quiet, with a dexterous turn and dive, both beak and head would disappear entirely under the wing and puffed-out feathers of the back, the bird now presenting the appearance of a perfectly round ball of feathers. In this position he would pass the night, sleepy but not generally asleep; for if I called him by his name, he would always answer by a little noise like a grunt. If I touched him in the night without first calling to him, he would start up broad awake. If, however, I spoke to him first, and then touched him, he would not move, but only give vent to a kind of purring grunt, which probably meant 'Can't you leave a fellow alone?' Toucans are far more intelligent and amusing birds than parrots, as far as my experience goes."

HUMMINGBIRDS

THERE are more than five hundred species of hummingbirds known to science, and each and every one of these is a resident of the western hemisphere; not a single member of this extraordinary group is found in any part of the old world.

Without a reasonable doubt more species will be discovered, for much of the western part of Brazil, and those portions of Colombia, Ecuador, Peru, and Bolivia east of the Andes have yet to be visited by a bird collector; and in these regions hummingbirds are especially numerous. Ecuador—a country about the size of the state of Texas—would seem to be the center of the universe so far as hummingbirds are concerned; for, according to Wetmore, one hundred forty-eight kinds have already been described from there.

It is estimated that there are on earth approximately fourteen thousand described species of birds. Simple arithmetic reveals that there is one species of hummingbird for twenty-seven of all other species. In Ecuador, where the avifauna is richer than in any other part of the world—nearly fifteen hundred species are recognized—there is, by the same method of calculation, one species of hummingbird for nine of all others. This superiority in number of species is almost as great in Colombia, where over one hundred forms are known; and, while there is a gradual reduction in Central American countries, there are many places where they are abundant. For instance, Belt gave it as his opinion that there were as many hummingbirds in Nicaragua as all the other birds put together.

The range of hummingbirds extends from Alaska (61 degrees North) to Tierra del Fuego (55 degrees South). The rufous hummingbird *(Selasphorus rufus)*, a normal summer resident of the Pacific and Rocky Mountain states, occurs as far north as Alaska; while *Trochilus forficatus*, according to Darwin, "is found over a space of 2,500 miles on the west coast [of South America], from the dry country of Lima, to the forests of Tierra del Fuego—where it may be seen flitting about in snow-storms."

The altitudinal distribution is fully as interesting as the latitudinal, for the dispersal of hummingbirds in equatorial America is from sea level to a point just below the level of perpetual snow. On Mt. Chimborazo this level is at approximately 16,000 feet, and hummingbirds have been observed at that altitude on this famous Andean peak. Four distinct altitudinal zones are recognized for the Andes: the tropical zone, extending from sea level to an altitude of 3,500 to 5,000 feet; the subtropical zone, reaching above the tropical to an elevation of 8,000 to 9,500 feet; the temperate zone, extending from the subtropical to an elevation of 11,000 to 12,000 feet; and the paramo or *puna* stretching from the temperate to the lower limits of snow at an elevation of 15,000 to 16,000 feet. The limits of these zones are surprisingly sharp, and each one has its quota of hummingbirds. Chapman wrote, "I have passed from one zone to another and experienced an almost complete change in bird-life within five minutes."

More than a century ago Humboldt pointed out that, as one travels from the equator, the mean temperature decreases about one degree Fahrenheit with each degree of latitude. In the ascent of the Andes it has been shown that the mean temperature decreases about one degree Fahrenheit with each three hundred feet. According to this reckoning, three hundred feet of altitude is the approximate equivalent of sixty-seven miles of latitude. Those birds living in the temperate zone of the Andes at an elevation of twelve thousand feet, although right on the equator, would find the latitudinal equivalent of this elevation some twenty-five hundred miles away either to the north or to the south.

Those hummingbirds that have been discovered in the temperate zone of Ecuador in all probability came from the zones immediately below them, although it is possible that they had their origin in the temperate zone of Chile or Argentina, in which case they simply increased their altitude as they moved north.

The most noteworthy feature of this distribution is the unusual degree of inflexibility manifest in the altitudinal range of birds. In some cases there is an overlapping of ranges; but the number of birds that spend the entire period of their existence within the narrow confines—three to four thousand feet—of their zone is surprisingly large. It is also worthy of comment that those hummingbirds which, in the past, extended their range from the tropical to the temperate zone—a distance of only some ten thousand feet—made an altitudinal journey as profound as though they had traveled from Peru to Arizona.

In spite of their abundance in the tropics, and their ability to range far to the north and to the south, the number of species of hummingbirds in temperate regions is not large. Only about a score of forms have been noted in the United States and Canada, and at least half of these are not found north of the Mexican border states. Just one species, the ruby-throated hummingbird, is indigenous to the states east of the Mississippi. It is equally surprising to learn that, as Hudson has pointed out, only about one dozen species are found in the Argentine.

This brief review of the distribution of hummingbirds is sufficient to show that they love the proximity of the equator; not more than 5 or 6 per cent of the total number of species has indicated a preference for nesting grounds in temperate climes. Even these return to the tropics or subtropics each fall after the young have been hatched and cared for to maturity. It is possible that the tropics were the original home of these few, and they moved either north or south with the sun in order to discover safer nesting sites and a greater quantity of food. The autumnal flight of the ruby-throated hummingbird to Central America may then be a journey to its former home.

It is not generally realized just how small hummingbirds are. The tiniest of the five hundred or more forms, in fact the smallest bird in the world, is Helena's hummingbird *(Calypte helenae)*, an inhabitant of Cuba, the weight of which is only about one gram. If that statement of fact is not sufficiently impressive, it may be pointed out that it would take something like five hundred of these feathered corpuscles to weigh one pound. From the tip of their pointed beaks to the end of their tails they are only two and one-half inches in length. Since both tail and beak are fairly long, the head, neck, and body together measure slightly less than an inch; and over half of this is probably neck. A large percentage of all the hummingbirds are not so very much larger than this species. The largest species of all is the giant hummingbird *(Patagona gigas)* found in southern South America, which measures eight and a half inches in length.

Hummingbirds vary tremendously in the detail of form. The beak is no more than one-half inch in length in some species and is fully five inches long in others; the sword-bearer *(Docimastes ensifera)* has a beak that is longer than the rest of the body. The greater number of hummingbirds have bills that are practically straight, yet the sicklebill carries a beak so strongly curved that it forms one-third of a circle.

The head is frequently adorned with a neck frill, pendent beard, or crest resulting in unusual effects. These ornamentations are generally associated with the males, for in hummingbirds there is pronounced sexual dimorphism. The tufts that grace the head may be erected in some cases and consist of elongate, brilliantly colored, and oddly shaped feathers. These secondary sex characters appear occasionally as parts of the tail, the tail feathers being greatly elongate in the males of some species, and having unusual shapes and colors in others. In a Nicaraguan form *(Florisuga mellivora)* the male has a tail that can be spread to form a half-circle. The effect created is quite striking, from the circumstance that the feathers are white and each one widens toward the end so that when the tail is expanded it resembles a beautiful white fan in miniature. According to Belt this tail is spread only during courtship; in feeding, or flying from station to station it is contracted. Belt witnessed the activities of two males as they displayed their physical charms before a female seated on a near-by limb. First one male and then the other would exhibit his expanded tail. Each bird would shoot up into the air and then slowly descend in front of the female, turning the body as it went so that the beauty of the caudal ornamentation could be viewed from both sides. After each exhibition the two males fought savagely, although Belt was unable to discover which one ultimately received the favors of the female.

Hummingbirds are noted for their extraordinary colorations although a few, such as the "hermits" *(Phaethornis)*, are quite modestly garbed. This coloration is of such rare beauty that it is generally described by comparing it with the ruby, emerald, topaz, or some other of the precious stones.

The color of a feather is determined by one of three factors: (1) pigment, (2) refraction of light, or (3) a combination of pigment and refraction. In hummingbirds color is dependent on refraction of light. If a feather of one of these creatures is examined under the microscope it is found to be divided and subdivided into many tiny branches, or barbules. In each of these reposes a dark substance covered with a sheath which may be polished in some instances, and ridged or pitted in others. Regardless of the configuration of this enveloping structure it acts as a series of prisms, producing the transient shades of color peculiar to hummingbirds. As the bird changes its position the angle of light is shifted and the hues vary accordingly. Coloration in a hummingbird, then, is only an illusion, for the many nuances of vermilion, turquoise, and emerald apparent to the eye are not what they seem. Moreover it is impossible to see all colors at one time even though the bird is held in one's hand. A hummingbird in one position may look dull, but if it is moved only slightly the body may suddenly "flash out with colour more brilliant than fire." It is consequently very difficult, if not impossible, for an artist to make a faithful reproduction of a hummingbird. As Im Thurn has said, "Hardly more than one of the points of colour is in reality ever visible in any one hummingbird at one and the same time, for each point only shows its peculiar and glittering colour when the light falls upon it from a particular direction. A true representation of one of these birds would show it in somewhat sober colours except just at the one point which, when the bird is in the position chosen for representation, meets the light at the requisite angle; and that point alone should be shown in full brilliance of colour. A flowering shrub is sometimes seen surrounded by a cloud of hummingbirds, all of the same species, and each, of course, in a different position. If some one would draw such a scene as that, showing a different detail of colouring in each bird, according to its position, then some idea of the actual appearance of hummingbirds might be given to one who had never seen an example."

Hummingbirds

For rapidity of muscular contraction, the whir of a rattlesnake tail or the teeth-clashing of a peccary simply cannot compare with the speed with which the wings of a hummingbird beat; no human eye can possibly follow it. According to evidence gathered through the aid of slowed-up moving pictures the ruby-throated hummingbird can beat its wings fifty to seventy times in one second. Some insects can do much better—two hundred to three hundred contractions per second—but among backboned animals the hummingbird is in a class by itself. It is the only bird capable of flying backward. Normally, the wing beats are fifty or fewer each second, but when going into reverse the beats may be increased to sixty, and even to seventy. The remarkable flying ability which these birds possess is correlated with extraordinarily well developed breast muscles.

The speed and agility of hummingbirds make it possible for them to elude enemies, and this ability seems to have engendered in them fearlessness and a predisposition for fighting. In their daily foragings they are continuously at war with other birds. It is not unusual to see a hummingbird put to flight a bird much larger than itself. What time they are not engaged in hostilities with other avians they spend in fighting among themselves. Beebe tells of observing a Guiana hummingbird that took possession of a limb of a tree and from that vantage point made war against every bird, irrespective of size, that came near it. "I have never," Beebe declares, "seen such a concentration of virile combative force in so condensed a form." Edwards writes that the hummingbirds along the Amazon often "meet in mid-air and furiously fight, their crests and the feathers upon their throats all erected and blazing, and altogether pictures of the most violent rage."

Of thirteen species of hummingbirds Belt saw around Santo Domingo, Nicaragua, the smallest *(Microchera parvirostris)* was the most pugnacious of all, and he often saw it driving away much larger birds. "They are all bold birds," Belt assures his readers, "suffering you to approach nearer than any other kinds and often flying up and hovering within two to three yards of you."

It is customarily supposed that the food of hummingbirds consists entirely of nectar which they sip from flowers with their long, needlelike bills. Waterton may have been the first observer to disprove this notion. Deep in the forests of Demerara he encountered innumerable hummingbirds, watched their feeding habits, and later examined their stomachs. In almost all of them insects were found. Darwin opened the stomachs of several in various parts of South America, and in every instance insects "were as numerous as in the stomach of a creeper." Belt observed these "winged gems of nature" on every opportunity and paid particular attention to the food they ate. To quote his conclusions: "I have no doubt many hummingbirds suck the honey from flowers, as I have seen it exude from their bills when shot; but others do not frequent them; and the principal food of all is small insects. I have examined scores of them, and never without finding insects in their crops." Belt noted one species *(Heliothrix Barroti,* Bourc. that spent much time searching the undersides of leaves for soft-bodied spiders and never once went near a flower.

Although Belt was an engineer by vocation, his *A Naturalist in Nicaragua* might well be the envy of any professional biologist. In continuing his studies on hummingbirds, he watched closely the manner in which they employ their mouth parts when feeding. "Their generally long bills," he asserted, "have been spoken of by some naturalists as tubes into which they suck the honey by a piston-like movement of the tongue; but suction in the usual way would be just as effective; and I am satisfied that this is not the primary use of the tongue; nor of the mechanism which enables it to be exerted to a great length beyond the end of the bill. The tongue, for one half of its length, is semi-horny and cleft in two, the two halves are laid flat against each other when at rest, but can be separated at the will of the bird and form a delicate pliable pair of forceps, most admirably adapted for picking out minute insects from amongst the stamens of the flowers." This theory proposed by Belt has not been proved nor disproved by ornithologists, although some naturalists consider that the tip of the tongue is scarcely rigid enough to make a very effective pair of forceps.

Americans frequently confuse the hummingbird with the sphinx or hawk moth. It is not at all surprising then that European naturalists who see these birds for the first time in the Americas are immediately struck with the very close resemblance between the two unrelated forms and frequently mistake the moth for the bird. Darwin's first words on hummingbirds, written shortly after he had landed in Brazil, were as follows: "Whenever I saw these little creatures buzzing round a flower, I was reminded of the sphinx moths: their movements and habits are indeed in many respects very similar."

Bates took some months in learning to distinguish quickly between the two and admitted that on several occasions he shot by mistake a hawk moth. In *The Naturalist on the River Amazon* he found that the natives of Brazil were firm in their belief that the one is metamorphosed into the other. All their lives they were accustomed to seeing ugly, wormlike larvae change into gorgeously marked butterflies; and, to their minds, there was nothing at all remarkable about the metamorphosis of a sphinx moth into a hummingbird, or vice versa.

The pronounced similarities between the two forms made an even stronger impression on Bates after he had examined both of them in his hands. "The shape of the head and position of the eyes in the moth," he wrote, "are seen to be nearly the same as in the bird, the extended proboscis representing the beak. At the tip of the moth's body there is a brush of long hair-scales resembling feathers which, being expanded, looks very much like a bird's tail. But, of course, all of these points of resemblance are merely superficial."

Bates was of the opinion, too, that the mental qualities of hummingbirds are more like those of insects than of any vertebrate animals. "The want of expression in their eyes, the small degree of versatility in their actions, the quickness and precision of their movements, are all so many points of resemblance between them and insects," he thought.

The admiration which most Americans feel for these "glittering fragments of the rainbow" is well expressed by Waterton, who was one of the first naturalists to write of them with an appreciative pen. "Though least in size," he wrote, "the glittering mantle of the hummingbird entitles it to the first place in the list of the birds of the New World. It may truly be called the Bird of Paradise; and had it existed in the Old World, it would have claimed the title instead of the bird which now has the honour to bear it."

COCK-OF-THE-ROCK

NOT many birds have been singled out from others of their kind as the major objective of a scientific expedition to a foreign land, yet the cock-of-the-rock has had that dubious honor thrust upon it. In 1915 Leo Miller, accompanied by Dr. Allen and Mr. Lloyd of Cornell University, made a long, hazardous journey into the southern part of Colombia which took him across the Andes to the headwaters of the Magdalena River. Miller sought many kinds of animals which would make desirable additions to the museum he represented, but he was interested primarily in collecting specimens of the cock-of-the-rock.

The expedition left the ancient city of Popayán in February, and several weeks intervened before the scientists discovered the birds of their search in a deep gorge of the Río Naranjos, a tributary of the Magdalena. At this point the river rushed madly through a canyon the walls of which, covered with dense tropical verdure, rose almost perpendicularly to a great height.

It was here that Miller hoped to find not only the adult birds, but the nests, eggs, and young, necessary for the completion of a museum group. The adults were common, but the nests with their desired contents were at first not to be found. The men left nothing to chance in the effort to locate them. With the help of Indians they began a systematic examination of the sides of the gorge. The search was difficult from the start; it rained a great deal, and the footing along the narrow ledges of the canyon wall was slippery. A rope was made, with which they tied themselves together, and this precaution saved more than one of them from falling onto the rocks in the stream below.

The search for nests continued for a considerable period of time without success. Finally a female cock-of-the-rock was seen flying back and forth from the bottom of the gorge to a point high on the face of a cliff. The men, from concealment, watched each movement of the bird in an effort to determine whether it was making journeys to and from its nest. At last Miller was able to make out a dark blotch high above on a narrow ledge which proved to be the object of their protracted search. The birds could scarcely have chosen a more inaccessible location if they had been forewarned of the catastrophe that was to befall them.

In order to get at the nest a tall tree was cut so that it fell against the side of the chasm; but the tree failed by several feet to reach its objective. It appeared now that all their efforts had been in vain. As a last resort, Miller and two of the Indians slowly climbed the precipice as far as they dared and then, with the aid of long bamboo poles spliced together, were just able to reach the nest and push it from its position on the ledge. It fell into a whirlpool below and was retrieved by an Indian who risked his life by diving after it. The nest contained a single young—drowned.

Later, under circumstances that were almost as thrilling, Miller secured other nests. Some of these contained eggs, others the young; and since the adults were not hard to find, all the material necessary for the group was eventually secured. Miller killed only the birds he needed; the others he "left to the eternal mystery of the wilderness, to dance in the shadows and to woo their mates beside the rushing waters; to rear their young and to lead the life that was intended for them from the beginning."

The cock-of-the-rock *(Rupicola)* is one of the most beautiful birds indigenous to tropical America. It is about the size of a pigeon and is a very brilliant orange in color with wings and tail of black; surmounting the head is a flat crest over an inch in height, also of orange, jutting forward to hide the saffron-colored beak. The female is garbed in a subdued dress of brown which is in marked contrast to the lively colors of her mate. When Wallace first saw the male cock-of-the-rock, with its orange color pre-eminent against a background of jungle green, he was reminded of "a mass of brilliant flame"; and Miller, as he watched a richly attired form fly through a mass of foliage, likened it to "a fiery comet."

Both native and naturalist seek this bird because of its unusual beauty. The former want it for feather work and for domestication; the latter, for display in zoological gardens and museums and for study in the laboratory.

The cock-of-the-rock has an extensive range, and in many parts of South America is quite common. Waterton, Schomburgk, Im Thurn and others found it at quite a few places in British Guiana; André reported it from the Caura in Venezuela; Wallace saw it on the Uaupés in southern Colombia and again on the highlands of Brazil, and von Hagen in the Jívaro country of Ecuador. According to Im Thurn it is not found at all in the lowlands but always in rocky, wooded mountain regions and seems to be especially partial to mountain ravines whose steep sides are covered with fruit-laden trees and bushes. It was under such conditions that Miller found it on the Río Naranjos in Colombia. It is known to inhabit the Kaieteur ravine below the great falls and Brown discovered it living under similar conditions in the gorge below the Amaila Falls.

The song of the cock-of-the-rock, if it can be called a song, is not in keeping with its delicate orange habiliment. The cries it emits from time to time can only be described as shrill, raucous croaks. Neither is the nest in keeping; for it is not an artistically built home of moss or tendril suspended gracefully from a limb or hidden away in a tangle of foliage, but is made of such prosaic material as mud and grass and plastered against a stone. The birds occupy the same nest year after year, Schomburgk wrote, and usually lay two black-dotted eggs. Several nests may be found in the same vicinity, conclusive evidence that these birds are social.

The cock-of-the-rock is celebrated for more than its exceptional beauty of plumage; at intervals it is said to choose a smooth, moss-covered plot of ground where it performs a remarkable kind of dance. Schomburgk had not resided long in British Guiana before he heard many stories of this bird and its innate disposition to dance. When at last his extensive wanderings took him into the forest where he might expect to encounter the cock-of-the-rock, he was constantly on the lookout for it. It was not, though, until he reached the Kanuku Mountains which form the watershed between the Amazon and Essequibo that he saw the first of these birds.

On the side of one of these ranges Schomburgk heard a peculiar cry which he mistook for that of some unidentified mammal. The Indians with him began to imitate the note, and within a few moments it was repeated close at hand. Suddenly a bird dressed in vivid orange and black alighted on a limb beside him, and he was treated to his first view of the much-sought-after cock-of-the rock.

Two or three days later Schomburgk and his men invaded another part of the Kanuku Mountains. Once again the notes of the *gallos,* now familiar to his ears, were heard. The Indians stealthily crept toward the birds, and in a few minutes one of them returned, beckoning Schomburgk to follow him. "We might have crept some thousand paces through the brush on hands and knees," Schomburgk wrote, "when my curiosity that had been aroused was satisfied, and on crouching down quietly beside the other Indians I witnessed a most interesting sight. On the smooth surface of a rocky crag a party of the beautiful birds were keeping up a dance; a performance that has been doubted by many ornithologists though not only my brother, but many of the Indians had already told me plenty concerning it. While about a score of birds perched upon the bushes surrounding the playground, were uttering the most peculiar notes, and apparently constituting an admiring audience, one of the males was cutting capers on the smooth boulder; in proud consciousness of self it cocked and dropped its outspread tail and flapped its likewise expanded wings, and thus continued to figure out the steps until it seemed to be exhausted, when it flew back onto the bush and its place was taken by another male. The females in the meantime uttered a peculiar note, watched unweariedly and on the return of the tired performer uttered a scream denoting applause."

At this point one of the Indians, who could not have known how he was circumventing the efforts of science, shot into the scene, ending the dance and leaving four of the birds wounded on the stage.

Schomburgk, so far as we have been able to ascertain, is the only naturalist who has witnessed this spectacular dance by the cock-of-the-rock. Two of the natives who were with Brown when he visited Amaila Falls reported to him that they saw the exihibition while hunting these birds early one morning; but Brown did not see it himself. Wallace, Im Thurn, Hudson, and others have described the dance, but they (with the exception of Wallace, who was repeating Indian versions) were paraphrasing Schomburgk's description.

TURTLES

THERE are more turtles in the South American waterways than in all of the remaining streams of the earth. They are in such abundance that the natives of many regions depend upon them for their food as the Comanches and Cheyennes of the Midwest relied upon the bison in pre-Columbian days and the Tehuelches of Patagonia rely upon the guanaco to this day. Their flesh is often the only meat available, and if some catastrophe should obliterate them from the Orinoco and Amazon and their tributaries, the Indians inhabiting the banks of these streams would find existence precarious, if not impossible. The presence of thousands upon thousands of turtles spread as thick as the stones of a pavement over a sand bar two to three miles long and several hundred yards wide would seem incredible if it had not been confirmed by so many travelers.

No adequate idea may be formed of the stupendous number of these creatures without visiting the inland waterways of the country at the time of the year when the turtles issue from the water to lay their eggs in the sand. They are shy and elusive to a rare degree and seek the depths of the river channels at the slightest noise, seldom leaving the water for any other purpose. For the small portion of a day—the fag-end of a night—they seek the land in order that their kind may be perpetuated, and then return to the water where they remain until the same instinct prompts them twelve months later.

Turtles were present in unbelievable numbers when Humboldt visited the Orinoco about 1800, and fifty years later when Bates lived on the Amazon; and their numbers have not been materially reduced since then.

The water turtles of South America of which we are speaking —and these should not be confused in any way with the land forms—are placed by Ditmars in the genus *Podocnemis*. According to him there are at least six species, all of which are giants among fresh-water forms. The ones seen by Humboldt on the Orinoco weighed from forty to fifty pounds, and those on the upper Amazon described by Bates had a shell three feet long and two feet wide. Brown and Lidstone asserted that they observed specimens four feet in length; some that Up de Graff saw had an average weight of seventy-five pounds, and a few must have weighed as much as one hundred fifty pounds. While none of these approach the weight of the giant terrestrial species found on the Galápagos Islands, nor the huge marine species, the green, loggerhead, and leatherback tortoises—the latter said to reach a weight of a thousand pounds—they nevertheless are of mammoth size in the world of fresh-water chelonians.

Egg-laying time, which has been characterized as "harvest time" in South America, varies in different regions. On the Orinoco, according to Humboldt and others, the turtles begin laying in March. On the upper Amazon the urge does not strike the turtles until September. This period coincides with the period when the waters are at their lowest—at the peak of the dry season, the "season of dearth." On the Orinoco the sand flats are uncovered from the first of January till near the end of March. With the vernal equinox the wet season sets in. The dry season is much later on the Amazon, the waters subsiding to their lowest point in August or September, and it is then that the turtles assemble there to lay their eggs.

Probably as a result of thousands of years of persecution by jaguars and other predaceous animals, these creatures have learned to select their egg-laying sites with extreme care. Turtles are unusually timid and mistrustful and will leave any location where man makes himself conspicuous. On the Orinoco, for instance, comparatively few turtles are to be found below the mouth of the Apure River. The great majority of the eggs are laid above this point, where man is an infrequent visitor. As a rule an island is chosen—the turtle has discovered in some way that an island is a safer place than the shore—which projects above the level of the water some thirty to forty feet at least. Just before the eggs are laid the reptiles gather around these islands in vast numbers and inspect the shore with an eye to safety. If they are frightened two to three days in succession by the natives, or other potential enemies, they are very likely to seek another spot promising greater security. The island must jut some distance above the general level of the stream to offset sudden unpredictable rises of the water. As Bates said: "These places are, of course, the last to go under water when, in unusually wet seasons, the river rises before the eggs are hatched by the heat of the sand. One could almost believe, from this, that the animals used forethought in choosing a place; but it is simply one of those many instances in animals where the unconscious habit has the same result as conscious prevision."

The rivers of South America are the largest on earth, and the islands and sand bars are proportionately large. Up de Graff mentions one that was three miles long and several hundred yards wide. This was not exceptionally large, for, as we shall see later, eggs are sometimes laid as much as a mile away from the water.

During the small hours—they are most active between midnight and dawn—the turtles crowd laboriously, like antediluvian armor-plated tanks, from their aquatic seclusion and seek a suitable place for the laying of the eggs. They look about them on all sides, and at the slightest noise or movement retreat to the stream. On each side of the shell, a double track is left by the feet in the sand, which to the natives is an index to the size of the reptile, and also to the number of eggs they may expect to find.

A site well above the water line having been chosen, the turtle sets to work and with the claws soon excavates a depression two to three feet deep in which the eggs are laid. No animal known can compete with the turtle as an egg-layer when actual quantity of yolk and albumen is taken into consideration. Fishes and insects lay thousands, even millions, of eggs at one time—a feat which is unsurpassable, considering the size of their bodies; but the total amount of protoplasm and inert yolk material in no way approximates that extruded by the turtle. It is probably safe to say that the female lays at least one hundred eggs—and each egg is as large as a chicken egg.

Up de Graff was so impressed with the egg-laying feat of the turtle that he tried mentally to get all of them back into the body of the reptile. To quote his words: "Needless to say, if an attempt were made to put so many eggs back into the shell of the reptile which laid them, it would be necessary to cut the whole of the flesh away in order to make room for them. This is a miracle of production which, I think, is not surpassed in the animal world, except by certain insects."

It is not clear whether more than one turtle lays in the same pit. The general impression is that a female lays her quota and then carefully covers them before traveling back to the water. Bates states specifically, however, that one female after laying her eggs, about 120, blankets them with sand and another then lays her allotment on top; these are covered, and a third turtle adds to the collection, and so on, until the hole is full. If this be true there may conceivably be three or four hundred eggs in a single nest. There are no references to the discovery of so many in one nest, but Humboldt was told: "These tortoises feel so pressing a desire to lay their eggs, that some of them descend into holes that have been dug by others, but which are not yet covered with earth. There they deposit a new layer of eggs on that which has been recently laid. In this tumultuous movement an immense number of eggs are broken. The missionary showed us, by removing the sand in several places, that this loss probably amounts to a fifth of the whole quantity."

Brown wrote that he "often obtained as many as 130 eggs from one nest," and Orton found nests on the Napo that contained 132, 114, 112, and 97 eggs. He had heard, he said, of as many as 160 in a single nest. Brown and Lidstone wrote that as many as 150 were often taken from a nest. All of these numbers more nearly parallel the aggregate laid by a single female than the sum total of three or four.

The turtle egg is much like a billiard ball in both size and shape. Its shell is not hard, like that of birds' eggs, but is flexible and leathery and gives with the pressure of the fingers. It is superior to the hard, brittle shell, for it is very tough and resistant and not easily cracked or broken.

The inside of the egg is peculiar in that the albumen refuses to coagulate when cooked. No matter how hot the fire, the white of the egg, which differs markedly in chemical composition from the white in the bird egg, refuses to part with its mucus consistency. The natives ordinarily throw away the albumen and cook only the yolk.

A period of fourteen to fifteen days elapses before all of the turtles have laid their eggs. The incubation is left entirely to nature. The heat which is necessary for development comes, of course, from the rays of the tropical sun, and the moisture, if any is needed, comes from the sand itself.

Even before the egg-laying begins, natives are on hand. At first these act as sentinels to ascertain the movements of the reptiles and to warn strangers in boats to keep to the middle of the river and to make no outcries. The annual egg hunt is the big time of the year for many of the natives in proximity to the large sand bars; it is for them what the salmon run is to the Columbia River fishermen, and elaborate preparations are made.

Two classic accounts of egg hunts in South America have been written. The first was by Humboldt on the Orinoco in 1799; the second, by Bates on the upper Amazon in 1850.

Humboldt's observations occurred on an island in the Orinoco not many miles above the mouth of the Apure, a comparatively large western tributary. When he and Bonpland and the remaining members of his expedition reached this island they were surprised to find on it at least three hundred natives, a few white traders, and a missionary. Humboldt had arrived at a very opportune moment. The natives of several different tribes had assembled from miles around for the yearly egg harvest. The missionary, a Franciscan monk, was on hand to supervise the proceedings. Chief among his duties was the selection of lieutenants who determined the extent of the egg-stratum and then apportioned the fruitful area among the various families present. Before the arrival of the Franciscan monks in this part of South America the Jesuits had had charge of the egg hunts. With the wisdom and foresight which characterized so many of their actions in the new world, they reserved a portion of the island on which the natives were forbidden to dig for eggs. The Jesuits wished to make certain that the harvest would not decrease with the passage of years. The Franciscans did not follow the laudable example set by their predecessors; not one square yard of the entire island was reserved, and there were natives who asserted that the eggs were not as abundant as they had been. However, the supervision of the Franciscans was a great improvement over the condition that obtained before the Jesuits, when there was a mad struggle for the eggs, resulting in a very unequal division and considerable losses.

The general procedure on the upper Amazon, as described by Bates, was very similar to that on the Orinoco. The operations were under the supervision of one individual, elected for the job by the municipal council of Ega and given the title of *commandante* of the *praia real* (royal beach). There were four *praias* in the Ega district, and each had its officially elected *commandante*. These men performed the same duties as the Franciscans on the Orinoco.

As soon as the sand bar is divided among the natives they start excavating. This consists in the removal of the sand from above the eggs, and the hands are the most practical tools for that purpose. Bates found that after the second day of digging each family had a mound of eggs four to five feet high in front of its quarters. The eggs are, of course, much in demand for food—many are eaten on the spot, and others dried for future consumption; but most of them are used in making oil. As soon as all of the eggs have been unearthed, those not intended for food are picked up and thrown into a canoe. They are usually broken with wooden implements manufactured for the purpose; but occasionally the Indians, particularly the children, unable to resist the opportunity of a lifetime, jump into the canoe and continue the maceration with their feet. After the eggs are well squashed and everyone is besmeared with yolk and albumen, water is poured on the mass, which is then left in the sun until the heat induces the oil to come to the top. As it reaches the surface, it is skimmed off and boiled. If properly and carefully prepared, the oil is clear and odorless and very like olive oil. It is used in lamps, and also for cooking, being an excellent substitute for lard and butter.

The amount of oil produced on the *praias* is the best index to the number of turtles in the South American rivers. There were three islands in the Orinoco that produced most of the oil at the time of Humboldt's visit. These three yielded approximately 5,000 jars, he said. According to his estimate 5,000 eggs were needed to fill a jar; but, since one-third of the eggs were broken at the time of laying, 6,666 were laid for each jar, or the stupendous total of 33,330,000 for the 5,000 jars. If each turtle lays 100 eggs 333,300 females would perforce have to be on hand. Since this estimate, which is probably far too low, concerns only the comparatively small region of the Orinoco close to the mouth of the Apure, the total number of turtles in the Orinoco basin is beyond comprehension.

It is interesting now to compare the above estimate with that of Bates for the upper Amazon. He wrote that 8,000 jars of oil were produced on the upper Amazon and Madeira, each year. Since 6,000 eggs were necessary for the production of a jar, 48,000,000 were needed for the 8,000 jars; and, since each female lays 120 eggs, 400,000 females must have been on duty.

Mention should be made here of the fact that male turtles are scarce at egg-laying time. The above figures are for females only and, going on the assumption that there are as many males as females—and we have no reason to believe otherwise, if our chromosomal theory of sex determination is correct—the total figures should be more nearly twice those suggested by Humboldt and Bates.

When the floods of the Amazon recede, many small ponds are left in the low-lying alluvial plains. In these may be found a large number of half-grown turtles. The natives make expeditions to these pools during the dry season and catch the turtles, sometimes hundreds of them at a time. Brown and Lidstone tell of a Señor Fonsica who came in with a catch of five hundred turtles after a day of hunting. On these the Indians may subsist for weeks, or even months. Bates accompanied the natives on one of these excursions and saw the way in which they secured the animals. The particular pool finally decided upon had an area of four or five acres, and was surrounded by a dense tangle of tropical vegetation which came down to the water on all sides; in no place was the depth over five feet. At first the men shot the turtles from their canoes with bows and arrows. Bates was astonished at their skill. They were able to detect the slightest motion of the turtles in the water, even though no part of the body was showing above the surface. The instant one was located, an arrow penetrated the shell of the reptile. The arrow, of a kind frequently employed in shooting fish, has a steel point rather loosely fixed into the end of the shaft, but secondarily connected to a thread thirty to forty yards long made from the fiber of the pineapple. When it is shot, the thread is wound around the upper part of the arrow; as soon as it pierces the victim the point disengages itself from the shaft which floats on the water. It is an easy matter for the hunter to recover it. He then plays the line until the turtle comes into view, when it is secured, or shot once more if it has much life remaining.

There is practically no difficulty in capturing a turtle if it is encountered out of the water. No guns are necessary, no nets, no clubs, only the strength to turn it over on its back. A man lying prone, gagged, and tied hand and foot is not so helpless as a turtle on its back. The man is able to roll over, to change his position from time to time, but turtles are as fixed as an oyster on its cultch. They are frequently captured in this manner as they return to the water after laying their eggs, but at that time the natives have to be on the sand bars before dawn if they wish to waylay many of them. The hunters must be extremely cautious: the slightest noise, like the grating of a boat on the sand, may alarm every turtle on the *praia*. If all goes well the men land, rush upon the unfortunate animals, and turn them over before they have a chance to regain the water. Sometimes a turtle is so far from the boat, and so large and heavy, that it is next to impossible to carry. In such a predicament it is frequently turned on its feet and driven to the edge of the water, where it is turned over again. The boatswain on the boat which Brown and Lidstone used in the surveys of the Amazon basin was driving a turtle to the boat when it suddenly eluded him and reached the water before he caught up with it. The boatswain was, of course, heavier than the turtle by several stone and was completely the master on land; but in the water the sailor fought a losing battle. In very short order he found that it was a question of severing all relations with the turtle or being towed under water.

There are two common methods of keeping turtles in captivity until they are desired for the pan. For a period no longer than two to three weeks, the animals are turned onto their backs, where they kick spasmodically as they observe the clouds in the daytime and the appearance and disappearance of moon, planets, and constellations at night. If they are intended for consumptior at a much later date, aquatic pens are staked off for them in pools near the hut of the owner. It is the presence of these reptiles in so many back-yard corrals that has given them the name "cattle of the Amazon."

Turtles supply an abundance of wholesome food in addition to the oil, and they are more sought after than any other animal in the Amazon basin. At Ega, Bates lived for the greater part of the year on turtles. He liked the meat but said it was satiating, as it might well be after a steady diet of it for a year. Most South American travelers have found the flesh very acceptable. There are more ways of preparing turtle than there are species in South America. Some of the choicest, as outlined by Bates, are:

1. Under flesh of breast minced, with *farinha.*
2. Steaks cut from breast and cooked with fat.
3. Sausages made from the thick-coated stomach.
4. Quarters cooked in kettle of *Tucupi* sauce.
5. Lean pieces roasted on spit and moistened with vinegar.
6. Entrails chopped up and made into a delicious soup called *sarapatel.*

At Manáos, Spruce had turtle meat not only every day, but every meal, and it was not unusual to have it in five different dishes at one meal. Edwards had a similar experience. "Turtle in every variety of preparation, from the soup to the roasted in the shell, tempted us," he wrote.

Cherrie was on the upper Paraguay in the Lenten season, but the natives consumed turtle meat in great quantities because—it was not meat. In the preparation they built a fire and placed the live turtle on it upside down. When Cherrie remonstrated at such an act of cruelty they seemed astounded and replied that that was the penalty the animal had to pay for being a turtle.

The infant turtles emerge into the world always under cover of darkness. It would be suicidal for them to emerge when the sun was up: if some predaceous animal did not gobble them up, the scorching sun would kill them. Up de Graff bears witness to this: "I once saw a practical demonstration of the fate which would overcome them if they came out by day, having disturbed, during an egg-hunt, a nestful which had been hatched out, and which would shortly have broken cover. The yolk of the egg, which remains attached to the underside of the young reptiles' shells, and from which they derive their nourishment, while gathering strength to break and run for the river, was in this case practically consumed, so that the turtles had enough strength to reach the river, had it not been that they were unearthed by me in the daytime. Once discovered there was nothing for it but to attempt to get to the water, which they started to do, streaming off more like a stampede of gigantic bed-bugs than anything else. Before covering ten yards, their legs shrivelled up, turned red as if cooked on the fire, and they immediately died."

Not many men, surely, have been present during the night when the young were actually escaping from their subterranean incubators. The boat of Brown and Lidstone stopped one day at a deserted place on the Juruá River called Pupunhazinha, to lay in a supply of wood; and the loading was not completed during the day. After darkness had fallen they crossed the river to a sand bar on the opposite side. They had been sitting on the sand only a few minutes when they heard a peculiar sound, like the pattering of little feet: "Taking the boat's lamp, we held it over the spot, and to our astonishment beheld a perfect stream of little turtles, each not two inches in length, bursting up through the compact sand, struggling out through it, and toddling off at a good pace to the river, into which they ran. They were the products of a turtle nest which had hatched out, and was now pouring forth its contents into the world. The spot from which they emerged had a few moments before looked firm and smooth, not hinting in the least at the existence of any kind of life beneath."

According to Bates some of the eggs are laid a mile from the water. Consider then the feat of a baby turtle only an inch or two in length, just out of the shell, toddling on very uncertain legs over a vast stretch of uneven sand toward a haven a mile away! Furthermore, the journey must be made under cover of darkness, and it is not certain that these infantile forms can see.

Another remarkable fact known about the young turtles is that instinct leads them straight to the water even though it be as much as a mile away. It is said that those hatching out on an island, although surrounded by water on all sides, will strike out for the shore line that is *nearest.* Bates was fascinated with the migration of the young turtles to the water. One morning just at dawn he discovered a beach that was literally swarming with them, all going in the same direction. He picked up several and turned their noses in the opposite direction, but they invariably about-faced and continued along the line already started. A more splendid example of the power of instinct could scarcely be found.

CAIMANS AND CROCODILES

THE caimans and crocodiles, together with their proximate kin—the alligators and gavials—are the living representatives of the reptilian order Crocodilia. They are the largest of existing saurians, at least two species, the Indian gavial and the Madagascar crocodile, reaching a maximum length of about thirty feet. Although huge, judged by current reptilian standards, they are fingerlings compared with their predecessors the Dinosaurs. Among these antediluvian monsters, Diplodocus and Brontosaurus measured seventy-five to a hundred feet from jaw to tip of tail; and Tyrannosaurus, built along more expansive lines, had a bulk approaching that of the elephant.

The Crocodilia now inhabit tropical and semitropical regions the world around. In general their haunts are sluggish shallows, hot, festering swamplands, and endless miles of monotonous waterway where humid atmosphere and tepid water prevail. They rarely go far from water, and only a few species, including the American alligator, find existence tenable beyond the limits of the Torrid Zone.

Ditmars recognizes two species of alligator, twelve species of crocodile, five species of caiman, and two species of gavial. These are much alike in general appearance; but to the eye of the trained scientist the differences are sufficiently pronounced to demand their division into the four separate groups. To the layman, however, crocodiles, caimans, and alligators—perhaps not the gavials—look so much alike that they are collectively designated as alligator by this person and crocodile by that. Practically every naturalist who has visited South America—Humboldt, Schomburgk, Edwards, Wallace, Spruce—makes reference to the "alligators" in the Essequibo, Orinoco, Magdalena, or Amazon. Yet, strictly speaking, there is not a single alligator native to the continent of South America—nor to any part of Central America, for that matter. Just two species are placed in the genus Alligator: the American alligator *(A. mississippiensis)*, the habitat of which extends along the Gulf of Mexico and the Atlantic from the Rio Grande to southern North Carolina; and the Chinese alligator *(A. sinensis)*, a much smaller form, found only in far eastern Asia in the Yangtze Kiang.

The species of crocodilians in South America are seven: two of crocodile and five of caiman. The crocodiles are the Orinoco crocodile *(Crocodilus intermedius)*, confined to the river of that name and its tributaries, and the American Crocodile *(C. americanus)*, with a range extending from Florida to Mexico and then south through Central America and the West Indies to Ecuador, Colombia, and Venezuela. This is a coastal form and inhabits, like the salt-water crocodile of India, both fresh and salt water. The known species of caiman range from the *jacaré-tinga*, or rough-backed caiman *(Caiman trigonotus)*, with a maximum length of six feet, to the large *jacaré-uassu*, or black caiman *(C. niger)*, with a maximum of near twenty feet. The spectacled caiman *(C. sclerops)*, the round-nosed caiman *(C. latirostris)*, and the banded caiman *(C. palpebrosus)* are intermediate in size, having lengths of seven to eight feet. The two species of crocodile mentioned above have maximum lengths of twelve and fourteen feet, respectively, according to Ditmars; the black caiman is then by considerable the largest of the lot. Honors for extent of distribution are easily captured by the spectacled caiman that ranges from southern Mexico through Central and South America as far south as northern Argentina.

The caimans are more closely related to the alligators than to the other forms, the two often being confused; but they differ in the arrangement of their ventral scutes, and the caimans lack the bony nasal septum present in the alligators. The caimans are said, too, to be more active, more vicious and to have larger teeth. In South America, where caiman must be distinguished from crocodile, certain difficulties arise. Crocodiles differ from alligators in having long, pointed snouts. Oddly enough the black and round-nosed caimans have the broad snout characteristic of the alligator while the other three species of caiman have a pointed snout much like that generally seen in crocodiles. The caimans have the fourth tooth of the lower jaw on each side—the largest one—fitting into a concavity in the upper jaw, while the crocodiles have this same tooth fitting into a notch or groove, so that when the jaws are closed it may be seen from the outside.

If the extent of the crocodile's dispersion in South America is kept in mind—roughly Ecuador, Colombia, and Venezuela—one may be reasonably certain that a crocodilian from any of the other republics, whatever its name, belongs in reality to one or another of the five species of caiman. There is, unfortunately, considerable overlapping in the ranges of the crocodile and caiman in Colombia and Venezuela, so that it is frequently impossible to tell from descriptions which form the author has in mind.

Of the abundance of these reptiles in the rivers and inland lakes and marshes there can be little doubt. Spruce wrote from the neighborhood of Villa Nova on the lower Amazon: "I can safely say that at no time during the whole thirty days were we without one or more alligators [caimans] in sight, when there was light enough to distinguish them; and we might hear their snorting and grunting all the night through." "It is scarcely exaggerating," Bates asserted, "to say that the waters of the Solimoens are as well stocked with large alligators [caimans] in the dry season, as a ditch in England is in summer with tadpoles. During a journey of five days which I once made in the Upper Amazons steamer, in November, alligators were seen along the coast almost every step of the way." Similar reports have been made by others from different parts of the country. In the Orinoco "they swarm like worms in the shallow waters of the river," Humboldt averred. "The Berbice River is the home par excellence of the cayman," if we are to believe Brown; and in one of the coastal streams of Ecuador, according to Up de Graff, "the water seemed to be made of mud and alligators [crocodiles]. The mud-bars were almost eclipsed by them." At one point along the Orinoco, Whitney said, "I saw more crocodiles than I thought the entire river held." They were so numerous it was a mystery to him how so many large animals could find subsistence.

Crocodiles and caimans, although generically different, have many points in common. The sides and belly are covered with scales having the texture of very hard, tough leather, and the back is reinforced with numerous keeled, bonelike plates that are set in the underskin and provide a strong protective armor. These dorsal plates have a definite arrangement and are of value to the systematist in classifying species. A popular misconception is that this skin is so hard and tough it will deflect bullets. Schomburgk, for one, had considerable to do with fostering the notion that it is impossible to kill a crocodile with a gun unless it is shot through the eye or the soft, fleshy parts of the front legs. On at least three occasions the German naturalist complained of being unable to kill a caiman because its stubborn hide was impervious to the shots he fired. In the light of what is known now it is rather difficult to understand Schomburgk's predicament; certain it is that the plated skins of these reptiles are easily pierced, not only by bullets, but by arrows.

The mouth is voluminous, utterly utilitarian, and holds a liberal collection of sharp, conical teeth, of which the anterior ones are longer. They are all similar in shape, there being no differentiation into incisors, canines, and molars as in mammals. They are not at all used for grinding purposes, only "for snatch and swallow," as Waterton aptly put it. The jaws are powerful, a single snap being capable of severing an entire limb from the body. The musculature employed in closing the mouth is much more highly developed than that for opening it; a man with strong fingers encircling the muzzle can hold the two jaws together without great effort.

On the bank of a stream, caimans and crocodiles frequently lie with their mouths open. The reason for this can only be conjectured—perhaps the mouth contains parasites that are killed by the sun.

Of more than passing importance in the life of these reptiles is the location of eyes and nose. These are so elevated above the head that they may remain above the water after the rest of the body is submerged. It is possible then for a caiman to immerse itself in the water and remain effectively hidden while it breathes and looks about, with its green irises like two miniature periscopes, for enemy or potential provender. For hours it will maintain its position, motionless as a sponge, except for the rhythmical kicking of the hind limbs.

The ear is equally well adapted to use under the water. Over each external meatus leading to the inner ear there is a flexible flap of skin, controlled by muscles in such a way that it may be lowered or raised. When the animal plunges into a stream this flap effectively prevents the entrance of water.

The tail is long and laterally compressed toward the end and is the chief organ of locomotion in the water, the feet playing no part at all. It is said to have an important role in stunning victims before they are grasped with the jaws; but this would seem to be an exaggeration. It appears more likely that it is used only when the intended prey cannot be reached with the jaws. The tail is then swept in an arc toward the head, the victim being thrown within easy distance of the mouth. There is no doubt but that caimans can deliver a sledge-hammer blow with the tail. Quite often they slap it down smartly on the surface of the water, causing a pistol-like report. The natives say they do this in order to attract fish.

The general coloration of the caiman or crocodile varies, probably according to the nature of the water it occupies. If the water is clear the reptile will in all likelihood be relatively light-colored. As a result some forms may have a yellowish cast while others will have a dark brown or even a black one. There is occasionally an albino. Spruce discovered one on the upper Amazon, and almost half a century later Up de Graff found another. It came as quite a surprise to Up de Graff, for he had not heard of such a thing as a "snow-white" caiman. This specimen was five feet long. Instead of preserving it, in the interests of science, Up de Graff and his companions ate it, and were pleasantly surprised at its sapidity.

Both Edwards and Bates declared that the caimans of the lower Amazon estivate, and Humboldt made the same claim for the crocodiles of the Venezuelan llanos. Estivation is similar to hibernation but occurs during the dry season of the perennial tropic summer. Estivation is an escape from drought (as hibernation is from cold) and a concomitant shortage of food. The lakes and ponds of the wet season that communicate with the lower Amazon and its larger tributaries, dry up soon after the cessation of rain, and the caimans can either migrate overland to the main streams or estivate. Thousands of caimans of the lower Amazon have been known to die in unsuccessful attempts to reach water. On one farm on the island of Marajó it is said eighty-five hundred were found dead from this cause. If caimans really estivate, and in the manner characteristic of lungfish, they burrow into the mud at the bottoms of small streams and ponds, fashion a sort of slime cocoon, and therein remain dormant until the rain falls again. On the upper Amazon where the dry season is not so protracted, the caimans did not estivate, Bates said.

Caimans sometimes migrate because of a superabundance of water as well as because of a scarcity. In those parts of Amazonica where heavy rains swell the rivers until they overflow their banks, inundating extensive areas, the caimans leave the parent streams and migrate to the inland reservoirs, where they stay until drier weather obtains. According to Bates there were practically no caimans in the main rivers while they were at flood height.

It may be logical that these beasts should be sensitive to floods; but that they should be sensitive to rainstorms is something else. "I was greatly astonished and amused," wrote Rusby, "by their behavior on the occurrence of a shower. Motionless in the sunshine, they would, on the falling of the first drops of rain, rise and make for the water, for all the world as if anxious to avoid getting wet, but slipping at once beneath the surface."

Some of the crocodilians lay their eggs in holes in the sand, but the caimans build nests. The female is both architect and contractor; for the male, after the mating season, plays no further part in the propagation of the species. The nest is located in some sequestered spot not far from water and is constructed of damp, decaying vegetation. The female collects leaves, sticks, and other material in her mouth and piles them in a rude heap. There is no definite size for the nest although it may be two or three feet high and four to five feet or more in diameter. Throughout the process of construction the reptile crawls over it again and again to make it compact. The nest is now left to settle and to allow heat to generate from the decomposition of the vegetable matter.

Several days later, according to Beebe, the female returns to the nest, rips off the top, and lays the eggs; then she replaces the superstructure. While the temperature may be appreciably raised in the nest it is not nearly so high there at midday as on the outside; neither is it so cold at night, the temperature remaining fairly constant. The leaves may be heaped high to maintain a high moisture content, too.

The egg is somewhat larger than a hen's egg, is ovoid, and weighs about three ounces. The shell is like porcelain and is quite rough from the lime incrustations. There would seem to be no order in the arrangement of the eggs as they are laid and there is no definite number. Beebe says 20 to 40; Schomburgk, 30 to 40; and Spruce, 40 to 60. Bates told of finding 20 in one nest, and Im Thurn counted 37 in another. The average number is probably near 30 for the caiman, but that may vary in the different species.

The female caimans, unlike the feminine turtles of that region, remain by the nest and are said to protect it against all comers Some authors maintain that no caiman is so dangerous or so willing to attack as the female standing guard over her eggs. This may be exaggeration, however, for Beebe declares that the caimans of British Guiana may often be driven away with little effort.

The eggs hatch about the same time of the year as turtle eggs, in order that the young may reach the safety of water before floods destroy them. The incubation lasts about seventy-five days; the female is apprised of the hatching by sounds from the nest. She immediately tears off the roof, removes the eggs that have been pipped and breaks the shells. Often the young are unable to escape from the eggs without maternal assistance, even though each one is generally equipped with an egg tooth. This is an exiguous structure sticking up from the anterior end of the upper jaw like the sight on the end of a rifle barrel.

Following their delivery into the world, they are looked after with considerable solicitude by their mother. The father takes no interest in the matter, which is just as well, as it is said that he sometimes eats the young. Schomburgk was of the opinion that the mothers are just as dangerous at this time as they are during incubation. He encountered a female caiman with her clutch of young and was completely taken aback at her viciousness. How long the mother stays with the young is apparently not known.

Some remarkable examples of instinctive behavior by newborn caimans have been noted by the naturalists. Spruce recorded that while traveling up one of the streams of the upper Amazon in company with two native helpers, he came to a place where the earth had fallen away at the side of the river, leaving the contents of a caiman's nest exposed. One of the men hurled two of the eggs into the water. The impact broke the shells, and two young ones emerged and immediately dived out of sight. Of this action Spruce said, "I never saw a finer example of instinct, or inherited reason, being called into play at the very moment of a creature's coming into the world."

Beebe picked up a caiman egg containing a young one which had been trying hard to get out into the world for several hours. Its efforts had been rather ineffectual, however, for only the tip of the snout was exposed. Beebe was in the act of breaking away a piece of the shell to help it gain its freedom when suddenly the baby saurian burst out and dived into a basin of water. Finding the depth of the water inconsiderable, it swam distractedly in all directions. "For a day and night, the past twenty-four hours," Beebe wrote, "only the snout had projected. In three seconds more the whole being of the perfect gatorling was functioning fully, launched on what would normally be a long and checkered career."

The young caiman, or crocodile, left to its own devices soon becomes a forager. Its food consists of small fish and insects. After reaching a length of approximately eighteen inches it supplements its diet with small amphibians, reptiles, and crustaceans. The food of the adult reptile, at one time or another, consists of practically every living animal that comes within reach of its capacious jaws. The young reptile confines its activities to the water, but with increased age it soon learns to slither out onto the sand bars and then to make short forays into the jungle. Later in life it may occasionally travel considerable distances from water. If human beings live near by the reptile soon has opportunity to sample an assortment of domesticated animals: chickens, pigs, goats, dogs, calves, and the like. The natives suffer a considerable loss of livestock each year because of caimans and crocodiles. The foraging of these brutes is often undertaken under cover of darkness. Bates awoke one night to find a large caiman walking around just beneath his hammock, which had been hung between two trees not far from the edge of a river. It had waddled up from the stream and was intent on capturing a dog owned by one of the natives.

Father Zahm, a veteran explorer of out-of-the-way places in South America, stated that the danger from caimans and crocodiles had been highly exaggerated. "On the contrary," he wrote, "they are, in their native state, very timid animals, and rarely exhibit hostility toward man, except when cornered. We often saw the natives enter rivers frequented by crocodiles and caymans, something they surely would not have done if the danger were as great as ordinarily imagined. In Venezuela the Indian, or mestizo, has a much greater dread of the ray, or carib fish, than the cayman."

Of these same animals Dickey, also an explorer of many years' experience in equatorial America, wrote: "They are my one great terror, as they are of every thinking person who frequents the great waterways of the southern continent. It is hard to bring home to Northern folk who are not accustomed to seeing the creatures, the fact that they are the most dreaded, even by Indians, of all the living things."

There is little question that the crocodilians are hated and feared by both native and traveler. Their general appearance is sufficient to stir up a certain amount of trepidation. That Bates was no different from the ordinary run of mortals is evident from this statement: "The enormous gape of their mouths, with their blood-red lining and long fringes of teeth, and the uncouth shape of their bodies, make a picture of unsurpassable ugliness." Miller was no less perturbed at the sight of these reptiles. "I know of no more repulsive sight," he wrote, "than to come suddenly upon one of the huge saurians lying quietly in wait among the shadows; the evil, grinning expression; the leering, green eyes and the glistening scaly body of the creature suggest treachery and cruelty, combined with agility and cunning." Waterton asserted, "Perhaps no animal in existence bears more decided marks in his countenance of cruelty and malice than the caiman."

Over and over again in the writings of the South American explorers we find the words "cowardly," "sneaking," "cruel," "despicable," "treacherous," applied to these beasts. The naturalists, inclined to be more conservative in their appraisals than others might be, use the same terms of opprobrium.

It is true as Father Zahm contended that these reptiles are timid, and that they will flee to the water when confronted by man; and it is also a fact that in certain places at least the natives fear the piranha more than the caiman. But these admissions of timidity and cowardice are only a prelude to the real character of the big-muzzled beasts. They instinctively lurk in deep shadows, sometimes near the water's edge and at other times in the forest, ready to pounce upon an unsuspecting foe; they are cunning enough to lie almost submerged near shore where they simulate old water-soaked logs onto which the incautious may step; they immerse their bodies near bathing places and rise quickly above the surface to grasp the heedless who come within reach of their large jaws. At no time, near their haunts, can one be free from apprehension—there is a permanent anxiety that is never completely dispelled. If caution is thrown overboard for even a second these beasts may be upon one rending limb from body. The caiman in sight is never dreaded; it is the one *not in sight* that is to be feared. It is only when unobserved that it suddenly appears with feline stealth.

The crocodiles and caimans, as may have been gathered, are not man-eaters by occupation. Ordinarily they will not go out of their way to attack a human being. Most fatalities are due purely to accident or carelessness and not to any noteworthy aggressiveness on the part of the reptile. It is rare that one of these animals will rush from the water, or from a sand bar where it has been basking in the sun, and deliberately attack or chase a person, as will the man-eating crocodile of the Nile; instead, with a pertinacity worthy of a better cause, it lies in furtive wait for the heedless unfortunate who comes within reach of its ample jaws. That it becomes a man-eater is probably a result of accident and not of nature. Ordinarily it will eat any animal into which it can set its teeth, and it will eat at any time. If one of these animals happens to be a man a taste may be developed for human blood. It plays a lone hand when foraging; it does not hunt in groups. It eats alone and, if not pursued, on the spot. There is some variance of opinion as to whether it prefers its meat fresh or in advanced decomposition. It is not true, as one or two of the naturalists have thought, that it is unable to eat under water. Much of the smaller food it grabs while submerged is swallowed immediately. If the food is too large to engulf at one bite, and requires chewing, it then raises its head above the surface.

Although Father Zahm and others had no experiences that awakened fear of either caiman or crocodile, circumstances in the lives of other explorers have been of a different nature. While Bates was in residence on the upper Amazon an inebriated sailor sauntered down to the beach for a swim, stumbled into the water and was immediately pulled under by a caiman. While Cherrie was collecting near the mouth of the Apure on the Orinoco an Indian woman took her child to the river's edge to give it a bath. She looked about but did not see the submerged crocodile until it threw itself from the stream and disappeared with the child in its jaws. This mugger, shot the next day by Cherrie, held the remains of the child's body in its stomach. McGovern related that an Indian boy of fourteen went swimming in the river while he was at Manacapurú. Suddenly the youth gave a shriek, and the next instant was pulled beneath the surface, apparently by a caiman.

These were deaths to which the scientists were witness; many others came to their attention. Wallace wrote, "In almost every village some persons may be seen maimed by these creatures and many children are killed every year." Colonel Rondon told Roosevelt that he "knew of repeated instances where men, women, and children had become their victims." Bates became acquainted with a certain native and his son who lived in the vicinity of Ega. The year before, these two had an experience with a caiman which, in spite of its seeming incredibility, Bates had reason to believe. The boy had gone to the river's shore and was starting to bathe when, with no warning whatsoever, a caiman shoved its head and shoulders above the water, grabbed him by the leg and quickly disappeared into the water. The boy's father was near and was immediately apprised of the tragedy. Without hesitation he raced to the river and dived after the beast. Incredibly enough, the father caught up with the caiman, shoved his thumbs into its eyes, and thus caused it to release its hold on the boy. Bates was shown the scars on his thigh.

It is no myth that the dorsal surface of a crocodilian has a definite resemblance to a log or lichen-covered stone. Beebe once remarked that in British Guiana there was an abundance of logs in the streams of that country, but that about three of every four were caimans. The animals will lie motionless for hours at a time in such a position that only their backs and the tips of their heads protrude from the water. After the sun has dried the scale-covered backs they look for all the world like old water-soaked tree trunks. Birds come and light on them, and still the reptiles do not betray by the slightest movement that they are alive. Humboldt once wrote, "I have often seen flamingoes resting on their heads while the other parts of the body were covered, like the trunk of a tree, with aquatic birds." Both Cherrie and Dickey admitted that they were never nearer death than when they came within inches of using the backs of these brutes as convenient stepping-stones. In each case the man mistook the back of a crocodile for a stone and was prevented in the nick of time from making the fatal step by some inner prompting of danger.

There are few animals known to science that have not been found of value to man in one capacity or another. The crocodilians have served as a valuable source of leather; they and their eggs are used for food; and the fat of their bodies is a reservoir of oil for the natives. The most unique manner, however, in which they have been of service to man was related by Humboldt. In the days when buccaneers sailed along the coast of the Spanish Main and the English and the Spaniards were not on speaking terms, unless by way of invective, many ingenious methods were used by the Spaniards in South America to protect themselves from their enemies. Humboldt told of visiting a fort at Cumana (northern Venezuela) that had a defense as unusual as it was practical. The Spaniards had simply relied upon their own native fauna and flora. The fort was located on a slight eminence, on the sides of which were dug several concentric ditches, large enough and deep enough to hold considerable water. The first step in the defense was the planting of a certain species of cactus, abundant in the environs of Cumana, all over the earthworks between the ditches.

This soon formed an impenetrable mass of thorns and spines. The second and final step, which certainly recommends itself, was the introduction into the moats, without advance publication, of a large number of crocodiles. Whether any of the hated enemy ever attempted to tàke this fort, and if so with what success, we are not told.

THE GIANT BOAS

AMONG the twenty-four hundred described species of present-day snakes there are two that surpass all others in size. These are the anaconda, or water boa *(Eunectes murinus),* of South America, and the regal python *(Python reticulatus)* of the Malay Peninsula and the Dutch East Indies. There are only three or four other snakes that closely approach these two. Just how large the anaconda and regal python are, and which of the two is the larger, is a matter upon which even the herpetologists disagree.

In his authoritative work *Reptiles of the World,* Ditmars says that the most colossal representative of the snake world in existence today is the regal python; and that there is an authenticated case of one having been measured that was 33 feet in length. Ditmars places the anaconda second with a maximum of about 25 feet. Pope agrees with Ditmars in all respects with the exception of the length of the anaconda. He says that it reaches a length of 28 feet.

More or less to the contrary, Curran and Kauffeld declare in their recent book *Snakes and Their Ways:* "For great size among snakes honors must go to the anaconda, or water boa. There are reliable records of twenty-nine foot specimens."

It may be pointed out here that the anaconda is a very bulky snake, quite a bit more so than the regal python. Ditmars says that a 17-foot anaconda weighs more than a 24-foot python, and that he weighed an anaconda 19 feet long that tipped the scales at 236 pounds. In contrast to this is the 28-foot regal python owned by Hagenbeck that weighed just 250 pounds.

It would seem then, that the regal python is the longest snake in the world but the anaconda is the heaviest.

In spite of the scientific evidence available the notion persists that even larger anacondas and pythons are in existence. There are two chief reasons for this belief: in the first place, the habitats of these serpents have been imperfectly explored by scientifically minded men armed with tape lines, and in the second place, numerous explorers, big-game hunters, and naturalists have emerged from the jungles of South America and the Far East alike willing to take solemn oath that they have seen snakes 40 and 50 feet in length and even longer. Some of these stories are suspected at once, but none of them can be proved false. With this in mind it will prove interesting to examine a few of the statements by naturalists concerning the behavior and dimensions of the anacondas.

Waterton wrote that the "Camoudi" (anaconda) grew to a length of 30 to 40 feet, and that a friend of his had killed one 22 feet in length that was swallowing a deer. It had proceeded as far as the horns, which furnished a temporary impasse, and was patiently waiting for the digestive action to take care of the bulk of the body and liberate the head and antlers.

Gardner stated that the anaconda reached a length of 40 feet and went on to relate a story that could in no possible way be construed as underestimating this serpent's capabilities. Before his arrival at a small town (Sapê) in the interior of Brazil, a certain gentleman had turned one of his horses out to pasture. Later, no trace of it could be found anywhere although an extensive search was made in all directions. At about this stage Dr. Gardner arrived, and it was only a few days later that a *vaquero* found a giant anaconda draped over the limb of a tree that grew near a stream. The snake was dead and had seemingly been carried down by high waters and had lodged in the tree. Two horses were necessary to drag the boa from its nesting place onto land, where it was found to measure 37 feet in length. Gardner apparently saw the snake, but he fails to make clear whether he measured it or he accepted some one else's figures. The anaconda was cut open, and on the inside were discovered the bones of a horse and a considerable amount of partially digested horse flesh. The bones of the head were intact. From this evidence, it was concluded the anaconda had swallowed the horse that had disappeared under such perplexing circumstances. In support of the contention that the horse had actually been swallowed *in toto* by the snake, Gardner pointed out that very small snakes were capable of swallowing animals several times their diameter and concluded by saying, "If such be the case with these smaller kinds, it is not to be wondered at that one 37 feet long should be able to swallow a horse, particularly when it is known that previously to doing so it breaks the bones of the animal by coiling itself round it and afterward lubricates it with a slimy matter which it has the power of secreting in its mouth."

Wallace considered Gardner to be a "competent scientific observer" and believed the account just related. "It is an undisputed fact," he wrote, "that they [anacondas] devour cattle and horses, and the general belief in the country is that they are sometimes from sixty to eighty feet long." However, in the same paragraph Wallace admitted he had not seen any that were over fifteen or twenty feet in length.

Im Thurn told of seeing an anaconda killed that was 20 feet in length and 3 feet in girth, and of measuring the skin of another that was 30 feet in length. Of the latter Im Thurn related a yarn that deserves position among the snakiest of stories. A friend had taken up residence in a remote district in British Guiana. He had, like other mortals, some idiosyncrasies, and one of these was a cup of coffee every morning just at dawn. His cook had the habit of striking matches on a particular corner post when she entered the kitchen each morning sometime before daylight. One morning she found it impossible to strike the matches; one after another was discarded as it failed to light, and she was forced to try another surface. As the kitchen was illuminated she turned to examine the post and was horrified to find an enormous anaconda coiled around it, on the scales of which she had been vainly attempting to strike fire. It was the skin of this that Im Thurn found by measurement to be 30 feet long.

Other stories of the huge size of these snakes may be read in travel books on South America. Algot Lange, the author of a fairly recent book entitled *In the Amazon Jungle,* wrote that he killed an anaconda which upon measurement proved to be 56 feet long and 25 inches in diameter. Up de Graff stated that he killed one 30 feet in length and saw another that was at least 50 feet from snout to tip of tail. "This I know," he said, "from the position in which it lay. Our canoe was a twenty-four footer; the snake's head was ten or twelve feet beyond the bow; its tail was a

Courtesy of Zoological Society of Philadelphia

BOA CONSTRICTOR

Courtesy of R. L. Ditmars (Reptiles of the World)

BUSHMASTER

Courtesy of N.Y. Zoological Society

CASCABEL, OR SOUTH AMERICAN RATTLESNAKE

good four feet beyond the stern; the center of its body was looped into a huge S, whose length was the length of our dugout and whose breadth was a good five feet."

Kermit Roosevelt, in the foreword to Up de Graff's most entertaining book *Head Hunters of the Amazon,* wrote that his experiences on the length of the anaconda were not in agreement with those of Up de Graff; that he had often heard of huge snakes forty to fifty feet in length but he had never seen one. His father made an offer of $5,000 for the skin and vertebral column, or either alone, of a snake that measured more than thirty feet. Although the men with whom Kermit and his father were associated in South America frequently told of seeing enormous reptiles, no one up to that time had put in a claim for the reward. In concluding Kermit Roosevelt said, "There may be snakes of more than thirty feet, no one can definitely deny their existence, but they must be exceedingly rare."

This last sentence probably expresses the opinion of most herpetologists who have made a study of the anaconda. While one may be convinced that there are no snakes in South America over thirty feet long, it cannot be proved that they are not there. No two observers are likely to agree about the details of an incident, and the most competent may easily be mistaken at times, particularly in regard to visual evidence. Brown once killed an anaconda in the interior of British Guiana that he found to be seventeen feet long although he confessed that it looked much longer before his tape line convinced him of its actual length. If there are snakes of such tremendous lengths, it is certainly a mystery how they have managed to keep out of the naturalist's way.

There is slight evidence that the anaconda will attack man. Schomburgk told of an attack made by one of these serpents upon an Indian who belonged to a Mission station in British Guiana. The native had gone hunting with his wife and had succeeded in shooting a bird, which fell into the water so that he had to wade out some distance. While so engaged he was seized by an anaconda that suddenly appeared and threw its coils around him. He had left his weapons on the bank, but his wife heard his cries and brought him a hunting knife, with which he inflicted deep wounds in the flesh of the beast that caused it to loosen its hold and escape. Schomburgk visited the Mission soon after and found everyone in a considerable degree of excitement over it.

McGovern was paddling up a tributary of the Rio Negro with several Indians, one of whom pointed out a large anaconda stretched on a limb over the water. He grabbed his gun and fired. The shot tore away the lower part of the jaw, and the boa dropped into the water where it immediately made itself the center of a good-sized whirlpool. Very soon it appeared to regain part of its equilibrium, and hurled its body through the water straight for the boat, which it hit with enough force almost to capsize it. Another shot put an end to the incident as well as the snake. It was McGovern's notion that this snake actually took the offensive and charged the boat. Another explanation might be that it was blinded by the shot which tore away a part of its head and was simply trying to escape when it struck the craft.

Ditmars related in *The Making of a Scientist* an attack on a man by a water boa. The story was told by a government ferryman whose duty it was to pull a scow by hand along a cable as he carried passengers and cars across a lagoon on the island of Trinidad. One day a lone passenger decided on a swim, stripped off all his clothes except one undergarment, and dived into the water. An instant later a long, sinuous form detached itself from the near-by shore and quietly swam toward the bather. The latter saw the approaching anaconda but not soon enough to prevent its jaws from closing on the lone garment. In the struggle that ensued the clothing was torn away and the bather succeeded in reaching the shore alive. This was the first authentic account Ditmars had heard of an anaconda attacking a man with possible intent to kill and swallow.

The evidence above to the contrary, the anaconda does not make a practice of attacking man; it prefers animals with fewer clothes. However, the fact that it generally shies away from human beings at meal time does not mean that it is incapable of swallowing a man. A twenty- or twenty-five-foot anaconda could, beyond any reasonable doubt, swallow a medium-sized man provided the shoulders were not too broad or the waist line too pronounced, and there would be no question as to its ability to engulf a child. The human body, when prone or supine, has just the stream-line contour that should appeal to one of these huge water-inhabiting serpents, and there are no spurs, antlers, tusks, or other pronounced excrescences which, in other animals, hinder the snake from taking its dinner *in toto*. When one considers these facts it is difficult to understand just why more of the South American natives are not attacked. It may be that the anaconda judges the size of a prospective animal in terms of its height. If that be true, a man would appear much larger than any of the other animals, and it would, accordingly, leave him alone. Then, too, in an environment where food is common enough, it is logical to suppose that the anaconda would rather swallow, with ease, two or three fairly small animals than exert itself to the limit with a single, huge one. If it were sufficiently hungry, though, it might attack any animal it was capable of ingesting. Many of the swallowing feats attributed to this serpent—swallowing horses and cattle, for example—are manifestly exaggerations. It could, and probably does, swallow peccaries and capybaras, and possibly young tapirs. It likes chickens and eats them—spurs, feathers, comb and all—whenever the opportunity presents itself. Some chickens were purloined from a boat on the Amazon by an anaconda one night when Bates was aboard.

Just how large an animal a 25-foot anaconda would swallow no one can say definitely. Ditmars fed an 80-pound pig to a 20-foot python and it swallowed it, although with great difficulty. From that experience he thought a 30-foot regal python would be able to swallow a 150-pound pig. Since the anaconda has a greater bulk than the python, a 25-foot one might be able to accomplish just as much as a 30-foot regal python.

The structure of the hard palate and the relationship of the lower jaw to the upper one are responsible for the unparalleled swallowing feats of which snakes are capable. The hard palate is not rigid in snakes as it is in mammals, because the pterygoid bones are movably articulated with the palatines; and the lower jawbones, of which there are two instead of one as in higher forms, are loosely attached to the cranium by elastic connections. In practically all vertebrates the lower jaw is firmly anchored to the upper, and no amount of pulling will sever the connection;

as a result the size of the throat, or pharynx, is limited, and only small morsels may be swallowed. The loose connections in snakes, on the contrary, permit the lower jaw to be pulled away from the upper, so that the size of the object engulfed sometimes reaches perfectly astounding proportions. The existence of two lower jawbones, connected in the chin region only by elastic ligaments, is also of advantage in increasing the size of the oral and pharyngeal cavities. Moreover it facilitates to a great extent the swallowing process, for snakes ingest their food by a process which may be called "jaw-walking." Each half of the lower jaw works independently. After the teeth of the snake have taken a firm grip on the animal—the head end is invariably engulfed first—one half of the lower jaw, the right side, for instance, is advanced a slight distance and then takes a new purchase while the left side holds and, at the same time, exerts a strong pull. The next step is for the right side to pull while the left advances for a new hold. In this manner the body of the intended victim is slowly but surely "walked" into the gullet of the serpent. Snakes probably swallow other snakes more rapidly than they do any other animals. Four- or five-foot snakes have been known to swallow others of their kind only slightly inferior in size within less than ten minutes.

While engaged in ingestion serpents can quickly disgorge all that has been swallowed if they are bothered or frightened. Frequently the entire animal has been swallowed and then regurgitated. In such a case the egested body is well covered with digestive and mucus secretions. This condition probably led to the fallacious notion quoted from Gardner that snakes invariably cover their prey with saliva before they attempt to swallow them.

The anacondas, as well as all boas and pythons, kill by constriction. The efficiency of this procedure may be judged from the speed with which they kill their prey; usually only a very few minutes elapse from the moment they throw their coils about the creature until it has gasped its last. Sometimes, of course, the animal they attack may be relatively large and death follows only after a prolonged struggle, or the animal may be too large for them to kill. The largest of the boas, though, would be able to kill almost any animal if they were able to throw their coils about the body. Fortunately constrictors are never poisonous, and poisonous snakes are never constrictors.

It is commonly believed that the constrictors crush the bones of their victims, often reducing the body to a shapeless pulplike mass; and that death is caused by suffocation superinduced by the enormous pressure on the lungs. The fact that death is so rapid makes it certain that suffocation is not the immediate cause. It is known, too, from examinations of animals killed by constriction that the bones are rarely crushed. Death, it is now thought, is to be attributed to stoppage of the heart. It would appear that the snake is very sensitive to the heartbeat of its victim and following each systolic action the snake, in perfect rhythm, increases the pressure. This deprives not only the lungs of the needed space for action, but the heart as well. As a result the heart soon stops its action, death following at once. Death from suffocation is never instantaneous.

The second largest American snake is the boa constrictor *(Constrictor constrictor)*. Unfortunately the term, "boa constrictor," is often used for any and all large serpents, regardless of whether they inhabit Asia, Africa, South America, or the Philippine Islands. Very frequently the anaconda is referred to by that name. The true boa constrictor is an inhabitant of South America. In comparison with the large pythons and the anaconda it is a relatively small serpent, rarely if ever exceeding eleven or twelve feet in length.

Both the anaconda and the boa constrictor bring forth their young alive. Parturition is a big event in their lives, for they give birth to as many as fifty, sixty, and even seventy at a time and, in the case of the anaconda, these young ones are thirty or more inches long. Pythons, although they belong to the same family as the boas, are egg layers—fifty to one hundred being a normal output for them at one time.

The anaconda is a strictly aquatic form, never being found far from water, although it is a good climber and is frequently seen on limbs of trees overhanging tropical streams; but the boa constrictor is decidedly terrestrial. The former is ill tempered and difficult to handle in captivity, while the latter is tractable and is sometimes found running at large around the homes of the South

American natives in a state approaching domesticity. It is a valuable rodent destroyer and may be counted upon to perform its offices to perfection. Edwards found a boa constrictor (he called it an anaconda but must have been in error) ten feet in length living with a family in the city of Pará. It was given *carte blanche* about the premises, and there was no doubt that the family preferred its presence to that of the rats. Miller also comments on the custom of having these snakes about the home. He says that they soon become quite tame, and that many of the natives keep them for the purpose of catching rats.

Among all the articles to be found in the markets of the cities along the Amazon from Pará to Iquitos designed to attract the eye and the pocketbook of the tourist, none would be more likely to lure the chance visitor than a large snake skin. Dickey told the interesting story of a man who made a specialty of collecting big snake skins to sell to transients. It was his rule that no skin should be less than twenty feet in length. Much of his material came from boa constrictors which, of course, seldom reach a length of over twelve feet. That, however, perturbed the dealer but little; by the time the skins were ready for delivery they were perfectly prepared, extremely attractive to the eye, and not an inch below twenty feet. This gentle dissembler had learned that the oil from the sea cow (manatee) had the auspicious merit of rendering leather, snake leather in particular, quite elastic. In his preparations then his skins were anointed with sea-cow oil. They were well lathered with it and left stretched in the hot tropical sun for a whole day. At the expiration of that time one end of each skin was fastened to a post while the other was laid hold of by two men who stretched it to the desired length. After the oil had done its work it was always possible to stretch the skin to double the original length.

POISONOUS SERPENTS

THE western hemisphere has five of the world's most poisonous serpents. The rattlesnake, water moccasin, and copperhead constitute a deadly triumvirate in the United States well known to most people, and the rattler, bushmaster, and fer-de-lance form an equally well-known trio in South America. There are other species of poisonous snakes in both continents but none are so large, so potentially dangerous, so widely distributed, or so generally feared as the forms just mentioned. For instance, the Sonoran coral snake and the Harlequin snake are two relatives of the cobra found in the United States; but both of these species are small, limited in their distribution, and relatively harmless.

It is not without interest that all five of the forms named above belong to a single group of serpents, the pit vipers. Between the eye and the nostril on each side of the head of these snakes there is a deep pit, or depression. The function of this pit is still a mystery. It would seem to be important, for there is a large cavity in the maxillary bone to receive it and there is a large nerve which runs from it to the brain; yet, in spite of much histological and embryological research, its function is just as obscure as ever. However, its presence makes easy the identification of any species suspected of being a pit viper. There are a few pit vipers found in the old world, but the majority are residents of the new world; from Maine to Montevideo they are common, and often abundant. They are thick-bodied serpents, an eight-foot diamond-back rattler having a diameter of four to five inches. They have exceedingly long fangs that fold against the roof of the mouth when it is closed and project forward when the mouth is wide open. In a bushmaster eleven to twelve feet long the fangs may be an inch and a half in length. It is a mistaken notion that the removal of the fangs will render a rattler or fer-de-lance innocuous. There is a series of subsidiary fangs at the rear of the functional ones, and if the latter are pulled, others soon take their place, so that the serpent is just as lethal as before. Poison glands are at the bases of the fangs, and the venom travels through the teeth to tiny openings near their ends. The hypodermic needle is very similar in plan to the fang of a pit viper. Indeed it might be said that when the first poison fang came into operation the hypodermic needle was invented. As much as a full teaspoonful of venom may be ejected from the glands at one time. Because the pit vipers are relatively large, have such long fangs capable of penetrating deep into the body, and eject large amounts of venom, they are among the most dangerous of snakes.

Just one species of rattlesnake is found in the southern continent. This may be considered strange, for in the United States there are fifteen species in all. These range in size from the pygmy rattlesnake *(Sistrurus miliarius),* not over twelve to fifteen inches in length, to the huge diamond-back rattler *(Crotalus adamanteus)* which is known to reach nine feet. They are found in every state in the Union. The South American rattler *(Crotalus terrificus)* has an extensive range; roughly, it embraces all of the western hemisphere between the Tropic of Cancer and the Tropic of Capricorn. It is five to six feet in length, and the body is heavy, as in all rattlers. In Central America and South America it goes by the name of *cascabel* ("rattle"). The scientific name *Crotalus terrificus* is apt for, according to Ditmars, it is "the most poisonous of the rattlers as well as the boldest." The *cascabel* will not voluntarily retreat from a human being and will actually take the initiative and crawl slowly toward the intruder; conditions being right, it may edge close enough to strike. This approach is all the more insidious for the reason the rattle, although well developed, may be employed little or not at all.

It is considered "the most poisonous of the rattlers" because its venom has a neurotoxic effect. Snake venoms are of two kinds: neurotoxic and hemolytic. The former attacks the nerves, and the latter the blood and vascular system. In reality, all snake venoms contain both elements in varying proportions. The venoms of pit vipers are for the most part hemolytic, while the venoms of cobras, mambas, and coral snakes are neurotoxic. The latter is said to be more dangerous to human beings since the rapidity with which it acts upon the nerves leaves but little time for effective treatment. Humans have been known to expire within one minute after being bitten by the African mamba, according to Curran and Kauffeld.

The venom of all the rattlers inhabiting the United States is hemolytic. Such a venom disintegrates the blood cells of the body, destroys the walls of the capillaries, and produces extensive hemorrhage.

The bite of a *cascabel* generally results in paralysis. The nerve center controlling respiration is paralyzed, and the victim dies of suffocation. Among certain natives the belief is widespread that the bite of this rattler will break a man's neck. The explanation probably lies in the action of the toxin on the spinal cord and the muscles of the neck. With this region of the body paralyzed the head falls forward on the chest or rolls from side to side just as it might if the neck were actually broken. The natives are said to fear the *cascabel* more than they do the fer-de-lance.

Cherrie came near being bitten by a *cascabel* near the Orinoco, as he was following a small species of warbler that he was eager to secure for his collection. The bird fell, at his shot, into some tall grass. Without hesitation, Cherrie thrust in his hand—to encounter, not a soft feather-covered body, but a hard scaly object. It was a rattler, and just why he was not bitten he does not yet know.

The largest of the South American poisonous snakes is the bushmaster *(Lachesis mutus),* known to reach a length of at least twelve feet. Specimens of this length, however, are rare. Indeed, the discovery of a bushmaster anywhere may be described as news, for it is abundant at no point in its range. It is probably more common in Costa Rica and Panama than elsewhere, according to Ditmars, although it is spread over much of Central America and the tropical portions of South America.

The bushmaster is moderately slender, more so than the other viperine forms. A four-foot diamônd-back rattler exceeds in weight a bushmaster six feet in length. The *surucucù,* as the bushmaster is called in Brazil, has habits similar to those already described for the *cascabel.* It is said to attack man occasionally; and, being larger than either fer-de-lance or *cascabel,* it has fangs proportionately longer.

The idea of being chased and attacked by a poisonous snake, especially by such a dangerous form as a bushmaster, is one fit for a nightmare. Popular notion has it that snakes travel very rapidly, and that a man chased by an angered racer or rattler would have just as much chance of outdistancing his pursuer as a sloth chased by an ocelot. Recently serious efforts have been made to determine the rate at which several of the North American snakes can travel. The results of these investigations will come as a distinct surprise to many, for they show that none of the snakes, not even those considered as the fastest, are able to do better than about three miles an hour. It is evident, then, that a man can walk faster than a snake can crawl. Each day the commuter in his early-morning dash for the express exceeds the best speed of which any snake is capable. Although this may come as a surprise, it should be received with relief and thanksgiving. Hereafter if a snake is encountered, even a twelve-foot bushmaster or a twenty-five-foot anaconda, one has only to remember that a walk at the rate of four miles per hour will outdistance the snake.

The markings on the bushmaster are striking, and have been admired by others than herpetologists. "The body hue is pale brown," according to Ditmars, "often pinkish. A series of large and bold, dark brown or black blotches extend along the body. These are wide on the back and abruptly narrow on the sides." Waterton wrote that this serpent is "unrivalled in his display of every color of the rainbow, and unmatched in the effects of his deadly poison. He is sole monarch of these forests."

Of all the new-world vipers the bushmaster is the only one to lay eggs. The female lays twelve or more at a time in a depression in the ground, after which she coils over the top of them and remains there until they hatch. There is a very interesting physiological fact associated with some if not all, of the oviparous serpents. After the eggs are laid and the female coils about them, the temperature of the body begins to rise. Captive specimens in cages have been found to develop a "temporary fever" of as much as twelve degrees. This temperature of the female, which is three to twelve degrees higher than that of the male in the same cage, persists until after the eggs are hatched. Ordinarily snakes have a temperature that is about one degree lower than the air or water about them.

Brown was one of the few explorers who had an unpleasant

experience with the bushmaster. On an excursion up the Mazaruni River in British Guiana he and his men had halted to cook their breakfast. Brown was startled by the cries of some of his helpers who pointed frantically into the woods just behind him. He turned quickly and saw a large bushmaster not more than ten yards off coming straight toward him. He grabbed his gun and fired. The smoke cleared within a few seconds, and there to his bewilderment was what he took for the same bushmaster still traveling for him. He fired again and waited with considerable apprehension for the smoke to clear a second time. This time he saw to his relief that he had found his mark. Upon investigation Brown found not one dead bushmaster but two; one was six feet nine inches long, and the other six feet four.

Miller had even a closer call than Brown. On a scientific expedition in one of the remoter regions of southern Colombia he and some companions were making their way toward camp along the bed of a small unknown stream. It was not an interesting spot, and they found it difficult to proceed rapidly on account of the slippery, moss-covered stones. Suddenly "a dark, shadowy form lunged from the blackness of a cavern among the boulders and clung for an instant to the cuff" of Miller's coat. It then fell to the ground and threaded its way out of his sight. It was a bushmaster four or five feet in length. Miller gives it as his observation that the bushmaster is "by nature sluggish; one person may pass close by without arousing the anger, while to a second individual, immediately following, it will show resentment, although it may not strike; but a third may consider himself fortunate indeed, if he does not draw the full measure of the reptile's fury."

Prior to the descent of the River of Doubt, the Roosevelt-Rondon expedition was divided into three parties: Roosevelt, Rondon, Cherrie, and others went down the Rio Duvida; Fiala and Lauriadó descended the Tocantins; while Miller and Captain Amilcar traveled by way of the Gy-Paraná and Madeira. This latter party was divided—Miller and certain of the men traveled in one group and collected while Captain Amilcar and his associates surveyed. Miller relates that one day the Brazilian captain's party had an experience that almost ended tragically. In order to make sights with the telemeter frequent stops were necessary, and it was their habit to drive the canoe into the growth along the shore. This method was highly successful until on one occasion a seven-foot bushmaster was dislodged from a limb and dropped into the bottom of the dugout. The native paddlers, and some of the scientists as well, immediately elected to take to the river. Captain Amilcar alone remained impassive—coolly he drew his gun and shot the reptile.

Schomburgk told of a snake bite which nearly resulted in two deaths. A few weeks before the German botanist arrived in Bartika Grove the son of a mulatto had been bitten on the cheek by a bushmaster. Shortly afterwards the boy's father discovered his son lying unconscious on the ground and, realizing what had happened, immediately dropped to his knees and sucked out the wound. Within fifteen minutes the father began to experience all the symptoms of snake poisoning; the bushmaster venom had entered his system through a defective tooth. The boy died and the father had not yet completely recovered when Schomburgk saw him.

The fer-de-lance occurs much more commonly in South America than either the rattlesnake or the bushmaster. It is the characteristic venomous snake of South America as the rattler is of the United States. Its range includes Mexico, Central America, certain islands of the West Indies, and South America from Colombia to northern Argentina. Almost everywhere within this region the fer-de-lance is an ever-present danger. There are said to be some three dozen different species, all belonging to the genus *Bothrops,* but *Bothrops atrox* is probably more abundant than any of the others; certainly it is the most widely distributed. It is three to four feet long ordinarily, but specimens measuring eight feet have been encountered. The name fer-de-lance (lance head) is Creole-French and originated in the West Indies. In Brazil the natives refer to this species as the *jararaca* (arrow); in Central America they call it *barba amarilla* (yellow beard); in the Guianas the name *labarri* or *labaria* is employed. In the Canal Zone it is called *tommigoff*. "Coloration is variable, from gray to olive, brown, or even reddish, with dark, light-edged cross-bands or triangles, the apex of these extending to the center of the back," according to Ditmars.

It is not to be wondered at that the fer-de-lance is abundant. The females produce astoundingly large litters; as many as sixty and seventy young are born at a time. The surprising feature is that fer-de-lances are not even more common than they are. Ditmars tells of three Honduran specimens that produced litters of 64, 65, and 71 respectively. Each young one is about a foot in length when born, and its fangs and poison glands are functional. Indeed, if the young are disturbed they instinctively begin striking and, such is the power of the toxin that a bite from a baby fer-de-lance may prove very serious. The toxin is extremely rapid in its action. The direct consequences of a fer-de-lance bite are described by Schomburgk. A young Indian and his wife joined the German botanist on a trip into the Kukenam River valley. At the time of the episode the party was walking single file along a rude trail; Schomburgk was near the rear of the procession with the Indian woman just behind him. He stopped for a minute to examine a flower and as he started on the woman screamed. She had been bitten twice by a fer-de-lance, just below the knee and a little farther down on the leg. Immediately Schomburgk applied a tourniquet, and several of the men took turns sucking the wound. The medicine chest was soon produced and the wound was scarified. In spite of these efforts convulsions seized the woman within a very few minutes. These were followed by vomiting, and hemorrhages of the eyes, and ears, and nose. The woman, until she became incapable of speech, complained of frightful pains in the leg, around the heart, and in the back. Her pulse was 120 to 130. The vomiting and hemorrhages continued up to the time of her death, sixty-three hours after the accident.

The extreme potency of the venom is further illustrated by an incident that occurred at the serum station at Tela, Honduras, that has been related by Ditmars. A native woman, in grating coconut at home had broken the skin at several points on her finger tips. In the midst of her labors her husband was brought from a near-by plantation suffering from the bite of a fer-de-lance. A native doctor was secured, but she assisted him by bathing the wound which was bleeding profusely. In spite of all their ministrations the husband died within a couple of hours. Shortly after this symptoms of snake poisoning developed in the woman, and she died the next day. Apparently she had absorbed a sufficient amount of venom through her lacerated fingers to cause death.

A native working for George Cherrie on the Orinoco was bitten by a fer-de-lance. Cherrie was not apprised of the accident until almost an hour afterward. He grabbed his first-aid kit and ran to the man as quickly as he could. Although bitten less than sixty minutes before, the man was dead; had probably died within thirty minutes, Cherrie says. The incident gave him an interesting sidelight on the native philosophy. The Indians are of one mind in believing that "what is to be, will be." This man having been bitten by the deadly viper, his companions conjectured that he was to die; and they squatted at his side and made no attempt to reach Cherrie until it was too late.

On the Approague River in French Guiana, Cherrie had reason to recall this Indian philosophy. At the time he was particularly interested in trapping small mammals and was living in an abandoned ranch house. He swung his hammock therein, noticing the tracks of many animals on the dirt floor, and set traps close to the house and almost immediately underneath his hammock. He customarily left a lantern burning on the floor and as the traps were sprung during the night he picked up the lantern, determined the identity of the catch, and then removed it to a jar containing preservative.

One night he did "a very foolish thing." He had walked far that day, and had made a large collection. By the time this had been taken care of, midnight had passed. He tumbled into his hammock and was almost immediately asleep. Sometime between then and dawn the springing of a trap awakened him. As he relates it, he was just too tired and sleepy to care; without getting his lantern he leaned over the edge of the hammock and felt about in the darkness for the trap, which he could hear thumping about. Finally he located it and lifted it into the light of the lantern. Incontinently he was wide awake, for the trap held a fer-de-lance that was striking again and again at his hand. Fortunately, he was not hit. The trap was dropped and Cherrie was out of his hammock in a second. He unscrewed the lid containing his preservative jar and, with the help of two sticks, dropped both snake and trap into the formalin.

Bates had as narrow an escape as any of the naturalists. While collecting in the forest near Pará he stepped on the tail of a *jararaca*. It turned quickly and bit into his trousers near the ankle. Before proceedings went further an Indian boy with him cut the serpent in two with a machete.

Of all the naturalists—from Humboldt, to Bates, to Beebe, who have written their travels—none was bitten by a poisonous snake. The sum total of their journeys took them to all parts of the continent, and they made no attempt to avoid the favorite haunts of the fer-de-lances, bushmasters, and rattlers. Even so there are many fatalities in South America among the natives, and the death rate is high enough to warrant serious attention. As a result antitoxins are now procurable for all the important viperine snakes of South America. Too much credit cannot be given to Dr. Vital Brazil and his Serum Institute at São Paulo, where the snake antitoxins were first manufactured. They now prepare five antivenins: one for the several species of *Bothrops,* of which the fer-de-lance is the chief offender; one for the rattlesnake; one for the bushmaster; one for the coral snakes; and a fifth, which is a combination of all four for use when the identity of the snake is unknown.

The explorer who wishes to make a long sojourn in the interior may secure these antitoxins and feel relatively safe on the score of *Crotalus* and *Lachesis* venoms. The native, if not too far from civilization, may be able to get an injection of serum before the toxin has completed its deadly work. However, the Indian frequently disregards the antivenin and puts his faith in the medicine man or local "snake doctor."

An antitoxin may be prepared for any of the true toxins. We use the word "toxin" very frequently as a synonym for poison. A toxin should be defined as any substance that, when injected in non-fatal doses into suitable animals, will produce a neutralizing substance called antitoxin. To date there are few such toxins known. The diphtheria, tetanus, and botulism germs produce powerful toxins; the locust produces one called robin, and the castor bean produces an even more powerful one in ricin. An experimental animal may be immunized against these, and against the venom of the various snakes, which also produce true toxins. As a result antitoxins may be prepared to nullify the effects of huge amounts of venom which may enter the human body. These antitoxins are prepared in the same way as those for diphtheria and tetanus. Suitable healthy animals are selected—the horse is used most often. Into this is injected a small amount of the toxin. The animal may have a mild reaction to this which quickly subsides. A slightly larger dose is then injected. The amounts of toxin are gradually increased over a period of weeks until almost any amount may be introduced into the blood stream of the experimental animal without ill effects. The animal is now immune: it has produced within its body a large quantity of the immunizing substance we call antibody. The particular antibody in this case is antitoxin.

A large vein is now opened and a quantity of blood drawn off. This may temporarily weaken the horse but has no other ill effect. The blood is allowed to stand, and in a short while a straw-colored liquid, the blood serum, rises to the top. This contains the antitoxin. After it has been standardized and preservatives have been added it becomes the antitoxin of commerce. Naturalists, missionaries, rubber prospectors, diamond hunters may feel relatively safe in the worst snake section of equinoctial America if they have the specially prepared antitoxins.

Some people have the mistaken idea that mongooses, peccaries, hedgehogs, etc., are immune to the venom of poisonous serpents. These animals are notorious as snake eaters, the mongoose in particular—they eat snakes as toads eat earthworms—but apparently nature has not endowed them with immunity. The peccaries have a very thick skin and subcutaneous layers of connective tissue which effectively prevent venom from reaching the blood vessels. The mongoose is so light on its feet that it seldom, if ever, gets bitten. The mongoose or peccary can eat the poisonous snake—poison and all—without ill effect, for any venom taken into the stomach by way of the mouth is neutralized by the digestive juices before it can reach the blood. A human being may swallow spoonfuls of rattlesnake or bushmaster venom and experience no ill effects whatever. A small part of a spoonful, introduced into one of the large veins or arteries, will quickly cause death unless counteracted.

THE PIRANHA

ON THE morning of the 3rd of April our Indians caught with a hook the fish known in the country by the name of *caribe,* or *carabito,* because no other fish has such a thirst for blood. It attacks bathers and swimmers, from whom it bites away considerable pieces of flesh. The Indians dread extremely these *caribes;* and several of them showed us the scars of deep wounds in the calf of the leg and in the thigh, made by these little animals. They swim at the bottom of rivers; but if a few drops of blood be shed on the water, they rise by thousands to the surface, so that if a person be only slighten bitten, it is difficult for him to get out of the water without receiving a severer wound. When we reflect on the numbers of these fish, the largest and most voracious of which are only four or five inches long, on the triangular form of their sharp and cutting teeth, and on the amplitude of their retractile mouths, we need not be surprised at the fear which the *caribe* excites in the inhabitants of the banks of the Apure and Orinoco. In places where the river was very limpid, where not a fish appeared, we threw into the water little morsels of raw flesh and in a few minutes a perfect cloud of *caribes* had come to dispute their prey."

In these words Humboldt gave to his readers what is probably the first accurate picture of a fish characterized by some scientists as the most ferocious in the world. Over a century has elapsed since the German scientist made its acquaintance in the clear waters of the Apure, and in that time science has learned a great deal more about it.

This fish is known locally in South America by several names. *Caribe* and *perai* are employed in the northern part of the continent. In Brazil it is called piranha (from two Tupi Indian words: *piro,* fish, and *sainha* tooth). By certain Indians of Bolivia it is styled ironically *palomita* (little dove), according to Rusby. English residents are inclined to designate it as cannibal fish, and water bulldog. Since the greater part of this fish's range is Brazilian, where Portuguese is the official language, it will be referred to here as the piranha.

The body of the piranha is short, broad, and laterally compressed, and in general outline resembles the bass and sunfish. A Guianan species measured by Schomburgk had a length of one foot and five inches and a dorso-ventral diameter of eight inches. The small species of the Apure referred to by Humboldt was ash-colored above, with a faint trace of green, and a rich orange below. Gardner described a larger species from southern Brazil as darkish brown on the dorsal side and yellowish white on the belly. Wherever found, it has a blunt face with the lower jaw projecting belligerently beyond the upper. Both jaws are strongly curved and well equipped with several triangular teeth, sharp as the fangs of a bushmaster. Rusby was impressed with the muscular development of the jaws, describing them as "strikingly large and powerful" and comparable to those of a bulldog.

There are many species: how many, no one seems to know. Schomburgk mentioned four from British Guiana (*Pygocentrus niger, P. piraya, Pygopristis fumarius,* and *Serrasalmo aureus*), and Hartley extended the list from that region to include at least four more. If there are eight species from the rivers of this small part of the piranha's range, the total number must be quite large when the Orinoco and Amazon basins are included. All of the species belong to the extensive South American family, *Characinidae.*

The majority of the piranhas are comparatively small, perhaps averaging less than a foot in length. The species Humboldt described from the Apure, it will be recalled, was only four to five inches long, and another on the Rio Negro encountered by Miller was no more than eight inches. Miller stated that he had collected a form in the Orinoco that exceeded eighteen inches from lip to end of caudal fin, and both Gardner and Dyott claimed to have seen others that were all of two feet. Cherrie says that they sometimes attain a weight of eight to ten pounds.

Piranhas are found east of the Andes from Venezuela and the Guianas south to Paraguay. Although inhabiting practically all streams in this area they prefer the placid waters above and below falls. This is fortunate, for the river men, compelled to wade while negotiating bad rapids, would find their presence very

Courtesy of N.Y. Aqua

PIRANHA

Courtesy of N.Y. Aquarium

PIRANHA DENTITION

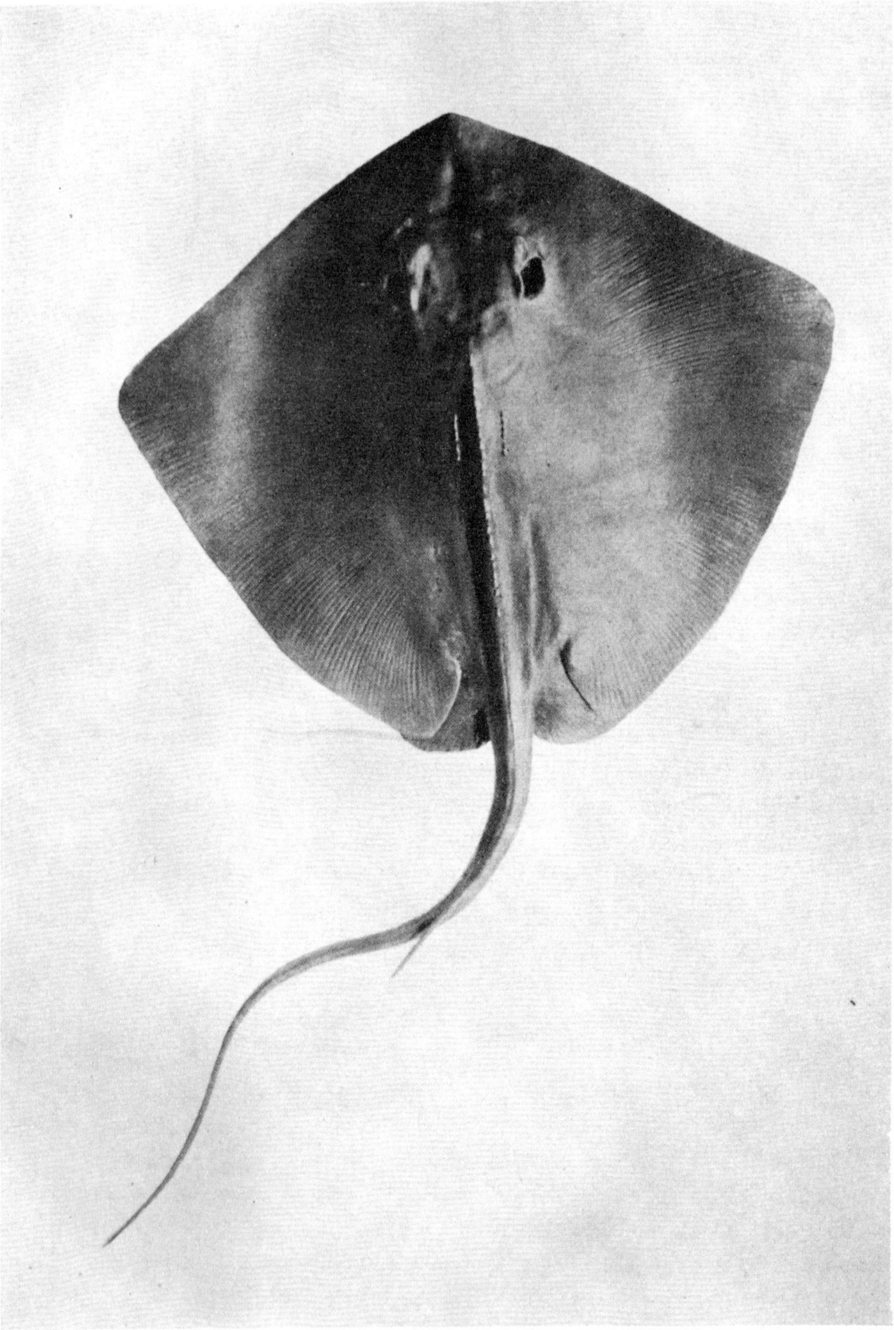

Courtesy of American Museum of Natural History

STING RAY

troublesome. The piranha thrives in countless hordes, and even though the species may be small it makes up for its lack of size in numbers and cold ferocity.

Humboldt declared the piranha to be a bottom fish, but the experience of others led them to believe it has no preference either for deep water or for shallow. It has been seen at all hours of the day both inshore and midstream.

According to Brown they lay their eggs on submerged vegetation in some secluded spot near the bank of a stream. The particular location he discovered was just beneath the surface of a Guiana river and consisted of a mat of roots with some associated aquatic plants. He became aware of the place when he saw two piranhas near the roots that were engaged, Indians said, in watching the eggs. He secured one of the roots and found not only eggs but tiny young already hatched. The eggs were approximately one-eighth of an inch in diameter and white in color with a hard shell. The young were not much larger than the eggs, and were covered with a gelatinous substance that had the effect of causing them to stick together in the water.

The piranha has the sinister reputation of being the fiercest in the world. Humboldt declared it to be "one of the greatest scourges of these climates"; Dyott wrote that he could think of no other fish that could compare with it in ferocity; and Im Thurn said that it "is probably as voracious an animal as exists."

Almost a century ago Bates wrote that "their taste is indiscriminate, and their appetite most ravenous." As scientists have become better acquainted with these fish they have discovered not only that they are omnivorous, but that they attack every form of life that ventures into their aquatic domain. Most carnivorous animals prey on smaller creatures: these fish attack a tapir or a peccary just as readily as they do creatures of their own size.

Most of their food must come from their own immediate environment; hence they prey without ceasing on the numerous other fish inhabiting the rivers and ponds and marshes. Fish is a staple to them as cecropia leaves are to the sloth; with this difference, however, that sloths rarely add anything else to their menu while the piranhas do. The life of other fish in tropical South America, must be one of constant vigilance; a single moment of languor may prove to be its undoing. Any number of the fish caught by the natives show scars and other evidences of piranha savagery; tail fins may be reduced to stumps, semilunar notches may have been cut in dorsal or ventral fins. The haimara is a fish of the Guiana rivers, much larger than any piranha. Brown witnessed the fierce onslaught of a mob of these fresh-water corsairs on a haimara that had been wounded with an arrow. The incident reminded Brown of "a parallel case on land—a stricken deer pursued by wolves."

Schomburgk contended that the piranhas, when attacking fish larger than themselves, "first of all bite off the tail fin and thereby rob it of its chief organ of locomotion while the remainder fall upon it like harpies, pull off the flesh, and tear it to pieces until the head only is left." It is possible that Schomburgk accepted the word of the natives for this behavior of the piranha without actually observing it.

Whitney wrote, "Blood, not flesh, is what the fish craves." The taste of blood to it is like the scent of powder to a war horse. The reaction is almost lightninglike: the fish is incontinently thrown into a paroxysm of passion and fury. A wounded animal in the water, or a bit of raw meat cast into a stream, acts like magic in drawing the piranhas from their subterranean retreats. A pool at one minute placid as an aquarium, and apparently as devoid of any danger, is the next instant so filled with writhing, contesting bodies that it resembles a vortex. A reptile or mammal may sometimes occupy a piranha-haunted stream for hours, provided there are no open wounds on the body. But if one of these beasts carries a laceration from which issues so much as a single drop of blood it will be fortunate if it escapes without serious injury.

Time and again a native hooks a fish but finds the flesh removed from the body in huge chunks before it can be pulled in. It was the experience of Miller and others that a wounded bird or mammal that dropped into a stream after being shot was rarely recovered. If a mammal, the carcass was quickly reduced to bones; if a bird, nothing was left except feathers which the current of the water soon swept away. Roosevelt shot a capybara that sank to the bottom of a stream. Ten minutes later half of it was gone. McGovern said he threw the body of a sheep into a river where piranhas were rife. It disappeared before their voracity in exactly two and one-half minutes.

The naturalists frequently dispose of skinned carcasses of monkeys and other animals by throwing them into the streams. Immediately these river carnivores surge upon them from all quarters and ravenously tear them to shreds. Miller said that at times the piranhas "threw one another out of the water in their mad struggles to reach the gory repast."

An incident that occurred during A. Hamilton Rice's journey to the upper Orinoco deserves more than passing comment. Rice saw a large hawk gliding swiftly near the surface of the river with a serpent in its curved talons. Whether the body of the snake struck the water, Rice does not say; but suddenly a piranha shot from the river, grabbed the reptile, and returned with it beneath the surface. An observation made by Hartley in British Guiana lends support to this remarkable account. The American scientist stated that a native species of bird, the kiskadee, makes periodical trips from bushes along a stream to the surface of the water, where it catches insects and an occasional minnow. The bird customarily hits the water with a distinct splash while seizing its prey. This splash is the cause of the bird's undoing for every so often an alert piranha splits the surface like a knife and seizes the luckless creature before it can continue its flight.

If any animal should enjoy safety in these turbulent tropical streams, it should be the caiman, clad in a heavy cuirass of horny plates. Ordinarily this reptile has nothing to fear from the piranha; but, if wounded, it quickly falls into the same predicament as any other wounded beast. Cherrie relates that he once shot a caiman as it lay sunning itself on the bank of the Paraguay River. The bullet tore a hole in its side and it immediately fled to the water. Almost instantly he was astounded to see the huge reptile actually leaping from the water in its desperation to regain the shore. The explanation was soon clear; to the wound, now bleeding profusely, there clung a dozen or more rabid piranhas, each more eager than the others to get its share of the sanguinary feast.

Although living flesh makes up the normal diet of the piranha, it will eat other foods. Cassava bread tossed into the stream is eagerly eaten, as are various fruits and seeds. Hartley told of a large citrate factory in British Guiana that, after extracting the oil from limes, dumped the skins into the river. Even these were engorged.

The naturalists are almost unanimous in saying that splashes attract the piranhas. The Indians, they state, take advantage of this fact whenever they wish to shoot these fish, and lash the water with sticks. The piranhas are attracted at once, and so unbridled is their gluttony that they actually snap pieces from the sticks. Brown declared that the piranhas of the Corentyne bit fragments out of the paddles while they were being drawn through the water. Could any better examples be given to illustrate the voracity of these mad fish?

There is some disagreement on the question of whether the piranha is cannibalistic. Miller threw the dead bodies of monkeys and birds into the Pilcomayo, and they were speedily stripped of every ounce of flesh. When he threw dead or stunned piranhas into the same stream they were not touched at all. Roosevelt, citing Miller's experience, gave it as his opinion that the piranhas did not consume their own kind.

Contrariwise, all the other naturalists who have expressed an opinion have stated that the piranhas are cannibalistic. Schomburgk caught a piranha, took it off the hook and dropped it not far from the river's edge. It came to life, however, and flopped back into the stream. In no time a score of piranhas were at it, soon reducing it to bones and fin-rays. André threw a paste containing carbolic acid into the Caura. As the poison floated on the surface it was speedily grabbed and devoured by piranhas. These, before many minutes, showed signs of being queasy, and were quickly attacked by their more fortunate kin who tore them to bits. Hartley caught many piranhas in the Mazaruni that had had pieces deftly removed from tail, fin, or body; he found that the entrails from piranhas made excellent bait for catching other piranhas, and that if these, in turn, were killed and thrown back into the river their uncles, aunts, and cousins showed no solicitude: they lost little time in devouring them.

The piranha relishes human flesh just as much as tapir or capybara. Evidence of that is encountered in every volume written by a South American naturalist or explorer, from Humboldt to Beebe. Miller had a piece taken out of a finger; Im Thurn had a similar experience; Cherrie was severely bitten when he fell from a tree into a piranha-inhabited stream; and Rusby lost considerable flesh from fingers on two separate occasions. Miller knew two persons who escaped the murderous jaws of the piranha only after being bitten cruelly; Im Thurn was present when one of his boatmen had the flesh torn from a toe; McGovern saw the effect of piranha greed on two natives—one had lost a toe, the other a finger; Cherrie knew the woman curator of the Museum of Pará who lost a finger while trailing her hand in the water during a boat ride; Schomburgk applied first aid to an Indian in his employ who had a respectable mouthful taken from his foot; and practically every other scientist with South American experience has testified that the natives frequently receive ugly wounds from the piranha as they bathe or swim along the banks of the river.

Cherrie came nearer death than any of the others. He was fishing for piranhas from a limb overhanging an equatorial stream. The fishing was good, for there were many of these fish in the water all eager to take the hook. He lost his balance and fell, tearing a gash in one of his arms. With his arm bleeding he was catapulted into the middle of a school of piranhas. The shore was not far distant, but before he reached it he was badly bitten in several places. He was convinced that if he had been stunned for only a few seconds, he would never have come out of the water alive.

Im Thurn knew of several men who had fallen into rivers of British Guiana to be found days later with practically every vestige of flesh torn from the bones.

Few men have had more experience in the Brazilian wilds than Colonel Rondon, who accompanied Theodore Roosevelt in his descent of the River of Doubt. He related his manifold adventures with the piranha to our former President in their hours and days together discussing the animal life of that country. Rondon himself had lost a toe to this fish. He knew of a twelve-year-old boy who, only a short time before, had gone for a swim, was attacked and torn to pieces. On another occasion a member of his party was wading a stream when he was attacked. The fish bit him cruelly on his legs, and on his hands, too, when he tried to beat them off. He did not recover completely for six months. On still another occasion Rondon had his men dynamite a stream for fish. Many were killed or stunned and soon floated on the surface. A lieutenant in his employ waded in after them and soon had his hands so full that he stuck one in his mouth for safe keeping. The fish was a piranha, suddenly came to life, and lived up to its evil reputation by taking a bite out of the man's tongue. The wound bled so profusely they feared he would die. One day a native rode away from camp on the back of a mule. Some time later the mule returned riderless. They followed the tracks left by the animal through the forests until they came to a ford. Here they discovered the skeleton of the unlucky man picked as clean of flesh as a fossilized cranium. They did not know whether he had drowned or been killed by the fish.

At least on one occasion an army was attacked by piranhas. The biographer of Bolívar, Ybarra, recounts that on May 26, 1819, while the famous Liberator was leading his army across the Venezuelan llanos to New Granada, some of his men were severely wounded as they swam a stream intercepting their route.

These and many other equally tragic episodes in the life of native and naturalist that might be enumerated, all tell the same story—a grim and harrowing story that no one familiar with this fish can possibly doubt.

The danger from piranhas is not over the moment they have been pulled from the water. If caught on a line it is always wise to club them into insensibility before trying to remove the hook. Lee Crandall, an assistant of Beebe in 1909, attempted to take a hook from the bony mouth of a piranha without first taking the precaution of reducing it to a subliminal state. The piranha turned itself into the correct position and adroitly removed a piece of flesh from his finger. Wickham suffered a similar loss.

Rusby can speak with more first-hand knowledge anent the viciousness of a piranha out of the water than any of the other naturalists, for he twice had fingers partially amputated. On the first occasion, he landed a piranha that, after a few preliminary struggles, lay perfectly quiet on the ground at his feet. Not being acquainted with its potentialities, he stooped over with the idea of removing the hook. The fish had a brighter idea, however, for as soon as his hand came within reach, it leaped, quick as a flash, and grabbed his forefinger, removing a piece of tissue about the size and shape of a kidney bean. On the next occasion, which left no lingering doubt in Rusby's mind as to the piranha's skill and cunning, the preliminaries were much the same; but he now had the advantage of experience and placed his foot on the side of the fish before proceeding to remove the hook. He had some difficulty, however, and for a second relaxed the pressure of his shoe. A second was entirely too long a period of time; the piranha, instantly taking advantage of its opportunity, squirmed free and leaped for Rusby's thumb. The aim was accurate, and he suffered a very nasty wound that took weeks in healing. Rusby said that in this case the piranha, instead of just biting once and then releasing its hold, clung to his thumb where it continued to chew vigorously until loosened.

Quite a few piranhas, first and last, were thrown onto the deck of the boat carrying Roosevelt into the interior of Brazil. "I never," he exclaimed, "witnessed an exhibition of such impotent, savage fury as was shown by these piranhas as they flopped on deck. One of them flopped into a cloth and seized it with a bulldog grip. Another grasped one of its fellows; another snapped at a piece of wood and left the teeth marks deep therein." Hartley declared that "the fish in the boat is nearly as bad as the fish in the water," and that the fisherman must be very careful not to get fingers or toes too close to the captive. According to him these fish exercise a certain amount of sagacity in that they will lie perfectly quiet until some part of man's anatomy comes within reach of their teeth.

Dyott was astounded as much at the piranha's vitality as its viciousness. He decapitated one of them and, when he reached down to pick up the body, the jaws snapped at him even though the head had been severed for nearly a minute. Up de Graff summed up this matter of the piranha's savagery very well when he wrote, "Either in the water or on dry land it is as vicious as a mad dog."

Could anything be more in keeping with the feral disposition of these fish than that they should, while out of the water, give vent to their rage by growling and squealing! This characteristic might reasonably be doubted if it had not been vouched for by at least four or five of the naturalists. The first mention of it that we have comes from Schomburgk, who said that it "grunts when drawn out of the water." Rusby said that, when his thumb was being masticated by a piranha, all of the time the fish was "emitting its peculiar growl," a noise very much like the low growling of a dog. Up de Graff declared that it "emits a noise that can only be described as a low-pitched bark—more striking, if not more formidable, even than its bite." The ones Roosevelt heard, on the contrary, produced an "extraordinary squealing sound."

The only redeeming feature of the piranha is its edibility. Most of the naturalists found its flesh quite to their liking although like most members of the family to which it belongs it is very bony. The sharpness of the piranha's teeth makes it more difficult to land than other fish of its size. Paez was eager to catch fish from the South American streams in order to sketch them, and came well equipped with all the customary Izaak Walton paraphernalia. His disgust was complete when, after each strike, his line was pulled in minus, not only a fish, but the hook as well. This kept up until his supply of "grappling irons" was exhausted. Not until later did he learn that his failure was attributable to the piranha.

The most successful fisherman is said to be the one who uses a long line with a wire leader and allows the bait to sink almost to the bottom of the stream. Without a wire leader the line is snipped in two every time. Although Roosevelt used large hooks and a leader made of double strands of copper wire, some of the fish snapped the hook in two and others bit through the wire with comparative ease. The piranha's hard, bony mouth makes it essential that a taut line be kept, and that the hook be anchored at once; otherwise the fish is likely to escape. It strikes hard as a rule, but after a few vigorous rushes tires quickly; and there remains little of a fight to warm the heart of the ardent angler.

In only one other way does the Indian find the piranha of any value. Practically all of the natives living in the equatorial forest use the blow-gun and poison-tipped darts. It is customary that the tip of the dart be almost severed before shooting, so that it will break off in the animal and remain to perform its sinister function. For severing the points the native carries with him the lower jaw of the piranha with its row of razorlike teeth.

STING RAYS

THE sting rays, or stingarees as they are often called, must be the outcome of some primordial era of extravagant depression, for they are, by all odds, the most utterly depressed of vertebrate animals. They are closely related to the sharks and dogfish, and they might well be likened to some of these predators that were unable to escape the leveling influence of a huge paleozoic steam roller. The extreme prostration of their bodies is due more immediately to the almost abnormal enlargement of the pectoral fins, which extend far on each side of the mid-line and are uninterruptedly confluent in front, where they form the tip of the snout. Extending from the posterior end of the rhomboid body, or disc, there is, in most sting rays, a long whiplike tail, one and one-half to two times the length of body. The size of these creatures varies a great deal, but the larger ones are at least three to four feet across. Of course these do not approach the proportions of the huge eagle rays, some of which have a width of nearly twenty feet.

Some ten genera and fifty species of sting rays have been described. They are found the world around in all warm seas, and a few forms are common in temperate oceans. The most surprising aspect of their distribution is the appearance of a few in the fresh-water streams of South America. Just what factor was responsible for their leaving salt water to embrace a circumscribed fluvial existence is not known, but such rivers as the Amazon, Orinoco, Corentyne, and Essequibo, with their large numbers of tributaries, are well stocked with them. Two genera, *Ellipesurus* and *Paratrygon,* are represented. Sabin's sting ray *(Dasyatis sabina),* normally a salt-water form, is known occasionally to enter the estuaries and rivers of Florida.

The weapon responsible for the name of these fish and for all the deviltry ascribed to them is a spine, or stinger, located on the dorsal side of the tail near its base. It is a fairly prominent structure which juts out menacingly like a miniature bayonet, making an angle of about twenty degrees with the horizontal. Observed under the binoculars, the stinger is suggestive of a tiny paleolithic harpoon fashioned by the hand of a Solutrean or Magdalenian artist. Whether it takes the place of a dorsal fin, as one author contends, is difficult to say. Its length is extremely variable, but in the larger species of sting rays it is eight to nine inches long at least. A stinger of this length protrudes approximately six to seven inches, the remainder being imbedded in the skin.

The length of the stinger is not its worst feature. Along each lateral margin there is a row of very sharply pointed, retrorse teeth. Without effort, the spine can be driven for a considerable distance into human flesh; and when it is pulled out it leaves a ragged wound.

There is usually just one spine; but two or three, and even more, may be present in some species, one behind the others. Brown wrote that the sting rays he observed in the streams of British Guiana were "armed with two bony processes or spines at the base of the tail." The spines are not of bone, however; there is not a single particle of bone in any of these fishes. The substance which is present is enamel, and it is found covering all of the sharply pointed scales which may be seen on the backs of the larger forms. In fact these scales, and the stingers, have much the same structure as the teeth of higher animals, including man —a covering of enamel surrounding a core of dentine. Future research will probably show that the stinger is a modified and greatly enlarged placoid scale.

The manner in which the sting ray manipulates its tail, with the attached spine, in order to get the most effective results in stinging is not clear; it is possible that different species employ different methods. It has been declared that the ray, when going into action, has the ability to lift the stinger several degrees above the normal horizontal position. Both Schomburgk and Im Thurn wrote that this spine might be raised at will. Since no muscles are attached to the organ this belief may be erroneous, the impression that it is elevated being created when the tail is bowed at the point where the stinger is attached. Whether the spine is brought into action by the tail being lashed upward and forward with precision, as one author declares, or whether the desired results are obtained by lateral movements, is not certain. Perhaps some other method is used, and here again it is possible that different species employ different methods.

The size of the mouth of these Elasmobranchs would preclude their eating anything very large. From this observation one is forced to the belief that the stinger is seldom, if ever, used as an offensive structure. It would be absurd to believe that the rays would try to harpoon crustaceans or the small fish upon which they feed. It seems most likely that the spine is purely a defensive organ. Roule, in *Fishes and Their Ways,* supports this opinion. "The sting rays when they lie buried in the sand," he writes, "never use the poisonous stings to attack their neighbors. Their life is usually passed as if they did not possess such an ornament."

The wound caused by the entrance of the spine into human flesh may be more serious than that caused by mere mechanical laceration. According to several naturalists, a person who has been stung by one of these aquatic hornets suffers excruciating pain for two to four hours, following which a numbness creeps up into the groin and armpit and these parts become very sore. More than that, the wound steadfastly refuses to heal, often remaining inflamed for weeks.

In the South American streams the rays are generally found on the bottom, where they lie partially submerged in the sand. The ordinary native has a dread of the ray born of experience, and treats it with the deference which is extended to those other fresh-water perils, the piranha and electric eel. However, the rays harmonize so well with the bottom that it is frequently impossible for the natives to see them when they have to jump from their boats or to walk in the streams. Most of the accidents happen at such times. One of Brown's interpreters was wading in water in order to haul a boat through a series of rapids and was unaware of the proximity of a ray until its serrated spine was driven deep into his instep, producing the characteristic jagged wound from which the blood issued freely. Brown at once administered first aid. He gave the man a strong drink of ammonia and applied laudanum to the wound. In spite of these ministrations, within fifteen minutes the unfortunate man "was writhing on the ground in great agony, actually screaming at times with the pain which he felt in the wounded part, in his groin and under one armpit. His foot and leg were so cold that he got one man to light a fire and support his foot over it, persisting in trying to put it in the flames." Brown gave him two additional doses of laudanum, but these did not relieve the pain. The man suffered for three hours before he felt any relief; but from time to time during the night which followed, there were recurrences of the pain. For one solid week he could not touch his foot to the ground, and six weeks passed before the wound entirely healed.

Bates once saw a native woman of the Amazon wounded by a ray while she was bathing. "She shrieked frightfully," Bates declared, "and was obliged to be carried to her hammock, where she lay for a week in great pain; I have known strong men to be lamed for many months by its sting."

In one day two of Schomburgk's native helpers were severely wounded by sting rays, one in the instep and the other on the sole of the foot. The reactions of the first wounded were, in Schomburgk's own words, as follows: "Directly the poor fellow was struck, he staggered on to the sandbank where he collapsed and, biting his lips with the raging agony, rolled about in the sand." The second boy, who was stung soon afterwards, "with a piercing cry of suffering, threw himself about on the ground, dug his face and head into the sand, and even bit into it." Schomburgk affirmed that both of these victims "felt the greatest pain in the groin, in the neighbourhood of the heart, and under the armpit," and that he had never "seen an epileptic suffering from convulsions to such an extent."

Schomburgk saw to it that the wounds were sucked out, were washed with laudanum, and that ligatures were applied. He also used soothing poultices made of cassava bread. In spite of these treatments, the convulsions of the younger of the boys took such an alarming turn they thought he would die.

"It is impossible," Schomburgk concluded, "that this absolute nervous breakdown can proceed from the mere wounding alone; very probably it must be ascribed to the poison combined with it. A powerful and lusty labourer who, shortly before our departure from Demerara, was struck by a sting-ray on Zeelandia Estate died in the most awful convulsions."

In support of Schomburgk's declaration that the wound of a sting ray may cause death Im Thurn states that, "for some not very obvious reason, it occasionally causes even death."

It should be pointed out that there is a remarkable sameness in these and other descriptions. There is, first, the intense pain which sets in almost immediately after the wound is made; second, the numbness which soon extends to the lymphatic centers; and third, the steadfastness with which the wound refuses to heal.

Even allowing for a certain amount of hyperbole in these accounts the fact remains that men have suffered terribly from the wounds of sting rays. There are too many cases on record to leave any room for doubt. The problem now is to determine the cause.

After reading the case histories described it would be only natural to suppose that there is a poison gland associated with the stinger. The existence of such an organ would seem necessary if, as Schomburgk and Im Thurn declared, strong men die from the wounds inflicted. In fact, some of our standard works of reference state that a poison gland is present, and that the venom issues through a duct which pierces the stinger.

Research, however, has failed to reveal the presence of any gland, and there certainly is no canalization of the stinger. There is, though, a sizable mass of mucous tissue immediately underneath the base of the spine. This produces copious amounts of mucus, and the spine is generously covered with it. Moreover, it is likely that the mucus is full of a certain species of bacterium. Since quite a few bacteria produce toxins, it is conceivable that the germs in this cutaneous secretion also produce a toxin, a virulent one which is capable of causing the results that have already been described.

On the contrary some authors state that all of the serious aftereffects from the sting are due to mechanical laceration and subsequent infection, and that alone. The existence of any poison whatsoever is denied, and it is claimed that the wound will heal readily enough if it is properly cleaned and antiseptics are applied.

Even though a positive decision cannot be rendered in our

present state of knowledge, the experiences related by Schomburgk, Im Thurn, Bates, Brown, and others serve notice that the sting ray is an ever present danger in river travel and an inhabitant of tropical streams to be avoided.

ELECTRIC EELS

STORAGE batteries are a commonplace in civilized countries, conveniences that are to be secured in every hardware store and five-and-ten-cent emporium. But how many people have seen, or even heard of, living storage batteries; batteries that consist of cells that are animate, that are filled with cytoplasm and chromatin—and deadly electricity? Some animals, notably the lightning beetles and certain crustaceans, are able to produce light, but of all the living creatures now known to science only the fish are capable of producing electricity. None of the higher vertebrates—amphibians, reptiles, birds, or mammals—are endowed with organs that manufacture this particular type of energy.

Peculiarly enough, the few species of fish that generate electricity do not all belong to the same family. Most of them have certain characteristics in common, though. For instance, they tend to be thin or naked-skinned, especially in the neighborhood of the electric organs, to have a sluggish nature, and to prefer shallow water.

The fish possessing electric batteries are the marine forms: the torpedo or electric rays which are found in the Mediterranean Sea and both the Atlantic and Pacific oceans; and the fresh-water forms: the electric catfish, the home of which is the Nile, the American stargazer *(Astroscopus)*, and the electric eel which frequents many South American streams.

The electric eel *(Electrophorus electricus)*, also called numbfish, *tremblador* and puraque, is an eel in name only. Scientifically speaking it is a degraded form of tiger fish that is entirely too long to be designated by any other name than "eel." It inhabits the fresh-water streams of Brazil, Venezuela, and the Guianas, and does not occur south of the Amazon system nor west of the Andes. Gardner found it to be quite common in the small streams of the upper Tocantins; Bates reported it from Ega on the Solimões; Wallace wrote that it was by no means uncommon on the upper Rio Negro; Edwards found it plentiful about Pará;

and Spruce stated that it was frequent in the Huallaga and Ucayali and even more so in the lakes connected with these rivers. The naturalists who traveled in British Guiana made many references to it from that part of the continent, and Humboldt and others reported it from the Orinoco system to the west.

It is an elongate, sinuous fish, almost cylindrical in cross section and entirely destitute of scales. The only prominent external structure is a continuous, ribbonlike fin extending ventrally from the head to a point near the end of the tail. The color of the smooth skin is described variously as bluish lead, olive-green, greenish black, and reddish. Whether these variations are due to sex, season, character of water inhabited, or to some other reason, is not known.

An average length for the eel is said to be about three feet, but it grows much longer. Humboldt captured one—his largest—that was five feet three inches long and Schomburgk's men brought him "two giant electric eels that were seven feet long and one and a half feet in girth." According to Ellis * the maximum size recorded is for an eel caught in British Guiana that was seven feet and four inches in length.

The eyes are situated far forward on the somewhat flattened head, almost on the upper lips. It has been found that most of the older eels are afflicted with cataract, a condition of the eye characterized by cloudiness or opacity of the crystalline lens. It seems likely that this derangement is the direct result either of the electricity generated in its body or of the shocks which it receives from others of its kind. Some support for this viewpoint is found in the fact that human beings have been known to develop cataracts after receiving severe electric shocks.

Of all the electric fish the electric eel generates by far the greatest amount of electricity and is the only one capable of regulating the intensity of the shock. There are three pairs of organs responsible: (1) the so-called large electric organs, (2) the organs of Hunter, and (3) the bundles of Sachs. These organs occupy the greater portion of the body cavity of the fish, the visceral organs being confined to the anterior one-fifth of the animal. If the pos-

* *The Gymnotid Eels of Tropical America,* by M. M. Ellis (Mem. Carnegie Mus. 6, No. 8, 1913).

terior four-fifths were to be lopped off there still would remain a complete animal minus, of course, its dynamo.

The three organs are not of equal size. The large organs in a seven-foot eel are approximately five feet long and extend from the viscera to the end of the tail. The organs of Hunter, lying just beneath the large organs, have almost the same length but are smaller in cross section. The bundles of Sachs are shorter, extending from near the middle of the animal to the tail.

Both the large organs and Hunter's organs are composed of a fairly constant number of electric plates that are separated by septa of connective tissue. In the large organs the number of these plates, irrespective of the length of the fish, is thirty to thirty-six, and in Hunter's organ fourteen to twenty.

The electric organs of the other electric fish are differently disposed, and there is not more than one pair in any of them. In the rays the single pair of organs is located on each side just behind the head while in the stargazer they are just beneath the naked skin on top of the head. In the electric catfish the organs are sheathlike and encase the body.

The weight of the electric eel is equally divided: one half fish, the other half electric organs. Apparently the latter have been evolved from swimming muscles; but whatever has been lost in locomotion has been more than compensated for in the generation of electricity. It is no wonder they are sluggish fish. They need never to hurry, either to escape an enemy or to catch their food material. Electricity keeps at arm's length the most voracious of enemies and at the same time renders insensible or kills the animals it needs as food.

The explanation for three pairs of organs, each of different size, is not entirely clear. The researches of Coates, Cox, and Granath* have thrown considerable light on the matter though. They have discovered that at times there is a very strong discharge that in fish of average size attains an electromotive force of about 300 volts. They have noted, too, a discharge of minor proportions, only about one-tenth that of the former and, again, a third discharge that varies in its intensity but that is intermedi-

* "The Electric Discharge of the Electric Eel," *Zoologica* (N.Y. Zool. Soc.), Vol. XXII (1937).

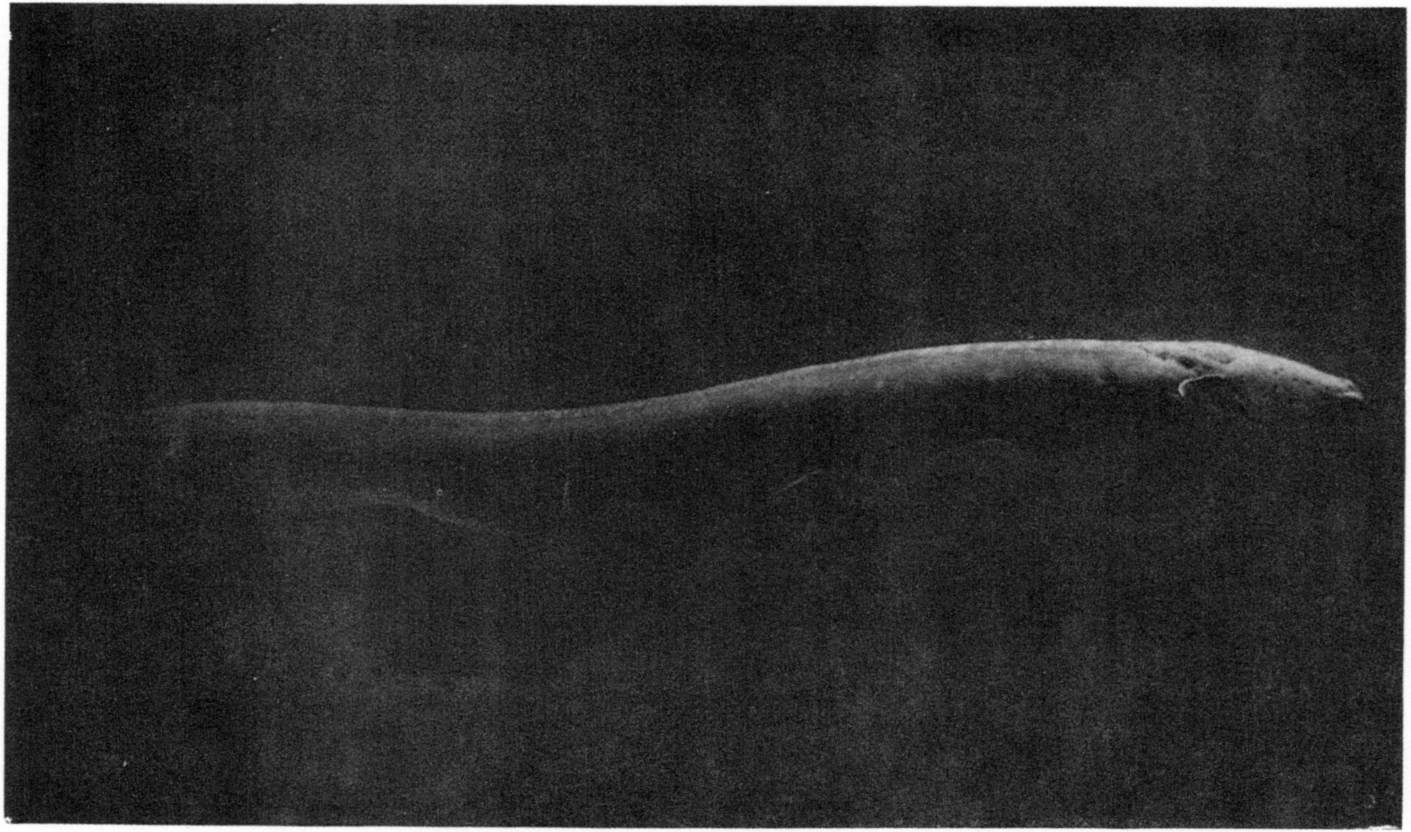

Courtesy of N.Y. Aquarium

ELECTRIC EEL

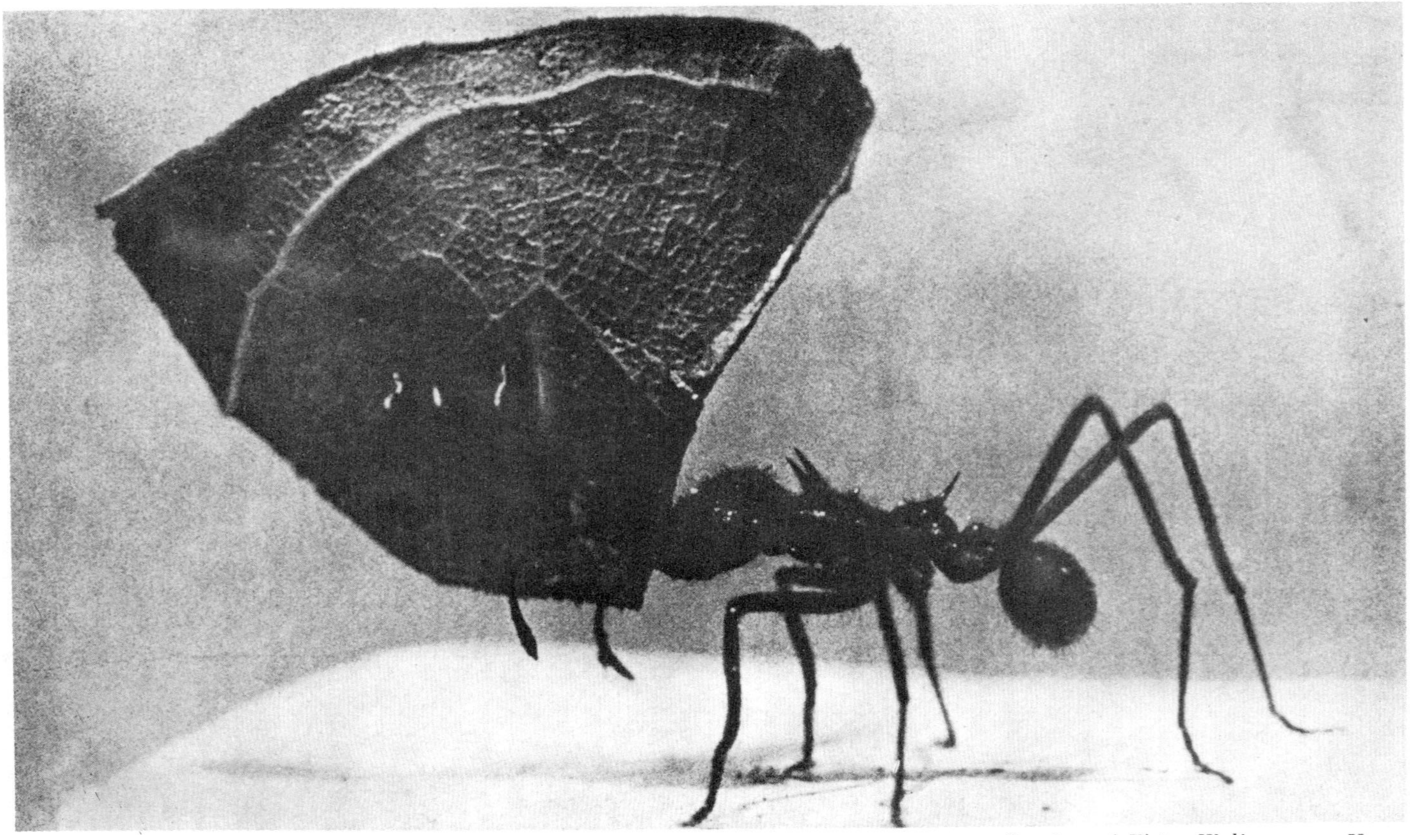

Courtesy of Victor Wolfgang von Hagen

PARASOL ANT

ate in voltage between the others. Accordingly it is thought that the large electric organs are responsible for the major discharge, the bundles of Sachs for the minor discharge, and the organs of Hunter for the variable one.

These findings raise the question as to what purpose, or purposes, might be served in releasing discharges of different intensities. The purpose of a major discharge seems to be evident. But what possible reason could there be for the minor discharge given off by the bundles of Sachs? Investigations have shown that as the eels lie quietly in the water they do not necessarily discharge at all, but when they begin to swim about the minor discharge is liberated. It would appear that they throw about them this mild electrical field in the nature of a protection or a warning as the owner of an estate runs a charged electric wire about his premises to protect against trespassers. The heavy guns of the large electric organs are brought into action only in case of an emergency or for the purpose of killing or paralyzing other animals for food. The explanation of the irregular shocks, apparently thrown off by Hunter's organs, remains yet to be explained.

Coates, Cox, and Granath* noted also that whenever a fish discharges its heavy artillery the other electric fish in the immediate vicinity swim to the source of the shock. In this way all of the eels within reach of the electric discharge are apprised that a kill has been made, and all are able to share in it.

Although the electromotive force of an average-size eel is about 300 volts, Cox† tells of one eel with a length of only forty inches that had an electromotive force of 500 volts. He thought, though, that this voltage would rarely be surpassed even in the very large ones with a length of six feet or more. Within limits the larger the eel, the greater is the discharge; but there is apparently no proportionate increase with length of body. Small eels only eight inches long, Cox wrote, had a force of 115 volts.

Humboldt's notion that the shocks of the fish become weaker with successive discharges has been found erroneous. Experiments have shown rather that as the eel becomes fatigued it discharges at the same power but at less frequent intervals.

* *Op. cit.*

† "The Electric Eel at Home," *Bull. N.Y. Zool. Soc.*, Vol. XLI, No. 2 (1938).

The discharge is not involuntary: it is entirely under the volition of the animal. It is possible then, for a person to touch the fish at certain times without receiving a shock. Humboldt said that when he grasped the eel by the head and Bonpland laid hold of it by the tail he might receive the full force of the shock while Bonpland would feel nothing. In recent experiments it has been found that it is impossible for one person and not another to receive a shock at the same instant provided they make a suitable electric current. As a matter of fact there seems to be no part of the body that is insulated, even though the organs are in the tail. On the other hand, if two fingers are placed on the fish at the anterior end of the electric organ, one centimeter apart, they receive a greater shock than two fingers laid on the posterior end of the electric organ one centimeter apart. This is because of the tapering of the organs toward the tail.

If the eel is cut in two only the anterior end is a potential sword of Damocles; the posterior end, deprived of its cerebral connection, is nerveless and inept. Also, if the nerve cord is cut at any point the discharge is blocked at all points posterior to the cut.

The electric eel's oxygen requirement is high, indicating a raised metabolism. Ordinarily it comes to the surface every four or five minutes to gulp air. If it is prevented from doing this for as long as fifteen minutes it will die. On the other hand if the eel is taken from the water into the air it will live for several hours.

It is known that frogs and small fish are electrocuted when placed in a tub or tank with an electric eel, even though they do not come in contact with it. Just how great the destruction of batrachians, reptiles, and fish is in the streams and ponds inhabited by the eels is not known, although Humboldt was informed that the streams of the llanos were practically devoid of all animal life exclusive of the electric fish. Where the eels are fairly abundant it is plausible that there would normally be considerable depopulation of other forms. On the other hand it is likely that most of the inhabitants are only paralyzed and, if not eaten, recover after a few minutes and are none the worse for the experience. Incidentally, the electric eel is probably the only electric fish that uses its singular energy in the capture of food; all the others use it only for defense, so far as is known.

It is not difficult to believe that frogs and snakes are quickly incapacitated by the electric shocks of the eels. But are horses, mules, and cattle prostrated by them? Many stories have been related which tend to show that, either directly or indirectly, the eel has been responsible for killing animals much larger than itself. One of the original stories, and certain the most interesting, was told by Humboldt.

On his way across Venezuela from Caracas to the Rio Apure, Humboldt found this fish to be quite common in the smaller streams and was so intrigued by its inherent physiological possibilities that he and Bonpland remained in one place for several days in order to study it. However, its abundance was one thing, and its actual capture something entirely different. The natives had such a dread of the eels that Humboldt was for a time unable to secure specimens alive and uninjured. This in spite of the belief that a person might handle the eels with impunity if he were chewing a good-sized quid of tobacco.

Finally a plan materialized for the capture of the fish which, if not laudable, was at least eminently successful. Some thirty horses were rounded up and driven to the margin of a small pool in which were a large number of eels. Upon a given signal the horses were prodded into the water, and the show was on. The eels, suddenly driven from their normal quarters near the bottom of the pool, rushed to the surface and incontinently started an offensive that was nothing if not superbly spectacular. Like a horde of angry venomous serpents they swam against the bellies of the horses and unleashed their invisible weapons. The horses, with eyes flashing terror and with manes erect, reared on their hind legs, dropped into the water with resounding splashes, floundered, sank beneath the surface, threw themselves into the air and plunged for the shore snorting and panting wildly. Here they were met by the natives armed with bamboo poles with which they drove them back into the pond where somewhat the same scene was reenacted. Two of the horses were drowned, and those that finally reached the bank were so benumbed and exhausted that the majority of them fell and remained prostrate until the effects of the electricity gradually waned.

In the meantime several of the fish had swum close to the edge of the pool, where they were caught by the natives with small harpoons tied to the ends of long dry cords. With these, and a few others secured later, Humboldt was able to experiment.

The question now arises as to the effect of the electric shock from the eel on human beings. "I do not remember," wrote Humboldt after imprudently placing both feet on an eel just removed from the water, "having ever received from the discharge of a large Leyden jar, a more dreadful shock than that which I experienced. I was affected during the rest of the day with a violent pain in the knees and in almost every joint." Im Thurn cautioned: "The electric eel is another fish to be avoided. Its power of inflicting an electric shock is well known and this shock is really very severe." McGovern saw an Indian boy receive the full force of a shock as the youngster was swimming in the waters of the Uaupés. The boy was hauled ashore, rigid and motionless. After vigorous first-aid measures had been resorted to he gradually regained consciousness, but the painful effects were noticeable for several hours afterward.

Up de Graff found that the Santiago River, a tributary of the upper Amazon in the Jívaro Indian country, was teeming with electric eels at certain points. They grew here to a length of three to four feet, he said, and because of their sluggish nature were easy to catch. His experience was that they were so heavily charged with electricity that a man was quite unable to keep his grasp on any metal object that came in contact with the fish or to hold onto a metal bucket in which an eel was swimming. He attempted to cut off the head of one with a machete. The weapon flew out of his hand and his arm was paralyzed for some minutes. "I might just as well have tried to cut a trolley wire with uninsulated pliers," was Up de Graff's comment. It was his belief that it would be far from safe for a man to try to swim across a river inhabited by these fish.

Occasional deaths to horses, cattle, and humans undoubtedly do occur; there are entirely too many reports to that effect for all to be discounted. However, in most cases at least, death is probably not due to the actual shock. Is it not much more likely that the bodies of these large animals, including man, are temporarily put of commission by the electricity, and drowning results before they are able to start functioning normally again?

Just how the electric eels respond to the dry seasons which occur at certain places in their range is not entirely clear. Bates found that the eels he discovered at Ega had made deep holes in the bottoms of the small streams they inhabited. Each fish had its own particular *cul-de-sac,* the depth of which was as much as eight feet. These had been fashioned, Bates said, by the turning of the body round and round in the soft mud. Herein the eels passed the dry season. Whether they became dormant when the holes dried up and actually estivated, as lungfish do, Bates did not state.

Although the economic importance of these *trembladores* is chiefly negative, they are beneficial in at least two respects. In the first place their non-electric parts are rather commonly used for food by the Indians. Humboldt said that they furnished "pretty good aliment," but most of the naturalists indicate that the meat is too fishy in taste, unless eaten with strong correctives. In the second place, they have been used by the natives in the treatment of rheumatism and various other bodily ills. Just when electrotherapy became fashionable among the Indians, and how effective it is, is unknown; but the aborigines of South America were probably the first people to use electricity in any manner, and the source was the electric eel

JUNGLE PESTS

"Our imagination is struck only by what is great; but the lover of natural history should reflect equally on little things," declared Humboldt in one of his more philosophical moments.

The traveler in the South American jungle, after he has been through weeks of torment from the bands of insect pests that make life almost unendurable there, is forced to reflect on the "little things" whether or no. The mosquitoes, ants, ticks, *bêtes rouges,* chigoes, and piums whose chief aim in life is to play fast and loose with some portion of the human periphery, are the chief threats to existence in South America. Such larger animals as the jaguar, peccary, caiman, piranha, and fer-de-lance, while dangerous under certain circumstances, do not compare with the insects and their kin as possible frustrators of well laid plans. On a protracted expedition into the jungle it is possible that the jaguar and the fer-de-lance may never be seen or, if seen, may be avoided; but the insects are ever present, holding high carnival at all hours of the day and the night. Some of these—mosquitoes, for instance—are ready to inject into the blood stream of man an organism just as capable of causing death as the venom which oozes from the fangs of the dreaded fer-de-lance; and for every fer-de-lance there are multitudes of these hungry, malignant creatures. There is always the chance that one of these probing pilferers is a carrier of tertian chills or quotidian fevers. Even though "fevers" may be averted, there still remain the incessant discomforts occasioned by bites, irritations, infections, and loss of sleep. If the explorer is on the move, these "baptisms of fire" may be only periodical; on the other hand they may persist for weeks at a time, even months, depending on the locality.

One of the worst pestholes in South America is the upper Orinoco, a region which has been referred to as the insect's paradise and the white man's hell. There seem to be especial concentrations at the great cataracts of the Orinoco (Atures and Maipures), at Esmeralda, and on the Casiquiare, that famous but seldom visited conjunction which allows an intermingling of the waters of the Orinoco and the Amazon. Miller and Cherrie spent a week collecting in the Chaco, northern Argentina. These veterans of exploration, hardened to the "bug brigades" of the Orinoco and the Guianas, found this the worst locality they had ever visited; the nights were a torment and the days a living inferno. But all over the immense area drained by the Amazon, Magdalena, Orinoco, Essequibo, and Paraguay there are, at least periodically, insect uprisings that drive men, including the natives, into a state bordering on madness. It is no wonder that Roosevelt said, "The very pathetic myth of a 'beneficent nature' could not deceive the least wise if he once saw for himself the iron cruelty of life in the tropics."

It does not follow that every South American explorer is tormented to the limits of his endurance by these "despoilers of the night," for many regions are relatively free from insect pests and others are harassed only during certain parts of the year. As a rule, however, the traveler who penetrates any distance into the jungle is attacked by one or more of these forms. If mosquitoes are not present, there are piums to contend with; if piums are on leave, there are always ants, or chigoes, or *bêtes rouges* to keep one from slipping into a state of tranquillity.

Before Humboldt's time it was generally thought that the natives of South America were immune to the bites of insects. The skins of the Indians are not so sensitive as those of a recently arrived European, Humboldt said, but the natives suffer a great deal and resort to all manner of devices to get away from the insect attacks. He found that many of the Indians on the Orinoco buried their bodies in the sand at night, leaving only their faces exposed, which they covered with a piece of cloth. Some built huts in the trees where they secured relief, for the insects were not so abundant twenty to thirty feet above the earth. Humboldt saved himself considerable pain by following this plan. Other Indians along the Orinoco spent the night on the islands in the center of the stream, where *la Plaga,* as they called these hordes of vicious malefactors, occurred in fewer numbers. Certain natives constructed ovenlike chambers that had no door or windows, only a small aperture at the ground, through which they came and went. Inside of these they made a smudge which drove out the pests. The door was then closed and the inmates, although nearly suffocated by the smoke and intense heat, gained a temporary respite. Bonpland resorted to one of these ovens in which to dry his plants while on the Casiquiare.

In regard to the large numbers of insects on the Orinoco, Humboldt wrote: "Persons who have not navigated the great rivers of equinoctial America can scarcely conceive how, at every instant, without intermission, you may be tormented by insects flying in the air; and how the multitude of these little animals may render vast regions almost uninhabitable. I doubt whether there be a country upon earth where man is exposed to more cruel torments in the rainy season." A common remark among the natives overheard by Humboldt was that there were more mosquitoes than air. Each morning the greeting was not some comment on the weather like, "It is a fine day," or "There may be rain today," as is customary in more salubrious climates, but "How were the mosquitoes last night?"

When Spruce visited Esmeralda, the last outpost of civilization on the Orinoco, he was struck with the beauty of the place, but amazed at the lack of industry among its inhabitants. For hours at a time, seven days in the week, self-imposed imprisonment was their order of the day. Years of exposure to insect attacks had not built up in their skins any appreciable lack of sensitivity to the punctures, bites, and stings of the flying hordes. Their lack of industry was a matter of necessity rather than of choice, Spruce decided.

Bates spent some days at Fonte Boa on the Solimões. "In addition to its other amenities," he wrote, "it has the reputation throughout the country of being the headquarters of mosquitoes, and it fully deserves the title." He found them abundant in the houses, particularly in the daytime, but much more numerous in the forest. While he was traveling through the woods a veritable cloud of these pests swarmed about him, and the hum of their wings was so loud he found difficulty in distinguishing bird notes.

Each and every explorer has his particular tale of woe to tell about some South American pesthole. No doubt they could appreciate the remark of a traveler who asserted that there were, broadly speaking, just two varieties of mosquitoes,* the day shift and the night shift."

Mosquitoes

Of all the jungle pests the mosquito is dreaded most, for at every turn it "holds out a welcoming proboscis" and, in many instances, "the needlelike sting is only the preamble." Chills and burning fever all too frequently follow, the natural sequelae of stabs from the ever present *Anopheles.*

The *Anopheles* mosquito, of which there are many species, is only the indirect cause of malaria, yet it has been given a greater part on the stage of the world's pathological history than any other animal. All of the evils of malaria have been placed on the fragile backs of these minute diptera. Our historians give *Anopheles* a dominating role in the destruction of two of the greatest civilizations of all time—those of Greece and Rome; it successfully prevented the French from building the Panama Canal; it delayed the colonizing of parts of Africa and America for many generations; and it has been a stumbling block in all equatorial regions to the carefully laid health programs of tropical doctors. Yet it is not *Anopheles* that *causes* malaria. The direct cause of malaria is the micro-organism which *Anopheles* unwittingly carries within its body—a microscopic Protozoan by the name of *Plasmodium.* If there were no such animal *Anopheles* would be harmless.

Three types of malaria are universally recognized: quartan, tertian, and subtertian (known also as pernicious, quotidian, and estivo-autumnal). The three types exist because there are three species of *Plasmodium.*

The explorer in Amazonia or on the upper Orinoco may be prostrated by any one of this malarial trio. If, by chance, *Plasmodium vivax* is injected into the blood stream by the proboscis of *Anopheles,* the result will be quartan malaria. This type is the rarest of the three and the least dangerous. It is characterized by the occurrence of chills and fever every seventy-two hours. If *Plasmodium malariae* is introduced into the body, the result will

* *Mosquito,* in Spanish, signifies any "little fly" and is applied by the South Americans to the small diptera which we of the United States call midges, gnats, or flies. For the real mosquito they use the term *zancudo.*

be tertian (benign tertian) malaria. This is the prevailing type and is characterized by chills which occur with clocklike regularity every forty-eight hours. If, however, *Plasmodium falciparum* finds its way into the circulatory channels subtertian malaria will be the result. This occurs oftener than quartan malaria but not so frequently as tertian. Of the three types it is by far the most severe, for the chills and fever occur as often as each twenty-four hours.

The victim of malaria is first apprised of the fact that he has the disease by a chill which is often so violent that he is thrown into convulsions. His temperature may rise seven or eight degrees above normal. This torment lasts for an indefinite period and is followed by profuse sweating. His temperature drops rapidly, sometimes below normal, ordinarily without any other discomfort than extreme weakness. If no remedies are available he will be subject to another attack at the end of forty-eight or seventy-two hours (depending on the type), and this may be more severe than the first. In subtertian malaria some of the effects are much more serious than those described above.

The universal remedy for malaria is quinine. Probably no single drug has alleviated more suffering and saved more lives. Although the naturalists who traveled in South America during the nineteenth century did not know the method of transmission of malaria—this discovery was made in 1898—they were acquainted with the merits of quinine, and they were usually supplied with it. The history of quinine, until the last few decades, is associated entirely with South America, for it is there that the tree grows from which it is obtained.

The first known use of quinine by white men was about the year 1600. At that early date Spanish missionaries used it in Loxa, Peru. The Indians, in all likelihood, were familiar with the remedial properties of the Peruvian bark long before that. In 1683 a supply was sent from Loxa to the Viceroy of Peru, who resided in Lima. His second wife, Francesca de Rivera, was suffering with malaria, and she was cured by it. Upon her return to Spain she carried some quinine with her, the first to enter the old world. The name *cinchona* was applied to it by Linnaeus in 1742. He made a mistake, however, in naming the drug after the first wife of the aforementioned Viceroy, the Countess of Chinchon.

Quinine may be used to prevent malaria, and it may be used to cure it. The preventive doses vary, although they seem to range from five to ten grains a day. The physician with Theodore Roosevelt's expedition gave each man one-half gram (about eight grains) of quinine daily and, on every third or fourth day, a double dose. Some physicians do not recommend preventive doses at all, arguing that too much quinine is hard on the system and that most of the doses are just shots in the dark, at that. If a curative dose is necessary the amount is generally increased. Dickey, a tropical physician of many years' experience, insists on sixty grains a day. He maintains that only through tremendous doses can the malignant forms be cleared from the vascular channels. Another program that is recommended for complete eradication of the disease requires ten grains of quinine sulphate by mouth three times a day for three to four days, followed by ten grains each night for eight weeks.*

The cure of malaria is not always as simple as one might think. This disease, according to Dr. Heiser,† is the most difficult of all tropical diseases to control, and "the method of its widespread control is not yet out of its swaddling clothes." Generally a stiff dose of quinine will quickly cause every single *Plasmodium* within the body to disappear as though by magic. At other times quinine may have no perceptible effect at all in reducing the number of the parasites. It would appear from this that certain stages of *Plasmodium* (of which there are several within the blood) are easily killed with quinine, while other stages are resistant to it; quinine, then, is not the absolute specific it has been claimed to be. Two new drugs on the market, plasmochin and atebrin, have attracted considerable attention because they seem to be effective in certain stages of malaria where quinine has been of little value. Quinine, however, is still considered indispensable; whereas plasmochin and atebrin have yet to prove their exact worth.

But, even though we know the cause of malaria and the agent of its transmission, and we have remedies for it in quinine,

* Chandler, *Introduction to Human Parasitology,* John Wiley & Son, N.Y., 1936.
† *An American Doctor's Odyssey,* W. W. Norton & Son, N.Y., 1936.

plasmochin, and atebrin, there seems to be almost as great an incidence of this disease in the world as ever. Moreover, any person from outside who attempts to live in the tropical forests of South America for any length of time will probably be forced by malaria to leave the country sooner or later, even though he is saturated with quinine. The greatest threat to life faced by the naturalists in South America has invariably been, and still is, malaria.

Wallace was so ill on the Rio Negro with malaria that he was not expected to live. His account of his sickness is interesting because it reveals his entire ignorance of the etiology or transmission of the disease. "I was attacked with severe ague, which recurred every two days," Wallace wrote. "I took quinine for some time without apparent effect, till, after nearly a fortnight, the fits ceased, and I only suffered from extreme emaciation and weakness. In a few days, however, the fits of ague returned, and now came every day. Their visits, thus frequent, were by no means agreeable; as, what with succeeding fever and perspiration, which lasted from before noon till night, I had little quiet repose. In this state I remained till the beginning of February, the ague continuing, but with diminished force; and though with an increasing appetite and eating heartily, yet gaining so little strength, that I could with difficulty stand alone, or walk across the room with the assistance of two sticks. The ague, however, now left me, and in another week, as I could walk with a stick down to the river-side, I went to São Gabriel, to see Mr. Spruce, who had arrived, and kindly been to see me a short time before."

Spruce, at this time, had no inkling of what he was to endure later, for none of the naturalists had such an experience with malaria as did the English botanist. Early in July, 1854, Spruce reached that outpost of civilization on the Orinoco, San Fernando de Atabapo. He had been ill with malaria for several days and, at the conclusion of his journey to this point, was too sick to care for himself. He relied upon his Indian helpers to wait on him, but they were a worthless lot. He gave them rum to put them into better spirits, and they repaid his kindness by stealing some of his supply of beef. This they sold and with the proceeds bought more rum, and got gloriously drunk. A day or so later a chance friend applied to Spruce for the loan of some of his boatmen in order that he might make a river trip. To this request Spruce acceded, but with the proviso that a nurse be secured who would care for him in his illness.

In due time a woman appeared who agreed to take care of him if he would move to her house. He was in no condition to move but, having no other recourse, packed up his belongings and did as requested. This woman, Spruce said, he would not easily forget. Although he was so weak he could only ask for his most urgent needs, she construed each action or request of his a complaint. In the way of medicine he had nothing but quinine and ipecac. These remedies brought about no improvement, and those recommended by his nurse (strong purgatives) only made him worse. For several days and nights his fever was so high he had no sleep at all. The only nourishment he could take was a spoonful or two of arrowroot gruel each day. He became so weak that those about him expected his death momentarily. Spruce himself prepared for this eventuality and gave directions for the disposal of his botanical specimens and other possessions.

During this period of extreme illness his nurse would close her house and leave Spruce alone for hours at a time. One evening she went out and did not return till after midnight. Another night she invited in a large group of friends, and they spent most of the time abusing him. They called him all the vile names they could think of, and he could not help overhearing his nurse shout, "Die, you English dog, that we may have a merry watch night with your dollars."

A night or two later, when she thought Spruce could not possibly live through it, she invited in all her friends and relatives again. As the hours dragged along and Spruce did not accommodate them by passing over the Great Divide, he heard them discussing the advisability of poisoning him.

After three interminably long weeks of this persistent nightmare Spruce started to improve; chiefly, he thought, because he had quit using the Indian's suggested remedies. Thirty-eight days after reaching San Fernando de Atabapo he was able to leave.

The last seven and a half years of Bates' stay were spent on the upper Amazon. Near the end of this extended visit he had a severe attack of malaria, which left him in a very weakened and shaken state of health. This attack, according to Bates, "seemed to be the culmination of a gradual deterioration of health, which had been going on for several years." Bates had quinine with him which he had bought at Pará in 1851. He had had no use for it until now (1858). He took regular doses of it, as much as he could get on the end of the blade of his penknife, and his malaria was relieved but, his general health failing to improve appreciably, he found it necessary to embark for Pará and England.

While collecting on the headwaters of the Orinoco, Cherrie was suddenly stricken with a violent attack of malaria. Large doses of quinine failed to alleviate his fever, and after a few days he realized that he must reach civilization soon if he wished to live. He gave directions to his boatmen, and they started down-river on a journey that, at the best, would take many days. Days later, still far from their objective, they made a stop at a small Indian village where the boatmen left Cherrie to look for some badly needed food. In their absence a native woman came down to the river bank to satisfy her curiosity. They conversed, and she discovered that Cherrie had at one time ministered to her husband when he was ill. She ordered him brought ashore, gave him nourishing food, and nursed him back to health. Cherrie felt that she saved his life.

These illustrations, only a few of many that might be cited, serve to show the dangers with which the explorer is faced from malaria in South America. In the cases of Spruce and Cherrie it would seem that only the intervention of Providence saved them from death in the heart of a truculent jungle. The malarial attacks suffered by Roosevelt in his descent of the River of Doubt unquestionably shortened his life.

The naturalists of the last century had not only malaria about which to be concerned. Yellow fever was then taking a huge annual toll of life in the cities. Schomburgk was stricken with it soon after he landed in Georgetown, and was so violently ill that physicians and friends despaired of his recovery. That he did recover was probably the result of a vigorous constitution more than of the ministrations of his doctor—very little is known about the treatment of yellow fever even today. Just a few years after this Wallace's brother made the trip from England to South America in order to assist him in his collecting. Shortly after he arrived in Pará he fell ill of the disease and died. Bates returned to Pará from the interior soon after this event to find that over 5 per cent of the city had died of yellow fever; he hoped to escape but was not so fortunate. However, his case was a light one, and he quickly recovered.

Piums

Im Thurn thought the pium *(Simulium amazonicum)*, wherever it occurred, a far more annoying pest than the mosquito.

Bates describes this species of black fly as "a minute fly, two-thirds of a line in length . . . with dark coloured body and pale legs and wings, the latter closed lengthwise over the back." According to him it alights on the body without being noticed and starts to work almost immediately. It has a broad snout with which it pierces the skin and sucks up the blood. After drinking its fill, it moves sluggishly away with its abdomen distended far beyond normal limits. It causes no pain while at work but leaves a small rounded elevation on the skin which soon becomes a source of irritation. If the blood is pressed from these spots the irritation may not follow; but it is difficult to perform several hundred operations each day on as many pium bites. These flies are sometimes so numerous, Bates continues, that they resemble "thin clouds of smoke" and now and then leave so many bites that strong men are incapacitated. Bates knew well a Portuguese man of middle age who was laid up for three weeks as a result of their bites. His legs were greatly swollen, and some of the punctures were badly infected.

The bites soon turn from red to black, according to Brown and Lidstone, so that "it is not unusual to see people, who have been traveling in a region where piums abound, with those parts of the body almost black by reason of the innumerable specks of coagulated blood which lie as thickly together as they could well be placed without transfusing themselves into one dark mass."

Wallace met with the piums on the Rio Negro. "The torments I suffered when skinning a bird or drawing a fish," he declared, "can scarcely be imagined by the unexperienced. My feet were so thickly covered with the little blood-spots produced by their bites, as to be of a dark purplish-red colour, and much swelled and inflamed. My hands suffered similarly, but in a less degree, being more constantly in motion. The only means of taking a little rest in the day was by wrapping up hands and feet in a blanket. The Indians close their houses, as these insects do not bite in the dark, but ours having no door, we could not resort to this expedient. Whence these pests could thus suddenly appear in such vast numbers is a mystery which I am quite unable to explain."

Spruce wrote that the activities of the pium start about seven in the morning and cease shortly after sunset, and that *if* the mosquitoes were absent it was possible to get some sleep, *unless* the pium bites previously received demanded too much attention.

Brown and Lidstone discovered that the piums have an enemy. One day when they were surrounded with a cloud of the insects, several small wasplike flies lit upon their clothes. At first they wondered what new pest had arrived. Their relief and delight may be imagined when they discovered that the wasps "were busily engaged in seizing the piums, tucking them up between their legs, and carrying them off." The wasplike insect was a species of ichneumon fly which carried away the piums after first paralyzing them with its sting.

These insects have well developed powers of discrimination, according to McGovern. In humorous vein he writes, "When I was alone I was driven frantic by their attacks, but if I could induce Mannling, the camera man, a very plump and well-rounded-out person, to sit by me, the midges [piums] would concentrate nearly the whole of their attentions upon him. I developed at this period a marked fondness for long conversations with my companion preferring him to my Brazilian attendants who were a rather scrawny lot."

Bête Rouge

If the reader has heard of the torments suffered by various and sundry explorers in tropical America from the *bête rouge,* he may be surprised to learn that this pest of the equinoctial jungles is none other than the chigger, or jigger, of the southern part of the United States.

The *bête rouge,* called red bug and *coloradito,* is extremely common, all too common, in many parts of South America. It is said to be unusually abundant during the rainy season, especially in the equatorial lowlands. It is, in reality, a harvest mite, a distant relative of the tick. The adult mite resembles a tick, but is built along less expansive lines. Other relatives of the mites, more distantly removed, are the granddaddy longlegs, scorpions, and spiders. It is not the adult that disturbs man, however, but the larva; and the latter does not burrow into the skin as often stated, but inserts only its mouth parts and feeds much as the tick does. These larvae have three pairs of legs, are a bright red, and are just visible to the unaided eye.

The larval activity in the skin is not immediately noticeable; but it sets up an irritation which, if the parasites are numerous, may become intolerable after a few hours. It seems that the insect injects a specific toxin which creates the discomfort. In speaking of the *bête rouge* and the fact that it attacks everyone, Beebe says it is a "great leveler of mankind, like a common disaster, doing more to make men 'free and equal,' than all the constitutions and doctrines ever signed."

Schomburgk insisted, "Only a person who has experienced the awful plague can have a full conception of the sufferings which of an evening convert the longed-for hammock into a real Laurentian grill, and of a day drive the sweat of anguish out of every pore."

Waterton declared that the bite of the *bête rouge* "causes an intolerable itching. The first year I was in British Guiana the *bête rouge,* and my own want of knowledge, created an ulcer above the ankle which annoyed me for six months." Simson, in his *Travels in the Wilds of Ecuador,* asserted, "The little animal is red and almost invisible to the naked eye; but he climbs up one's legs and all over the body and buries himself in the epidermis, setting up, in thin-skinned persons like myself, such intense irritation for about three days that I have been driven almost to the verge of madness by it."

Beebe's experience was that, while abundant in the Guianas,

these insects were no worse than "on some parts of Long Island and never nearly as bad as I have known them on the coast of Virginia." According to Hingston practically all of the mammals, birds, and reptiles in the Guiana forest show some evidences of being attacked by these pests.

On the authority of one writer the *bête rouge* is a "small thing, but mighty; a torturer—a murderer of sleep; the tormentor of entomologists, botanists, and others who encroach on its domains; not that it bites or stings—it does neither; worse than either, it just tickles."

Chigoes

In many parts of South America, also in the West Indies, Mexico, and Central America, there occurs a very tiny insect pest referred to as the chigoe (also *bicho,* sand flea, jigger, and chigger). This animal is a flea, is not even closely related to the chigger, and is known to the entomologist as *Pulex penetrans.*

Both male and female bite people and suck blood just as ordinary fleas do; but the female, to use the words of Humboldt, "gets under the toe-nails, and there acquires the size of a small pea by the quick increase of its eggs." It does not always manage to get under the toenails—although that does seem to be a haven devoutly to be desired by the chigoe for its incubation purposes—but may enter the body at almost any point. Since its natural habitat is the ground, the skin of the feet stands a better chance of making its acquaintance than that of any other part of the body.

Soon after the flea makes its entrance it sets up an irritation. If the parasite is not carefully removed within a short time it may cause a severe infection and even gangrene. This flea, which is more completely parasitic than any of the other species, is about 1 to 1.2 mm. in size, brown in color and quite active. It is said to be especially common in dry, sandy soil and in the dust on the floor of native huts. In the latter places it frequently multiplies to such an extent that it forces the inhabitants to seek new quarters. Both Wallace and Brown found abandoned native huts in the jungle, the floors of which were literally alive with chigoes. Brown, faced with the alternative of sleeping outside in a swampy spot, threw dry leaves onto the floor and set fire to them, as one means of making his cabin habitable for the night.

The operation described by Waterton for the removal of the procreant females is still in vogue. "As soon as you perceive that you have got the chigoe in your flesh," he wrote, "you must take a needle, or a sharp-pointed knife, and take it out. If the nest be formed, great care must be taken not to break it, otherwise some of the eggs remain in the flesh, and then you will soon be annoyed with more chigoes. After removing the nest, it is well to drop spirit of turpentine into the hole. Sometimes I have taken four nests out of my feet in the course of a day. Every evening, before sundown, it was part of my toilette to examine my feet, and see that they were clear of chigoes. Now and then a nest would escape the scrutiny, and then I had to smart for it a day or two after. A chigoe once lit upon the back of my hand; wishful to see how he worked, I allowed him to take possession. He immediately set to work, head foremost, and in about half an hour he had completely buried himself in the skin. I then let him feel the point of my knife, and exterminated him."

The natives are as a rule careful to examine their bodies each evening for the fleas, but Schomburgk found some of the Warrau Indians with feet and thighs in a very sorry condition. They had not removed the insects; as a result, ulceration had supervened and their feet were frightfully swollen and in an extreme state of infection.

Waterton spoke with pride of having removed as many as four pregnant females from his skin within the course of a day. Schomburgk said that a native operated on him on one occasion and extracted 83 of them within half an hour.

Waterton implied that the eggs were laid in the flesh of the victim; but this does not seem to be true. Two explanations are given: one, that the eggs are expelled through the opening in the skin made when the insect entered, after which the mother dies to be discharged later on; the other, that the female leaves the skin just before the eggs are laid and deposits them in the ground.

Ants

The forest conditions in South America, the equable temperature, the profusion of all kinds of life, the perennial abundance of food, form an environment that is highly salubrious for the everyday existence of ants. As a natural outcome they are everywhere: big ones, little ones; stay-at-homes, nomads; carnivores, herbivores; biting kinds, stinging kinds; recluses, socialites. Some live in trees, others build elaborate homes in the ground, and still others are constantly on the move—formicine globe-trotters. It has been said that "man is lord of all that he surveys." In South America man is often at the mercy of these fearless, voracious denizens of the soil and of the trees; when they invade his domain he makes way for them.

Parasol Ants

Of all the ants that live in the tropical forests from Mexico to southern Brazil, the most abundant are the parasol ants *(Atta)* also called leaf-cutting, umbrella, and sauba ants. In addition, they are the greatest defoliators known, their ravages far exceeding those of other famous leaf destroyers such as the Japanese beetle and the gypsy moth.

The visitor to tropical America soon becomes acquainted with the parasol ants. He probably notices them first as they march in an unending stream along a slender, deviating path that has become bare through the activity of countless thousands of these six-legged creatures. These highways radiate from the nests in all directions and extend long distances through forest or plantation—some of them over half a mile, according to Belt. Near the nest they may be as much as seven to eight inches wide.

The ants seen on these roads are of two kinds. One form is about half an inch in length and the other only about one-fourth as large. In the nests is still another kind that is larger than either of these. All three are undeveloped females that carry on the work of the colony. They are chestnut-colored and bear conspicuous spines on the head and thorax. The large ones in the nest are called soldiers, also maxims; the next in size mediums; and the smallest of all, minims. Each has definite functions to perform in connection with the life of the colony.

The mediums and minims leave the nest and travel along the paths they have made, usually to some tree or shrub. With their strong dentate jaws the mediums snip pieces out of the leaves, raise them above their heads parasol-like, and then carry them away to the nest. It is while they are engaged in this transportation that they are most conspicuous. Each procession looked to Bates "like a multitude of animated leaves on the march" and to Belt "like a mimic representation of a moving Birnam wood." The leaf fragments they carry are frequently larger than the ants themselves, so large in some instances that the bearers appear to be collapsing under their load.

These defoliating activities are carried on chiefly at dawn and dusk although on moonlit nights they may be active. The ants cannot stand the glare of the sun, and they are unable to continue their labors in heavy wind or rain.

The minims that are found associating with the mediums never make any attempt to cut or carry away leaves. They have special duties to perform in the subterranean chambers. It is not known just what their function is while above ground. They may come out for relaxation, as one author has suggested, or for the purpose of protecting the mediums, as another writer believes. They are perfectly willing to fight if necessary, but they are no help to their larger mates in carrying leaves to the nest. On the contrary they would seem to be a hindrance, for practically every leaf fragment has one or more minims hanging to it. Very frequently as many as six or seven may enjoy a free ride at the expense of one medium.

The nests, or formicaries, may be surprisingly large. They not infrequently stand four or five feet above the general level of the ground and extend eight to nine feet into the earth. Bates described one as having a circumference of forty yards, and Guenther wrote that a dozen men worked for six hours with mattocks and, at the end of that time, had not exposed all of one nest. The entrances lead to subterranean chambers, of which there may be a great number, depending on the size of the colony. These underground rooms are connected by passageways.

The early naturalists took it for granted that the leaves were used for only one purpose—food. The idea that they might have another function apparently did not occur to anyone until Bates arrived on the Amazon. After the young English naturalist had completed a careful examination of a sauba nest he reached the conclusion that the leaves were used "to thatch the domes which cover the entrances to their subterranean dwellings, thereby protecting from the deluging rains the young broods in the nests beneath." This explanation, however, was not the true one. About 1870 a more careful study of these ants was made in Nicaragua by Belt. He excavated a nest and made the remarkable discovery that the leaves were employed as a soil, or compost, upon which the ants raised a particular kind of fungus *(Rhozites gonglyophora)*. He found that there was a mass of this fungus in each of the chambers. In some the growth was no larger than a closed fist, in others the size of a watermelon. The color of the plant was grayish white, and the texture soft and spongy; if handled it tended to crumble.

The relationship between the parasol ants and the fungus is one of mutual benefit. Neither could exist, it is thought, without the other. The fungus depends upon the ants for its culture and the ants, in turn, depend upon the fungus for their food; they eat nothing else so far as is known. *Rhozites gonglyophora* has never been found elsewhere than in the sauba cellars. The attempts of scientists to rear it outside of the formicaries, without help from the ants, have ended in failure.

A close examination of the fungus reveals many globe-shaped nodules at the ends of the filaments, or hyphae, which make up the plant. These tiny spheroids were called kohlrabi by their discoverer (Moeller). They are said to be filled with a nutritive liquid and to supply the nourishment upon which the ants subsist. These ants are alone responsible for the kohlrabi, apparently. If the fungus is deserted by the ants for any reason the hyphae no longer produce the nodules but, instead, develop pinkish growths, two to three inches long, not unlike the common mushroom in size and shape.

Each fungus garden is more than a mass of interlacing filaments, for in the crevices is a veritable menagerie. There are parasol ants in all stages of development; there are mature males, females, and workers; and there are frequently several other insects totally unrelated. A detailed list of these inhabitants would include: (a) eggs, (b) larvae, (c) pupae, (d) the small workers, (e) the medium-sized workers, (f) the big workers, or soldiers, (g) the males, (h) the females, and, (i) other insects such as rove beetles and roaches. Infrequently there may be spiders and scorpions and other invertebrates.

Careful observation of these inmates in and about the fungus garden discloses the role that each plays in the life of the colony. Even though the chamber has been opened to the light of day the medium-sized workers continue their job of bringing in leaves. That apparently is their sole function, for as soon as they reach the underground rooms the leaves are immediately attacked by the small workers, or minims. They take complete charge of the leaf material now, and at once chew it to bits and shape it into small pellets. These in turn are placed at advantageous points in the crevices of the fungus where they may best serve to fertilize the mycelium. It is the role, too, of these tiniest workers to feed the larvae. They do this by regurgitation. They may also feed some of the adult workers which are too busy to do their own eating. And it is their task to carry away the leafy material after it has served its purpose as a compost. Special places may be discovered in the formicary where this useless leaf mold is regularly unloaded.

The duty of the large big-jawed, big-headed workers is easily discovered. Just as soon as an ant nest is dug into, they charge forth and attack the offender. They bite viciously and with enough force to cause bleeding. Moreover they hang on with bulldog tenacity, and the heads retain their grip even though abdomen and thorax are severed. Guenther wrote that when he stuck his umbrella into a nest it was immediately seized by several of these big fellows. Several hours later, after he had returned to his quarters, he noticed that several of them were still clinging to the cloth of the umbrella. Beebe wore high-top boots, well covered with vaseline, when excavating parasol nests. In spite of these precautions the soldiers sank their jaws into the leather and refused to let go. Once, while unpacking after his return to New York from British Guiana, he found the heads of two of these ants still clinging to the shoes. The Indians are said to use these ants in closing wounds that would normally require stitches. They pull the two sides of a gash together and then apply the head of a soldier sauba to the edges. The two jaws come together and remain fixed. Other ants are similarly attached. The natives then tear off all but the heads and these are left *in situ* until the wound has healed.

New colonies are founded by the females. These are winged forms that are almost the size of bumblebees. At a certain time of the year—at the beginning of the rainy season, according to Bates—the males and females emerge from their nests and start their nuptial flights. There is generally more than one female in a nest, but the number is never great. On the other hand the males are numerous, and each is intermediate in size between the female and the soldier. Before leaving the nest on her conjugal adventure, the female performs a remarkable task. She provides herself with a small pill of the fungus which is packed away in a small pouch at the back of the mouth. All is ready then for the flight. The sexual forms pour forth from the nest in huge swarms. Many enemies await them, and only a few of the ants survive. The males die anyway after impregnating the females, so that of the thousands which left the nest only a few of the females live to carry on the evolution of the *Attas*. Each of these soon discovers a hole under some stone or root that suits her purposes. Here she prepares to found a new colony. She first breaks off her wings, which are now of no use. She then removes from her oral cavity the morsel of fungus, which she plants in an advantageous spot and carefully fertilizes with her own excretions. She is then ready to begin laying her eggs. Only a small percentage of them actually develop into adults; the others—some 90 per cent, according to Guenther—she either eats or feeds to the developing larvae.

After a few days the larvae pupate and hatch into the adults. From this point the female works no more; her sole function is that of producing eggs. All other functions are relegated to the workers. The female is not even allowed to eat any more of the eggs. As they are laid the workers place them in the fungus gardens, where all subsequent development takes place.

Some of the newly created mediums soon emerge from the nests and initiate the very important work that is to follow above ground. They construct trails, locate desirable plants, and then begin defoliation. If all has gone well a new formicine colony is now well under way.

Parasol ants eat many of the wild plants found in the tropical forests, but they have a predilection for cultivated vegetables, shrubs, and flowers. It is impossible to estimate the damage they do in South America each year. In some places they are so destructive that the natives find it almost impossible to cultivate any sort of plant. A garden may have been successfully tended until it is almost ready to be harvested; then, seemingly from nowhere, a host of leaf cutters descends on it at night and at dawn nothing remains but leafless stalks.

Belt's experiences at agriculture are more or less typical. He attempted to raise fruits and vegetables and subsequently discovered that the leaves were rapidly disappearing into subterranean passageways. He immediately followed the line of ants to their nest, a hundred yards away. It was a low mound about four feet in diameter; but when he tried to lay bare all of the underground passageways he found them so extensive as to be impossible of destruction without a prodigious amount of labor. At that point it was suggested by a medical officer that he try carbolic acid. The idea was a good one. Following instructions Belt mixed a pint of the acid with four buckets of water, and poured this into the burrows. The ants in his garden were at once notified to come home, and the next day were busy moving to new quarters. They absconded completely, and it was a whole year before he was bothered again. The next time the ants invaded his garden he used the carbolic acid once more with gratifying results. He tried also corrosive sublimate, another deterrent that had been recommended to him, sprinkling a small amount of it across the ant path. When the *Attas* came in contact with it the reaction was as surprising as it was effective. They immediately ran amuck and began attacking their fellows. All that touched the sublimate reacted in the same way, so that in a short while ants were rolling in balls about the path, rabidly biting one another. Before long ants were seen minus antennae or legs, or abdomen. Reports of this internecine conflict reached the formicary, and a platoon of soldiers appeared on the scene, apparently to settle the matter once and for all. Some of them came in contact with the acid, and they, too, entered whole-heartedly into the mêlée. Only by utilizing these highly successful methods was Belt able to raise his plants.

The leaf-cutters do not confine their activities to defoliation. According to von Hagen they "attack everything containing cellulose." They carry away pieces of clothing, fruits of many kinds, flowers, and various foodstuffs. Bates awoke one night and found that they were spiriting away a supply of mandioca meal that he had in a container. He got rid of them by laying gunpowder across the trail and setting fire to it.

Army Ants

The army ants *(Eciton)*, also called foraging, driver, and migratory ants, are widely distributed over most of tropical and semitropical America and are famed for their predatory raids. There are many species that vary in size, color, habit, and other respects. Bates described ten species for the Amazon alone. Unlike the parasol ants, the army ants are carnivorous and hunt their prey in large, well organized groups. No living animal can stand against their invasion.

Each of the various forms has its own method of hunting. One species described by Bates *(E. rapax)* marches through the forest in single file. Another *(E. praedator)* organizes its members into a phalanx that may cover as much as four to six square yards. The majority of these freebooting species, however, dispose themselves into long, swiftly moving columns. The width of these formations varies with the species. In some they are only three to four ants wide; in others, three to four feet. Several columns may radiate from the nest, like the spokes of a wheel, and each may be hundreds of yards long and consist of untold thousands of ants.

Army ants, like all ants, are polymorphic. There are, as usual, males, females, and undeveloped females which are the workers. The latter are extremely abundant and, in several of the species, are readily divisible into at least two classes or groups: the workers proper, and the much larger soldiers. The soldiers are easily distinguished from the workers by their enormously enlarged mandibles. These are elongate, scimitarlike structures that extend from the head much like the tusks borne by certain prehistoric elephants. In some species these are so large that the ants have to hold their heads high to keep them off the ground. The biggest soldiers are only about one-half inch in length while the workers of certain species may be no more than one-fifth of an inch. The depredations of the army ants are such that one can scarcely credit their being caused by such small creatures.

The armies are invariably accompanied by a number of birds, and the cries of the latter may be a means of apprising man of the presence of the ants. Trogons, wood hewers, flycatchers, ant birds, and many others may be seen flitting from limb to limb above the line of march. The majority have been attracted by the beetles, moths, grasshoppers, and other insects that fly up from the floor of the forest when endangered by the ants. It is said that only a few of the tropical birds feed on the ants themselves.

As these armies rush through open woods or dense jungle growth the "whole animal world is set in commotion" (Bates). "Every creature aroused by the ants seems to know instinctively of the awful danger" (Beebe). Insects that are in the path take flight, and many escape. On the contrary many others are immediately snapped up by the birds. Still others, seemingly as a result of their terror, realight in the middle of the column, where they are immediately overwhelmed by scores of ants. Those animals incapable of rapid flight, such as spiders, millipedes, harvestmen, worms, and amphibia, are at the mercy of these six-legged plunderers. Some are able to scurry up the nearest herb or shrub or tree; sooner or later, however, an army ant will follow the same route and discover them. This ant will immediately relay the information to the main column, and soon a whole platoon will rush to the scene, where the unfortunate creature is summarily killed, dismembered and carried away. Everywhere along the line of march an observer will see veritable balls of ants, the size depending on the size of the beetle or spider that forms the nucleus of the sphere. The ants attack all animals, and they kill any beast, regardless of its size, if it has no ready means of escape. In addition to insects, which furnish the chief source of sustenance for army ants, the spiders, centipedes, scorpions, and harvestmen are probably most frequently victimized. Undoubtedly many nestling birds are killed. Adult birds, as well as large lizards and mammals, would quickly be dispatched if they did not flee.

If a man has the temerity to stand close to a column of army ants for any length of time he will discover why they are such formidable creatures. They not only bite deeply with their mandibles but double in their abdomens and sting for all they are worth; and each sting is like a stab of fire. Each ant has to be removed separately, and the head and jaws commonly remain adhering to the integument. According to von Hagen the combined bite and sting is worse than the sting of a wasp. Man is capable of coping with an army of these ants in only one way—retreat. No one can long withstand the fury of hundreds of these pests. The naturalists have had no first-hand knowledge of persons killed by army ants, but Verrill heard of two Brazilian officers who, after being reported missing, were found to have been victims of their voracity. The insects had left nothing but the skeletons. It was concluded that the men had dropped in a drunken stupor by the wayside, where the ants had found them.

In each column there are two streams of ants: one moving forward to the attack, the other carrying the spoils—legs, heads, wings, bits of lizard skin, small portions of flesh—in the opposite direction. If the prey is small it may be handled by one or more ants *in toto;* if large it is dismembered.

The manner in which some of the animals contrive to escape is of considerable interest. Belt thought that spiders showed the greatest ingenuity. He often saw them far ahead of the moving column "apparently determined to put a good distance between themselves and the foe." Many, trapped at the end of a limb, escaped the ants by descending a thread of silk of their own creation. Midway between their enemies above and below, they remained suspended until the horde passed on.

Harvestmen (granddaddy longlegs), surrounded by the ants, took advantage of their eight elongate legs. As the ants came near any appendage the harvestman raised it from the ground as far out of reach as he could, while supporting himself on the remaining seven. Belt saw one terrified creature with five legs pulled up near the thorax while it stood on the other three. In this way the harvestmen may occasionally save their lives, but probably not often.

Other animals feign death. A green, leaflike locust stood motionless surrounded by ants while many of them ran across its legs, apparently unaware that it was alive. Belt picked it up and placed it in another spot without its evidencing any signs of life. It was so much like a green leaf that he thought the ants were completely deceived. Beebe saw a large toad escape in much the same manner. It had fallen into a pit, and when an army of ants came along they descended into it. The toad remained motionless though the ants swarmed over it and some of them sank their jaws into its warty epidermis. Eventually the ants went their way, and the toad was left to do likewise.

Every so often an army of migratory ants converges upon the habitation of some native. Instead of being in despair the native is ordinarily so pleased that he moves out and gives the ants full control. His complacency is easily explained: the jungle home of the Indian is a haunt of cockroaches, centipedes, lizards, snakes, and all sorts of vermin. He is unable, or unwilling, to cope with these pests, and they swarm about the premises. After an army of foraging ants has ransacked the place, however, the whir of a cockroach and the squeak of a mouse are sounds unheard for several weeks. The ants penetrate every crevice in floor, wall, and roof and allow nothing to remain alive.

Some of the naturalists had their most intimate experiences with army ants when these overran their houses. Miller's quarters in Colombia were invaded one day while he was busy with his work. Dozens of cockroaches, centipedes, and scorpions suddenly began scurrying about the walls. These were followed by spiders and other arthropods. Following these came the ants, and there was nothing for Miller to do but remove his equipment to a point of safety.

On two different occasions, once on the forest slope of Mt. Campana in the eastern Peruvian Andes, and another time on the Danle River near Guayaquil, Spruce was visited by the army ants. In each case the residents, Spruce included, quickly vacated their quarters, and the ants took possession. After the ants had killed all the vermin and had begun to look for food in the family pantry the owners routed them by sprinkling water on them. When a brigade of army ants entered von Hagen's quarters in eastern Ecuador he was able to get rid of them in the same manner.

Verrill was visited one night. He was in his hammock and was not bothered. However, everything else alive in the house was killed, and a good-sized tapir that had been shot the previous afternoon and suspended outside was devoured, nothing being left except the hide and bones.

The nest of the army ants is not often found. It is temporary and is frequently moved. As a rule it is in some crevice in the ground or under a convenient log or stone. Here congregates a huge mass of ants, with the males, females, eggs, larvae, and pupae forming the core and the multitudinous workers composing the periphery. One such mass, according to Belt, was "at least a cubic yard in bulk, and contained hundreds of thousands of individuals, although many columns were outside, some bringing in the pupae of ants, others the legs and dissected bodies of various insects." He noted definite passageways leading to the center of the nest. These constituted the main avenues of approach and exit and were kept open. He thought that the developing forms were kept warm by the mass of closely associated bodies.

The activities of army ants are all the more striking when we learn that most of them are totally blind. None of them have the compound eyes characteristic of most insects. A few species have very small eyes consisting of a single lens. Others have only vestiges, while still others have neither sockets nor eyes, only a faint ring marking the place where the eyes formerly were. So we come to the amazing realization that many of these ants march endlessly through the forest, engage in warfare, and carry on their manifold activities, yet are entirely blind. Belt thought that this deficiency was of advantage to the ants, considering their communal life and manner of hunting. He reasoned that, if the ants could see, many of them would wander afield after prey and become lost, whereas the lack of vision had the effect of keeping them together.

Army ants follow one another by scent and not by sight. This sense is highly developed and is located in the long, quivering antennae that are constantly in action. "I believe," wrote Belt, "they can communicate the presence of danger, of booty or other intelligence to a distance by the different intensity or qualities of the odours given off."

The army ants are always accompanied by many strange companions. These are chiefly beetles and flies. Some chance along, but others consort with the ants at all times. Most remarkable of all is the fact that some beetles and flies mimic the ants so perfectly in shape, size, and color that they may be told from them only with difficulty. The ants kill all other animal life, but they do not molest these forms. The flies repay good with evil. They lay their eggs on the bodies of the ants. Later larvae emerge from the eggs and burrow into the abdomen of the ants, killing them.

"Amongst the ants of Central America," Belt wrote, "I place the Eciton as the first in intelligence." He based his belief on his personal observations. One day while watching a column of army ants he chose one from among many and placed a stone on top of it. Very soon another worker happened along and discovered its mate in distress. This one soon informed others of the predicament and all of them came to the rescue. Some attacked the stone while others pulled at the legs of the prisoner so lustily Belt thought they would be torn from the thorax. They persisted in their efforts until the captive ant was freed. Belt next covered another one, all but its antennae, with a bit of moistened clay. The ants found this one and quickly liberated it by biting away the clay in small pieces. On another day Belt found a straggler that was some distance from any of its fellow workers. He covered all but the head of this one with clay. Some time later a companion found it and tried in vain to free it. It then left, apparently for good. However, it returned in a few moments with about a dozen others. They set to work at once, and quickly liberated the captive one. "It was sympathetic help," Belt reasoned, "such as man only among the higher mammalia shows. The excitement and ardour with which they carried on their unflagging exertions for the rescue of their comrade would not have been greater if they had been human beings, and this to meet a danger that can be only of the rarest occurrence."

INSECTS AS FOOD

There is no accounting for tastes where food is concerned. In France snails are considered one of the greatest of delicacies; in China a *pièce de résistance* of the highest order is soup made from bird's nests; and in the South American "forest primeval" the natives feast from time to time on various and sundry insects—ants, termites, moth larvae, and the like.

These dishes, no matter how carefully prepared or how toothsome, evoke no enthusiasm from a North American. However, ants and termites represent unusual delicacies to the South American natives, and they go out of their way to hunt for them; on the other hand they would definitely spurn some of our choicest viands. For instance, a chicken is a pet to certain Indians of British Guiana, and they would no more think of eating one than we would our favorite wire-haired terrier.

Of course insects are eaten outside South America, and they have kept the wolf from the door on many occasions and among many peoples. Grasshoppers, in particular, have satisfied the hunger of primitive tribes in all historic times including the present. It is a matter of record that the Digger Indians of the Far West protested to our government a few years back about the scarcity of food after the numbers of migratory grasshoppers had declined almost to the vanishing point.

In looking through the writings of the South American naturalists we find frequent references to the consumption of insects by the natives. After all, these tiny arthropodan forms do constitute an enormous amount of nourishing food material, and it is rather surprising than otherwise that so-called civilized peoples have not included them in their diets more than they have. Many of the fish, reptiles, birds, and mammals thrive upon a menu which consists almost entirely of insects. Perhaps the future—as gustatory fashions change—will find fricasseed grasshoppers or scalloped termites being served at famous hostelries while epicures exclaim long and loudly upon their salutary merits, as others have done in the past about spinach and acidophilus milk. Perhaps, then, the lines from Charles Edward Carryl's nursery rhyme, "Robin Crusoe's Story,"

> For I live on toasted lizards,
> Prickly pears, and parrot gizzards,
> And I'm really very fond of beetle pie,

will be entirely apropos in northern countries as they are pretty much today in equatorial America.

Not so many months after the great Humboldt landed in South America he was far in the interior, on the Rio Negro. Here he discovered a small group of Indians eating a meal the like of which he had probably never heard. They "were seated round a fire of brushwood, and they were eating a sort of white paste with black spots which much excited our curiosity." These black spots proved to be ants which the Indians had dried and smoked. Several bags of them were hanging above a fire at the time to be used in subsequent repasts.

Just how many species of ants the Indians find palatable and which kinds they prefer is not known; but several of the naturalists speak of their eating sauba, or parasol, ants. These are the hymenoptera which are such outstanding defoliators. Spruce wrote: "I have many times seen Indians eat the sauba ant (called *bachaco* in Venezuela). The large kinds only are eaten, and at those times when the *bachacos* pour forth from their holes in great numbers (probably sending forth colonies after the manner of bees), if it be near any pueblo at all the unoccupied Indians in the place turn out to collect them. The head and thorax is the part eaten, the abdomen being nipped off (at San Carlos I constantly see them eaten entire), and it is eaten uncooked. The taste to me is strong, fiery, and disagreeable, but those who have eaten the *bachaco* fixed in turtle oil tell me it is quite palatable."

Bates found Indians on the Tapajós who made a sauce from the cassava plant which they called *Tucupi,* and they were in the habit of seasoning this with sauba ants. References to the use of sauba ants by the Indians are also made by both Wallace and Schomburgk, so that the custom must be rather widespread—especially since the observations of these different men were made at widely separated places.

McGovern has written the most interesting account of the way in which the natives capture and prepare the sauba ants for eating. His observations were made on the headwaters of the Uaupés River, a westerly tributary of the Rio Negro, and not far from the eastern boundary of the Republic of Colombia. After a long day of paddling up this stream he and the rest of his party made camp one evening in a small hut which had been deserted by its former inhabitants. The initial preparations for supper had no more than been made when two canoes, carrying altogether eight or nine natives, unexpectedly arrived at their camp. These were carrying baskets and explained that they were hunting ants.

A hunt for ants was something new to McGovern and he immediately decided to join this expedition, wherever it might lead him. After certain preliminaries they started, and before long discovered several nests of the well-known sauba ants. A low buzzing note was coming from the nests, and McGovern realized that they had arrived just in time for the swarming of these insects. He was perplexed as to how the Indians had gauged their arrival so accurately, for almost at once thousands of the queens and drones began to take wing. The natives turned the baskets upside down over the various exits, and the ants flew into them and were caught. All of the baskets were quickly filled, and the ant-hunting expedition returned to camp jubilant.

The ants were not very large, but some ninety to a hundred of them made a very satisfactory meal, according to McGovern. The Indians ate some of them raw, and others they roasted. Of the raw ants they ate only the heads. However, the whole bodies were eaten if they were roasted. The Indians had large earthenware pans in which they roasted the insects over the fire. McGovern, a true scientific spirit ever eager for new experiences, tried the ants both cooked and raw. He found the uncooked heads too oily, but the roasted ants tasted to him like crisp bacon; and he could not understand why anyone should object to eating them. These Indians considered ants a great delicacy.

Although ants are much sought after to replenish the domestic larder, termites are equally in demand. At the small settlement of Pirara on Lake Amacu between the Rupununi and Pirara rivers, Schomburgk found, as harbingers of the rainy season, dense flights of termites (*Termes destructor*)—which were a signal for the Indians to congregate from points near and far; they assembled at nightfall along the edges of the forests and started huge fires. The termites were attracted by the bright lights; and as they flew toward the bonfires the natives caught them in great numbers, using baskets and other large receptacles. These nocturnal experiences made a deep impression on Schomburgk. Of them he wrote in the following words: "I never missed these trips; they had a peculiar fascination for me for it was the most illusive realization of the Brocken scene in Goethe's *Faust* or the *Saga of the Harz,* when the wild brown figures, young and old, would caper wildly around the huge bonfires, and at the same time raise their voices, which to my German ear seemed to represent the unbridled gambols of a crowd of underground hobgoblins rather than those of my fellow brothers and sisters."

The natives capture termites at times when they are not swarming. While on his way to visit the celebrated Mt. Roraima, Brown watched them. "They capture these insects," he wrote, "by inserting a dry grass stalk into their nests to which the termites adhered by their mandibles, and were drawn out in hundreds." These were afterwards roasted and eaten.

Highly prized, too, for their appetizing qualities are the larvae of certain moths and of a few beetles. Schomburgk found that the Guiana Indians ate the larval forms of several different kinds of moths and beetles. All of these were eaten raw, usually with a piece of cassava bread. Spruce included in his journal this paragraph: "Indians of the Rio Negro, Uaupés, Cassiquiari, Orinoco (and perhaps of the Amazon) eat the large grubs bred on various growing palm stems. They are said to be of the size of the forefinger. The animal is roasted on the budar, or mandiocca, oven. There is another grub or caterpillar found on marima trees which they are very fond of. When this insect is in season, it constitutes a principal part of the food of the Maquiritari Indians, and Don Diego Pina related to me that, traveling once on the Alto Orinoco with a crew of these Indians, he was near perishing of hunger, for they would neither fish nor seek after any sort of food but these caterpillars, and wherever they stopped by the way they climbed into the marima trees in search of them."

This custom of eating the moth larvae which feed on the cabbage palm, previously referred to by Schomburgk and Spruce, is widespread. Brown mentions having seen the Guiana Indians eat them, and André found that they were considered "one of the daintiest of delicacies" by the natives living on the Caura. Guise, who spent several years in Bolivia as an engineer, one day saw several peons cutting into some palm trees that had been cut down to make way for a road. Becoming curious, he strolled over to the group and found them busily opening up the fibrous centers of the logs and extracting numerous fat white grubs which they carefully put into a tin can. The peons, when asked for an explanation, replied that these larvae were *tutuyus*—and that they were a great delicacy. That night they fried them over a fire and ate them with unmistakable relish.

McGovern related that the Pogsa Indians were prone to eat caterpillars which they secured from certain trees. Whether the trees were the cabbage palm is not made clear. The way in which they went about eating these larvae is described by McGovern in these words: "The 'innards' were carefully squeezed out, and only the skins were thrown into the cooking pot. They were boiled for half an hour and the banquet was then declared ready. I was surprised how tough these boiled caterpillars were. They required careful mastication, and both in consistency and in taste, they reminded me rather forcibly of rubber bands."

In British Guiana, and elsewhere, the natives find that wasp larvae make satisfactory eating. Brown once overtook a party of Wapisiana Indians that were "busily engaged in picking out and eating the larvae of a wasp from the comb of a nest of that insect which they had knocked from the overhanging branches of a tree. The children, especially, seemed to enjoy the little white grub-like larvae, as a civilized child would sugar-plums."

Waterton recounted that the wasps (or *maribuntas)* are great pests in the Guiana forests. Also that "the Indians make a fire under the nest (which hangs from the branch of a tree), and after killing or driving away the old ones, they roast the young grubs in the comb and eat them." "I tried them once by way of dessert after dinner," Waterton added; "but my stomach was offended at their intrusion."

BUTTERFLIES

South America is the lepidopterist's utopia; on no other continent are there such a variety and profusion of butterflies. Just one paragraph—no more—from Bates is sufficient to bring this home. "It will convey some idea of the diversity of butterflies," he declared, "when I mention that about 700 species of that tribe are found within an hour's walk of the town [Pará]; whilst the total number found in the British Islands does not exceed 66, and the whole of Europe supports only 390."

The full import of that statement is not grasped immediately. A man can walk in an hour's time about three miles. Here, then, within a tract of land which had an area of about 30 square miles, there were 700 species of butterflies, or 23 for each square mile. Europe has approximately 3,800,000 square miles or one species of butterfly for every 10,000 square miles.

A day of collecting on the outskirts of any town in the United States is considered highly successful if as many as twenty species are netted for the cyanide jar; and if that many were caught the next day the total number of new species secured would be negligible. Day after day Bates collected twenty or more different species in the immediate neighborhood of Pará. He wrote that one day he caught thirty-seven species and the next day thirty-five, twenty-seven of which were different from those taken on the day before; and these were not exceptional days. Bates lived in or near Pará for a year and a half before he left for his exploration of the upper Amazon, so that he had ample time in which to make a thorough survey of the insects in that region. He was struck with the fact that there was "a great paucity of individuals compared with species, in both Lepidoptera and Coleoptera."

The butterflies were most numerous in the vicinity of Pará when the dry season was at its height, he wrote, and particularly if there were occasional showers. At such periods of the year the number of species captured was almost unbelievable. Many of them were quite rare, and remarkable for their mode of flight, diversity of habit, and unusual coloration. Practically all tints of the spectrum were represented in the wings—red, green, purple, blue—and in a few the wings were perfectly transparent. One clear wing in particular *(Hetaira esmeralda)* attracted Bates because of its delicate beauty. When flying low through the forests it reminded him of "a wandering petal of a flower."

Years later he established his residence at Ega (Teffé), some fifteen hundred miles up the Amazon. Here, during a protracted stay, he discovered that butterflies were almost, if not quite, as numerous as at Pará. In the course of his collections at this tiny *ultima Thule* of civilization he assembled 550 distinct species. Bates wrote that those who had some knowledge of insects would be in a position to judge as to the wealth of butterflies from his finding eighteen species of swallowtails *(Papilio)* within ten minutes' stroll of his quarters. This fact spoke more eloquently "for the surpassing exuberance of the vegetation, the varied nature of the land, and the perennial warmth and humidity of the climate" than any other he might mention. But no word picture, he thought, could do justice to "the beauty and diversity in form and colour of this class of insects in the neighbourhood of Ega." In a short visit to a lake near Ega, he identified eighty distinct species. They were so numerous that large flocks were disturbed at the edge of the water every few steps. They were of all shapes, sizes, and colors.

This great profusion of butterflies in South America is not limited to the Amazon basin by any means. Father Zahm wrote that "in the immediate vicinity of Rio de Janeiro there are no fewer than eight hundred species," and Rodway declared that more butterflies have already been described for British Guiana than for all of Europe; and new species are being discovered regularly.

Im Thurn wrote that of all the South American butterflies the most striking are "the huge Morphos, the large wings of which are entirely blue, and so gorgeous, brilliant, and shining, that the insect as it comes flaunting lazily down through the dark alleys between the tree-trunks, seems even from a considerable distance like a flash of blue light. They generally fly high, at the tops of the trees; but for a short time every morning, apparently when the sun is at a particular point in the horizon, they come down into the open."

The gorgeously colored Morphos, some with a wing expanse of seven inches, preferred the dark shades of the forest, Bates wrote, although occasionally they were seen in the bright sunlight. When he was living at Nazareth he admired the *Morpho menelaus* but said it looked drab in comparison with *Morpho rhetenor,* the wings of which had a luster almost dazzling to the human eye. This form frequented the sunlit alleys of the forests, but flew so high that specimens were almost never captured. It rarely came lower than twenty feet, and when the sunlight was reflected from its huge wings it could be seen a quarter of a mile away. Another closely allied form was *Morpho eugenia.* This species had wings of a satiny-white appearance, and it was just as hard to capture as *rhetenor.* The wings of the female were a pale lavender instead of white.

Bates found several species of Morphos at Villa Nova, and most of these were quite common. "It is a grand sight," he exclaimed, "to see these colossal butterflies by twos and threes floating at a great height in the still air of a tropical morning." Only now and then did they flap their wings and frequently they sailed for long distances without a single stroke. The wing musculature was poorly developed considering the size of the wings, Bates said, but he thought the wide surface must compensate for this lack of contractile tissue. He found here *Morpho cisseis,* the largest specimens of which had a width of seven and one-half inches.

Wallace found the Morphos to be more abundant at Javita, a small settlement on the Temí, a tributary of the Atabapo, than at any other place he visited in South America; and they were on the ground instead of up in the air out of reach, as they usually were. "In certain places in the road," he said, "I found them by dozens sitting on the ground or on twigs by the roadside and could easily have captured a dozen or twenty a day if I had wanted them."

The outstanding beauty of the Morphos and numerous other forms of life along the equator could not be attributed to the tropical climate, Bates contended. He pointed to the fact that it was the males of the species that were highly colored and not the females. If climate were such an important factor, why would not both sexes be equally affected? He noted, too, that while there were many examples of animals with resplendent coloration there were just as many that have a dull coloration. Also that while there were more species in the tropical zone than in temperate zones, nevertheless the proportion of brilliantly colored forms did not increase with proximity to the line.

The existence of a greater number and variety of forms is probably due, as Bates said, to several factors: "the abundance of food, the high temperature, absence of seasons of extreme cold and dearth, and the variety of stations. This, perhaps, is all we can say with regard to the influence of climatal conditions. The causes which have produced the great beauty that astonishes us, if we really wish to investigate them, must be sought in other directions."

Next to the Morphos, the group of South American butterflies most likely to attract the eye of the visitor is that containing the Heliconias. These have long narrow wings that are of entirely different shape from those of most butterflies. The Heliconias are found only in tropical America. Bates saw them soon after arriving in Pará. "The prevailing ground colour of the wings of these insects is a deep black," he wrote, "and on this are depicted spots and streaks of crimson, white, and bright yellow, in different patterns according to the species. Their elegant shape, showy colours, and slow, sailing mode of flight make them very attractive objects, and their numbers are so great that they form quite a feature in the physiognomy of the forest, compensating for the scarcity of flowers."

According to Belt the Heliconias are distasteful to animals. He saw spiders that threw them from their nests, and monkeys invariably refused them although they did not hesitate to eat other butterflies. If this is a characteristic of the species everywhere throughout its range, the explanation of its abundance is quite obvious.

It is not generally known that butterflies often set out on long journeys that take them over land or sea for hundreds of miles. A great many species of butterflies are known definitely to migrate, and as observations on other species are continued the number in all likelihood will be materially increased. In some of these flights the number of individuals participating is not numerically great. In others the number is in the millions.

A few of the greatest of these Lepidopteran Marco Polos reside permanently in South America, while others visit it only on periodical southerly flights from the West Indies and North America. Quite a few of the naturalists have been spectators to these inexplicable pilgrimages.

One of the earliest observations was made by Darwin. He was on board the *Beagle* at the time, off the coast of Argentina some ten miles from the bay of San Blas. A tremendous flock of butterflies put in its appearance, consisting of countless thousands. In no direction could he find a space that was free of them, even with the aid of a telescope. They were in such profusion that the sailors exclaimed it was "snowing butterflies." The majority were of a species similar to the English *Colias edusa,* although other forms were represented.

Darwin does not state in which direction the butterflies were moving, but the impression is left that they were flying east, or southeast. The observation was made in December, a summer month in that part of the world.

Just a few years later Schomburgk witnessed a migration in which the butterflies were traveling north. This observation was made in September, 1842, near the mouth of the Cotinga in northern Brazil, not far from the British Guiana line.

As Schomburgk described it, "We had already struck large swarms of white butterflies, flying regularly from S.E. to N.W., on our departure from Pirara. They were still continually increasing. In the coloration of their wings they resembled the 'Cabbage White,' but the thoracic segment showed up more yellow, and a black border tipped the colouring. During the midday hour and shortly before sunset they would settle down in endless numbers to rest on the muddy heaps along the bank, or on the sand banks at the edge of the water."

Seven years later Bates saw a migration on the Amazon below Obydos. Huge numbers of butterflies belonging to the genus Callidryas kept passing over his boat for two whole days. They kept moving without any perceptible interruption from daylight till dusk. The direction of the migration was, in this case, from north to south and, in so far as Bates could make out, all were males. For this reason he thought that the migration could not have extended far. The date of this observation was October, 1849.

In November of the same year, Spruce witnessed a similiar migration on the Amazon near the mouth of the Xingú, between Pará and Santarem. To give this description in his own words:

"We saw a vast multitude of butterflies flying across the Amazon, from the northern to the southern side, in a direction about from N.N.W. to S.S.E. They were evidently in the last stage of fatigue; some of them attained the shore, but a large proportion fell exhausted into the water, and we caught several in our hands as they passed over the canoe. They were all of common white and orange-yellow species, such as are bred in cultivated and waste grounds."

Spruce considered that the outstanding circumstance of the flight was the consistency with which the butterflies moved always to the south. When he wrote this description—quite a few years afterwards—he was acquainted with Bates' statement that all the members seen were males. Spruce was unable to say whether all of the butterflies he had seen near the mouth of the Xingú were of one sex, or not; but he was quite positive that both sexes were represented in some migrations subsequently seen.

It is remarkable that two famous scientists, on entirely independent expeditions, should witness very similar migrations within two hundred miles of each other and almost at the same time. These may have been parts of the same general extensive movement; for such processions have been known to occur on a 250-mile front and to continue steadily in the same direction for days, if not weeks. Both of these migrations occurred—if there were two—in about the same latitude; 2° South.

In 1862 Spruce resided for several weeks at a little coastal village (Chanduy) north of Guayaquil in the Republic of Ecuador. Normally the rainfall of that section is meager, but that year there had been one heavy rainfall after another and, as happens now and then in arid regions, the desert was covered almost overnight with flowers. Shortly after, a huge migration of butterflies and moths appeared from the east. Many of the butterflies laid their eggs in clusters on the leaves and in a few days the place was overrun with caterpillars. During all of this time, additional butterflies, great hosts of them, were streaming in from the western slopes of the Andes. The late-comers, finding the plants eaten up, struck out over the Pacific Ocean, there to perish. This flight took place in the month of April, and the latitude was about 2° South.

The experiences of Belt in Nicaragua, and in Brazil, were that the flights were always to the south or southeast. He observed several of these pilgrimages, some of them lasting "three to five weeks" and consisting of "millions upon millions of individuals, comprising many different species and genera." He speaks of their southerly journeys as occurring in both April and June. He was continuously on the lookout for a return flight during his five years' stay in Central America, but at no time did he see any flight to the north.

In *The Edge of the Jungle,* Beebe writes of the several migrations he had seen in British Guiana. In every case, he says, the direction of the flight was north-northwest; and, of even more interest, each and every individual in the multitude was a male.

One of the most common migrants is the yellow *Callidryas eubule.* Since the time of Columbus its migrations have been noted, the great Genoese navigator having seen a great flock of them off the coast of Cuba that was dispersed by a tropical storm. Rodway said that he saw huge numbers of this species crossing the Demerara River. They flew in a southerly direction for hours at a time, maintaining a steady unbroken advance, and at a distance had the appearance of a yellow line against the sky. So far as he could tell, all of the butterflies were males.

It will have been noted that not only Rodway but Bates and Beebe observed migrating flocks in which all the individuals seemed to be males. Rodway thought that perhaps the males were off in search of females but added that he had no difficulty in finding plenty of females at many places in the colony.

A score of years ago it was thought that none of the butterflies ever returned from their flights. Evidence now proves conclusively that some forms do make a return journey. The species the migration of which is best known is the monarch, or milkweed butterfly *(Danaus plexippus)*. Its range includes practically all of the United States and a part of Canada. More than that it has, within comparatively recent years, spread to such distant lands as New Zealand and Australia, in both of which it is now established, and to continental Europe, where occasional specimens are collected.

The monarchs that are found in Canada in the summer start south in August. When the flight begins, the number of butterflies is not large; but large flocks congregate from east and west, and by the time it reaches the middle Atlantic states and the region to the west it attains proportions defying all calculation. The progress is a leisurely one, probably somewhere between three to ten miles an hour. The direction which the flight takes is as a rule due south and it does not end until the Gulf states are reached. Here the butterflies pass the winter in semihibernation. By March the weather has become warm enough to stimulate them to start traveling again. The stimulus, as in birds, may be associated with the physiology of the sex glands.

The return north is radically different from the southern flight. Starting in March, they fly individually—not in large groups; no one except an expert on the lookout for their movements would recognize that a northern migration was in progress. Those butterflies that go as far as Canada arrive about the last of May or the first of June. The females lay their eggs on the way, and it is the young from these eggs that go south in the fall. The parents die so that individuals make only one round trip. The monarch is rarely, if ever, seen in the north during the winter.

Butterfly migrations occur in all parts of the world. In most cases there is no evidence of a return flight but, as one author puts it, "absence of evidence is not evidence of absence." As with the monarch it is possible that the flights in one direction are quite thin and accordingly overlooked.

For the most part the spring flights are away from the equator; the fall flights toward it. However, there are exceptions. The experience of Belt in the spring months, when all the flights observed by him were to the south, is one example. Another is that of Schomburgk, who witnessed a migration toward the north in September.

The beginning of the flights has been attributed to food shortage, to a plethora of parasites, to unfavorable climatic conditions, and to overcrowding. There are some facts which support the last theory but not enough to make it tenable.

The force which impels the insects to travel hundreds of miles in a given direction is amazingly powerful. They have been seen to dash themselves against the sides of buildings rather than swerve a few feet, either to left or to right. They have flown in at the window on one side of a home and out at another on the opposite side; and of course no body of water, however large, stops them for an instant.

Attempts have been made to explain how the butterflies stick to a definite course while migrating, but thus far each theory has run up against too many obstacles to be considered really workable. The notion that they orient themselves by the sun, or that they are guided by a magnetic sense, is clearly unsatisfactory, almost as much so as another hypothesis based on memory of the route traveled. If all butterflies migrate just once, as do the monarchs, the memory concept naturally must be ruled out.

The mystery deepens when we consider the stopping places of the migrating butterflies. In some instances, such as in that of the monarchs, there is a definite, reasonable objective; but all too frequently the flying hordes pass by what might be considered the Elysian Fields and continue out over the ocean where certain death awaits. Two such flights have already been described, the one observed by Darwin and the other by Spruce. Apparently the biological urge is such that it must be completely satisfied before a stop is made.

BIBLIOGRAPHY

General Literature

Anthony, H. E., ed., Animals of America. New York: Garden City Publishing Co., 1937.

Beddard, F. E., Mammalia (Cambridge Natural History, Vol. X). London: Macmillan & Co., 1909.

Bruhns, Karl, and Lassell, J. and C., Life of Alexander von Humboldt. 2 vols. Boston: Lee & Shepard, 1873.

Chandler, A. C., Introduction to Human Parasitology (5th ed.). New York: John Wiley & Sons, 1936.

Cooke, W. W., and others, The Book of Birds. Washington: National Geographic Society, 1925.

Curran, C. H., and Kauffeld, C., Snakes and Their Ways. New York: Harper & Brothers, 1937.

Darwin, Francis, The Life and Letters of Charles Darwin. 2 vols. New York: D. Appleton & Co., 1897.

Ditmars, R. L., Reptiles of North America. New York: Doubleday, Doran & Co., 1936.

———, Reptiles of the World. New York: The Macmillan Co., 1933.

———, Snakes of the World. New York: The Macmillan Co., 1937.

Evans, A. H., Birds (Cambridge Natural History, Vol. IX). London: Macmillan & Co., 1935.

Grosvenor, G., and Wetmore, A., eds., The Book of Birds. 2 vols. Washington: National Geographic Society, 1937.

Hildebrand, S. F., Gilmore, C. W., and Cochran, D. M., Cold-Blooded Vertebrates (Smithsonian Scientific Series, Vol. VIII). New York: Smithsonian Scientific Series, Inc., 1930.

Hooton, E. A., Up from the Ape. New York: The Macmillan Co., 1931.

Hornaday, W. T., The American Natural History. New York: Charles Scribner's Sons, 1926.

Ingersoll, E., The Life of Animals. New York: The Macmillan Co., 1906.

Mann, W. M., Wild Animals in and out of the Zoo (Smithsonian Scientific Series, Vol. VI). New York: Smithsonian Scientific Series, Inc., 1930.

Nelson, E. W., The Larger North American Mammals. Washington: National Geographic Society, 1916.

Newman, H. H., Evolution, Genetics, and Eugenics (3rd rev. ed.). Chicago: University of Chicago Press, 1932.

Parker, E., Hesketh Prichard. New York: E. P. Dutton & Co., 1925.
Pearson, T. G. (ed.-in-chief), Birds of America. New York: Garden City Publishing Co., 1936.
Peattie, D. C., Green Laurels: The Lives and Achievements of the Great Naturalists. New York: Simon & Schuster, 1936.
Pope, C. H., Snakes Alive, and How They Live. New York: Viking Press, 1937.
Prescott, W. H., History of the Conquest of Peru. 2 vols. London: Richard Bentley, 1847.
Riley, W. A., and Johannsen, O. A., Medical Entomology. New York: McGraw-Hill Book Company, 1932.
Scott, W. B., A History of Land Mammals in the Western Hemisphere (rev. ed.). New York: The Macmillan Co., 1937.
Wallace, A. R., My Life. 2 vols. New York: Dodd, Mead & Co., 1905.
Wetmore, A., Miller, G. S., Jr., and Gidley, J. W., Warm-Blooded Vertebrates (Smithsonian Scientific Series, Vol. IX). New York: Smithsonian Scientific Series, Inc., 1931.
Ybarra, T. R., Bolívar: The Passionate Warrior. New York: Ives Washburn, 1929.

South American Literature

Adalbert, Prince of Prussia, Travels in the South of Europe and in Brazil. Trans. by Sir Robert H. Schomburgk and John Edward Taylor. 2 vols. London: David Bogue, 1849.
Agassiz, Prof. and Mrs. Louis, A Journey in Brazil. Boston: Ticknor & Fields, 1868.
André, Eugène, A Naturalist in the Guianas. London: Smith, Elder, & Co., 1904.
Azara, Don Felix de, The Natural History of the Quadrupeds of Paraguay and the River La Plata. Edinburgh: Adam & Charles Black, 1838.
Ball, J., Notes of a Naturalist in South America. London: Kegan Paul, Trench & Co., 1887.
Bates, H. W., The Naturalist on the River Amazons. 2 vols. London: John Murray, 1863.
Beebe, Mary Blair, and Beebe, C. William, Our Search for a Wilderness. New York: Henry Holt & Co., 1910.
Beebe, William, The Edge of the Jungle. New York: Henry Holt & Co., 1921.
——, Jungle Days. New York: G. P. Putnam's Sons, 1925.
——, Jungle Peace. New York: Henry Holt & Co., 1918.
——, Hartley, G. I., and Howes, P. G., Tropical Wild Life in British Guiana. New York: N. Y. Zoological Society, 1917.
Beerbohm, J., Wanderings in Patagonia. London: Chatto & Windus, 1879.

Bibliography

Belt, Thomas, The Naturalist in Nicaragua. London: John Murray, 1874.

Bigg-Wither, T. P., Pioneering in South Brazil. 2 vols. London: John Murray, 1878.

Boddam-Whetham, J. W., Roraima and British Guiana. London: Hurst & Blackett, 1879.

Brown, C. B., Canoe and Camp Life in British Guiana. London: Edward Stanford, 1877.

——— and Lidstone, W., Fifteen Thousand Miles on the Amazon and Its Tributaries. London: Edward Stanford, 1878.

Burton, Capt. Richard F., The Highlands of the Brazil. 2 vols. London: Tinsley Brothers, 1869.

Carpenter, C. R., A Field Study of the Behavior and Social Relations of Howling Monkeys (Comparative Psychology Monographs, Vol. 10, No. 2, serial no. 48). Baltimore: Johns Hopkins Press, 1934.

Chapman, F. M., Autobiography of a Bird-Lover. New York: D. Appleton-Century Co., 1933.

———, Handbook of Birds of Eastern North America. New York: D. Appleton & Co., 1926.

———, Life in an Air Castle. New York: D. Appleton-Century Co., 1938.

———, My Tropical Air Castle. New York: D. Appleton & Co., 1929.

Cherrie, G. K., Dark Trails. New York: G. P. Putnam's Sons, 1930.

Cunningham, R. O., Notes on the Natural History of the Strait of Magellan and West Coast of Patagonia. Edinburgh: Edmonston & Douglas, 1871.

Cunninghame Graham, R. B., The Conquest of the River Plata. New York: Doubleday, Page & Co., 1924.

Darwin, Charles, A Diary of the Voyage of H.M.S. "Beagle" (ed. from the MS. by Nora Barlow). London: Cambridge University Press, 1933.

———, Journal of Researches into the Natural History and Geology of the Countries Visited During the Voyage of H.M.S. "Beagle" Round the World. London: Ward, Lock, & Co., 1890.

Dickey, H. S., My Jungle Book. Boston: Little, Brown, and Co., 1932.

——— and Daniel, Hawthorne, Misadventures of a Tropical Medico. New York: Dodd, Mead & Co., 1929.

Ditmars, R. L., Confessions of a Scientist. New York: The Macmillan Co., 1934.

———, The Making of a Scientist. New York: The Macmillan Co., 1937.

———, Thrills of a Naturalist's Quest. New York: The Macmillan Co., 1932.

——— and Bridges, W., Snake-Hunters' Holiday. New York: D. Appleton-Century Co., 1935.

Bibliography

Domville-Fife, C. W., Among Wild Tribes of the Amazons. Philadelphia: J. B. Lippincott Co., 1924.
Duguid, Julian, Green Hell. New York: The Century Co., 1931.
———, Tiger-Man. New York: The Century Co., 1932.
Dyott, G. M., Man Hunting in the Jungle, Indianapolis: Bobbs-Merrill, 1930.
———, Silent Highways of the Jungle (2nd ed.). London: Chapman & Dodd, 1924.
Edwards, W. H., A Voyage Up the River Amazon. London: John Murray, 1847.
Enders, R. K., Mammalian Life Histories from Barro Colorado Island, Panama (Bull. 78, No. 4). Cambridge, Mass.: Museum of Comparative Zoology, 1935.
Friel, A. O., The River of Seven Stars. New York: Harper & Brothers, 1924.
Gardner, G., Travels in the Interior of Brazil. London: Reeve, Benham, & Reeve, 1849.
Gates, R. R., A Botanist in the Amazon Valley. London: H. F. & G. Witherby, 1927.
Guenther, Konrad, A Naturalist in Brazil. Boston: Houghton Mifflin Co., 1931.
Guise, A. V. L., Six Years in Bolivia. New York: E. P. Dutton & Co.
von Hagen, V. W., Off With Their Heads. New York: The Macmillan Co., 1937.
Hanson, E. P., Journey to Manáos. New York: Reynal & Hitchcock, 1938.
Herndon, W. L., and Gibbon, L., Exploration of the Valley of the Amazon Made Under Direction of the Navy Department. Washington: Robert Armstrong, 1854.
Hingston, Major R. W. G., A Naturalist in the Guiana Forest. London: Edward Arnold & Co., 1932.
Holdridge, Desmond, Pindorama. New York: Minton, Balch & Co., 1933.
Hudson, W. H., Birds of La Plata. 2 vols. New York: E. P. Dutton & Co., 1920.
———, Far Away and Long Ago: A History of My Early Life. New York: E. P. Dutton & Co., 1924.
———, Idle Days in Patagonia. New York: E. P. Dutton & Co., 1917.
———, The Naturalist in La Plata. London: J. M. Dent & Co., 1903.
von Humboldt, Alexander, Views of Nature. London: Henry G. Bohn, 1850.
——— and Bonpland, A., Personal Narrative of Travels to the Equinoctial Regions of America. Trans. and ed. by Thomasina Ross. 3 vols. London: Henry G. Bohn, 1852.

Bibliography

Im Thurn, E. F., Among the Indians of Guiana. London: Kegan Paul, Trench & Co., 1883.
Keller, F., The Amazon and Madeira Rivers. Philadelphia: J. B. Lippincott and Co., 1875.
Kennedy, Admiral, Sporting Sketches in South America. London, 1892.
Koebel, W. H., British Exploits in South America. New York: The Century Co., 1917.
Lange, A., In the Amazon Jungle. New York: G. P. Putnam's Sons, 1912.
LaVarre, William J., Gold, Diamonds and Orchids. New York: Fleming H. Revell Co., 1935.
———, Up the Mazaruni for Diamonds. Boston: Marshall Jones Co., 1927.
MacCreagh, Gordon, White Waters and Black. New York: The Century Co., 1926.
McGovern, W. M., Jungle Paths and Inca Ruins. New York: The Century Co., 1927.
Miller, L. E., In the Wilds of South America. New York: Charles Scribner's Sons, 1918.
Mozans, H. J. (Father Zahm), Along the Andes and Down the Amazon. New York: D. Appleton & Co., 1911.
———, The Quest of El Dorado. New York: D. Appleton & Co., 1917.
———, Through South America's Southland. New York: D. Appleton & Co., 1916.
———, Up the Orinoco and Down the Magdalena. New York: D. Appleton & Co., 1910.
Murphy, R. C., Bird Islands of Peru. New York: G. P. Putnam's Sons, 1925.
———, Oceanic Birds of South America. 2 vols. New York: American Museum of Natural History, 1936.
Musters, G. C., At Home with the Patagonians. London: John Murray, 1871.
Nesbit, L. M., Desolate Marches. New York: Harcourt, Brace & Co., 1936.
Orton, J., The Andes and the Amazon. London: Sampson Low, Son, & Marston, 1870.
Paez, Don Ramón, Wild Scenes in South America. New York: Charles Scribner, 1862.
Pérez Triana, S., Down the Orinoco in a Canoe. New York: Thomas Y. Crowell & Co., 1902.
Post, C. J., Across the Andes. New York: Outing Publishing Co., 1912.
Prichard, H. H., Through the Heart of Patagonia. New York: D. Appleton & Co., 1902.

Bibliography

Ralegh, Sir W., The Discovery of the Large, Rich, and Beautiful Empire of Guiana. Reprinted from 1596 ed. Ed. by Sir Robert H. Schomburgk. London, 1848.

Rodway, James, Guiana: British, Dutch, and French. New York: Charles Scribner's Sons, 1912.

——, In the Guiana Forest. London: T. Fisher Unwin, 1911.

Roosevelt, Theodore, Through the Brazilian Wilderness. New York: Charles Scribner's Sons, 1914.

Rusby, H. H., Jungle Memories. New York: McGraw-Hill Book Co., 1933.

Schomburgk, Richard, Travels in British Guiana 1840–1844. Trans. and ed. by Walter E. Roth. 2 vols. Georgetown: *Daily Chronicle* Office, 1922.

Simpson, G. G., Attending Marvels. New York: The Macmillan Co., 1934.

Simson, A., Travels in the Wilds of Ecuador. London: Sampson Low, Marston, Searle, & Rivington, 1886.

Spruce, Richard, Notes of a Botanist on the Amazon & Andes. Ed. and condensed by Alfred Russel Wallace. 2 vols. London: Macmillan & Co., 1908.

Tschiffely, A. F., Tschiffely's Ride. New York: Simon & Schuster, 1933.

von Tschudi, J. J., Travels in Peru. London: David Bogue, 1847.

Ulloa, Don Antonio de, A Voyage to South America. Trans. by John Adams. 4th ed. 2 vols. London: Printed for J. Stockdale, 1806.

Up de Graff, F. W., Head Hunters of the Amazon. New York: Duffield & Co., 1923.

Verrill, A. H., Thirty Years in the Jungle. London: John Lane, The Bodley Head, 1929.

Wallace, A. R., A Narrative of Travels on the Amazon and Rio Negro. London: Reeve & Co., 1853.

——, Tropical Nature. London: Macmillan & Co., 1878.

Waterton, Charles, Wanderings in South America. London: Printed for J. Mawman, 1825.

Wells, James W., Exploring and Traveling Three Thousand Miles Through Brazil from Rio de Janeiro to Maranhão. 2 vols. Philadelphia: J. B. Lippincott Co., 1886.

Whitney, Caspar, The Flowing Road. Philadelphia: J. B. Lippincott Co., 1912.

Wickham, H. A., Rough Notes of a Journey Through the Wilderness from Trinidad to Pará. London: W. H. J. Carter, 1872.

INDEX

Index

Index

Index

Index

Index

Index